CHEMISTRY
AT WORK

DEDICATION

We dedicate this book to each other and to Tia.

CHEMISTRY AT WORK

BRENDA SHAPIRO, Ph.D.

Winston Churchill Collegiate Institute
Scarborough Board of Education

STAN SHAPIRO, Ph.D.

Dr. Norman Bethune Collegiate Institute
Scarborough Board of Education

Copp Clark Pitman Ltd.
A Longman Company
Toronto

ISBN 0-7730-4730-1

Editorial development: Michael Webb

Editing: Dennis Cheung

Design: Michael van Elsen Design Inc.

Cover: Zena Denchik

Technical art: Catherine Aikens and Velentino Sanna

Creative art: William Kimber and William Laughton

Photo research: Jane Affleck

Typesetting: Compeer Typographic Services Ltd.

Printing and binding: The Bryant Press

The publisher wishes to thank the following reviewers for their comments and suggestions as the manuscript was being developed: David Cash, Mohawk College, Hamilton, Ontario; Don Garrett, Scarborough Board of Education, Scarborough, Ontario; and Gord Smith, The Elgin County Board of Education, St. Thomas, Ontario.

Copp Clark Pitman Ltd.
2775 Matheson Blvd. East
Mississauga, Ontario
L4W 4P7

Printed and bound in Canada

Contents

PHOTO CREDITS

Every effort has been made to contact the copyright holders of material included in this book.

Further information pertaining to rights would be welcome.

Abitibi-Price: 195 (Fig. 19).

American Institute of Physics/Niels Bohr Library: 131, 337 (Fig. 12), 398, 399 (all).

Banting and Best Department of Medical Research, University of Toronto: 37 (bottom).

Minerals America: 79.

Canadian Council for the Advancement of Food Technologies/John Narvali: 415.

Canapress Photo Service: 43, 51 (Fig. 8), 54 (Jonathan Eastland), 58 (Fig. 17), 70 (Fig. 2), 83 (Calgary Herald), 85 (Leslie Jackman), 108, 117, 118, 147 (Fred Chartrand), 150 (Geraldine Prentice), 156, 186, 194, (Fig. 16–Bruno Schlumberger), 195 (Fig. 18–Ottawa Citizen), 235 (Benoit Gysembergh), 239 (Rick Loughran/Vancouver Province), 246 (Toronto Star–Michael Stuparyk), 298 (Fig. 1–Blaise Edwards), 302 (Toronto Star–Erin Combs), 324, 334, 336 (Fig. 10), 341 (Lockheed Co.), 353, 367 (Halifax Chronicle Herald), 368 (Fig. 2–Hendersen), 371, 373 (Fig. 7), 380 (Vancouver Sun/Peter Battistoni), 384 (Toronto Star), 394 (Toronto Star), 396 (Fig. 3–Winnipeg Free Press), 396 (Fig. 4–Ryan Remiorz), 397 (Fig. 5), 408, 409, 410, 413 (both), 416 (Fig. 33), 417.

Centre for Forensic Science: 103 (spectrometers).

Dofasco Steel: 397 (Fig. 6).

From Gems, Robert R. Webster: 103.

Geological Survey of Canada: (202481-C) 34.

Imperial Oil Limited: 364.

Instructional Media Service, University of Toronto: 57, 416 (Fig. 32).

Bill Ivy: 92.

Jeremy Jones: 14, 17, 18, 19, 21, 28, 45 (Fig. 2, 3, 4), 52, 53, 64, 70 (Fig. 3), 73 (Fig. 5), 75, 84 (Fig. 17), 98, 99 (Fig. 8), 120, 146, 152, 157, 162, 188 (Fig. 3, 4, 5, 6, 8, 9, 10), 189, 191, 195 (Fig. 20, 21), 212 (Fig. 34), 215, 225, 232, 237, 240, 272, 276, 280, 282, 286, 287, 289, 307, 309, 312, 315, 321, 326, 336 (Fig. 8, 9), 337 (Fig. 14), 360, 373 (Fig. 8), 386, 387, 390.

Kidd Creek Mines Ltd.: 194 (Fig. 14).

Metropolitan Toronto Reference Library, Picture Collection: 36, 76, 114, 119 (gas masks), 169, 303, 335 (Fig. 4).

Miller Comstock: 69, 45 (Fig. 4, 6), 103 (Gems), 137 (Brian Thompson), 245 (R. Harrington); from Grant Heilman: 130 (Runk/Schoenberger), 187, 268; from Harold M. Lambert: 58 (Fig. 16), 80, 194 (Fig. 15), 195 (Fig. 17), 294, 335; from H. Armstrong Roberts: 26, 37 (top–C. Seghers), 39, 68, 142, 175, 233, 298 (Fig. 2), 311, 317, 347, 396 (Fig. 1).

NASA: 335 (Fig. 6), 336 (Fig. 11).

NCIVS Camera Club/Ken Coulthart: 51 (Fig. 9), 73 (Fig. 6), 368 (Fig. 3).

Nutrasweet Co.: 388.

Ontario Hydro: 82, 337 (Fig. 13), 396 (Fig. 2), 405, 407 (both).

Ontario Ministry of Energy: 119 (pool), 171, 374, 383.

Ontario Ministry of the Environment/Acid Rain Office: 188 (Fig. 7), 224.

Ontario Place Corporation: 90.

Rohm and Haas Canada Inc.: 166, 391, 392, 393.

Royal Ontario Museum/Conservation Department: 358.

Sargent Welch Scientific: 212 (Fig. 35).

Sears Canada: 181, 355.

SSC Photo Centre, Ottawa: 71, 283.

Stelco Technical Services: 88, 89.

Superior Propane Inc.: 84 (Fig. 18).

Sunshine Beach Water Park: 194 (Fig. 13).

TV Ontario: 59 (Fig. 19), 263, 335 (Fig. 4).

"Copyright 1988: Tribune Media Services Inc. Reprinted with permission–The Toronto Star Syndicate" 308.

Union Carbide Canada Limited: 27.

Valan Photos: 97 (Jean Bruneau), 99 (Fig. 9–Pierre Chabot), 125 (Jean-Marie Jro), 266 (Denis Roy), 288 (Tom W. Parkin).

Special thanks to Susan Jones for help co-ordinating photo sessions, and Elaine Freedman for research assistance.

Between the two of us, we have been teaching applications of chemistry for over 35 years! When we were approached to write this textbook, we jumped at the idea. At long last we have been able to put in print our philosophy of how applied chemistry can be taught so as to make it more personal and exciting for the learners.

Since students do not all learn the same way, the chapters in this book have been written to satisfy a wide variety of learning styles. Students have different priorities when it comes to learning. For some, the need to personalize a concept is paramount. They learn best by utilizing their experience and by discussion. Others enjoy learning facts and what experts say about a concept. Research, books, and the teacher's knowledge satisfy these learners. Another group of students prefer to practise and apply what they have learned. These students learn best with a hands-on approach. There is also a group of students who enjoy modifying and extending what they have learned. Creative projects with built-in flexibility meet the needs of these learners. We feel we have accommodated the needs of all these kinds of learners in this text.

Every effort has been made to include a variety of types of activities and student groupings. Students are asked to participate in class discussions, to work in small groups or in pairs, and to undertake individual projects. Students are also given opportunities to discuss consumer issues and concerns. Many activities encourage creativity and improve thinking skills.

We have attempted to highlight the interdisciplinary nature of chemistry throughout the text, and have also included a chapter on the use of chemistry in the craft world.

Without sounding like we've just won an Academy Award, we would like to thank a number of people. Our biggest offer of thanks goes to all our students for the interest they have shown in our materials and their appreciation of our philosophy of teaching chemistry. Thanks also go to Mike Webb, Rob Devine, Don Garratt, Jennifer Ludbrook, Dennis Cheung, Jane Affleck, Susan Jones, Linda Scott, Marion Elliott, and our reviewers. Since no one lives or works in a vacuum, we also pay tribute to all our colleagues for ideas and discussions we've shared over the years.

Finally, a note to the students using this textbook.

We have written this textbook in the belief that experiencing chemistry can be both interesting and fun for all types of learners! If we have succeeded in persuading you that chemicals and the effects of chemicals are a part of your very being and your everyday life and enjoyment, and that you can make informed judgements as a consumer, we feel that the effort of writing this book has been well worthwhile!

SETTING THE SCENE

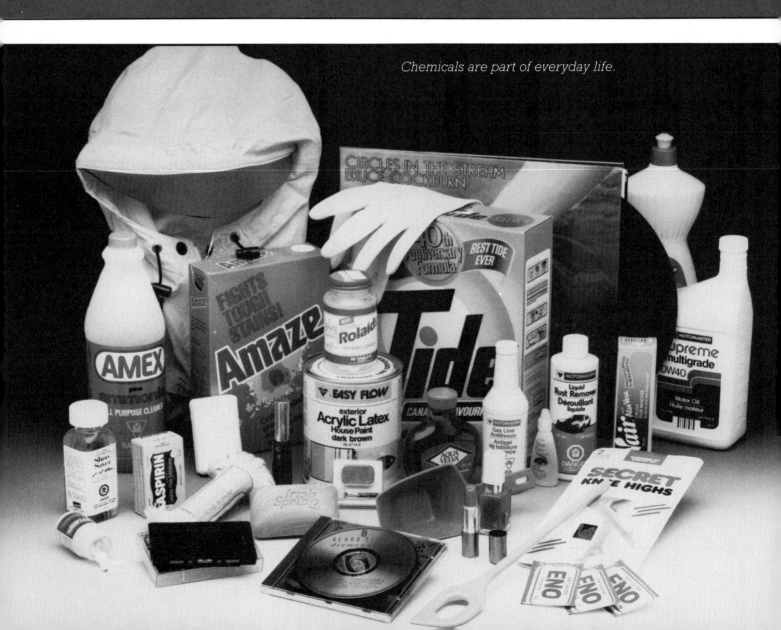

Chemicals are part of everyday life.

CONTENTS

Fig. 1 *Where are the chemicals in these rooms?*

1.1 You're Surrounded

Let us begin with a group activity. Form your group with three other students. Pick a room in the house in Figure 1 that no other group has chosen.

15

List all the items found or stored in your chosen room that are made up of chemicals. Use felt markers to write your list on a large piece of paper. When you have written everything you can think of, post your list in the classroom.

Study the lists produced by all the groups. In the rooms, is there anything that is not made up of chemicals?

You now know that you are surrounded by chemicals. But what about your own body? Is it made up of chemicals? In fact, the human body is a chemical factory second to none. All the time chemical reactions take place in the cells of our bodies. All the foods that we eat are also made up of chemicals. The idea that naturally grown vegetables and fruits have no chemicals is not true. What they don't have are contaminants such as insecticides and fungicides.

1.2 Don't Live to Regret Something

Chemicals exist all around us, and it is fun to experiment with them. But remember, a laboratory accident may have serious consequences.

To help you understand how important it is to avoid laboratory accidents, try the following activity. First, choose one of these three situations:

- *Pretend that you are blind.* (Wear a blindfold. Another student will watch you so you cannot hurt yourself.)

- *Pretend that you have lost the use of your writing hand and the thumb and forefinger of the other hand.* (Tie your writing hand behind you, and tape the thumb and forefinger of your other hand.)

- *Pretend that you have been badly hurt and have lost all your fingers.* (Tape all your fingers to your palms.)

Then carry out the following tasks:

1. Set up a retort stand and fix a small ring clamp onto the rod.

2. Place a funnel in the ring clamp so that the end of the funnel is inside a 250-mL flask and about 2 cm below the rim of the flask.

3. Pour 50 mL of water from a graduated cylinder through the funnel into the flask.

4. Pour 5 mL of water from the flask into a 10-mL graduated cylinder.

Write down your personal feeling and frustration while doing the above. Then, in groups of four, discuss how an accident could affect your lives.

Draw your image of the word "safety" on a large piece of paper and put the drawing up in the classroom. Alternatively, perform a charade on the word "safety."

Fig. 2 *Goggles protect your eyes from shattered glass and splashed chemicals.*

1.3 Safety First

The following are some important safety rules in the laboratory. As long as instructions and safety precautions are followed, chemicals don't have to be dangerous!

- *Always read the safety instructions before you start any part of an experiment.* This will reduce the chance of accidents.

- *Wear goggles* (Figure 2) throughout activities that involve glassware or liquid chemicals.

- *Tie back long hair (Figure 3) and do not wear loose clothing.*

Fig. 3 *Long hair or loose clothing may catch fire in a Bunsen flame. What precautions are these students taking?*

- *Always wear shoes* (but not open-toed ones) in the laboratory. Some chemicals may have been spilled on the floor.

- *Always stand while doing an experiment.* In case of accident, you can get away faster if you are standing.

- *Never sit on laboratory benches.* Some chemicals may have been spilled on them.

- *Learn the fire-exit route.* In a fire, you need to get to the exit quickly and safely.

- *Learn the location of the fire alarm* nearest to the laboratory. You should warn others immediately of fires. Never pull a fire alarm as a joke.

- *Learn the location of the fire blanket.* If your clothes catch fire, you will need a fire blanket quickly. Wrap yourself in the blanket and roll on the floor.

- *Use tongs to handle hot equipment.* Remember hot metal and glass look like cold metal and glass.

- If your Bunsen burner does not light as soon as you turn on the gas and use a match or a spark, *turn off the gas.* Wait a few minutes for the gas to clear and try again. When the gas is turned on, it comes out of the Bunsen burner. The longer the burner remains unlit, the more gas surrounds you. When it eventually lights up, you may be burned!

- *Never leave a lighted Bunsen burner unattended.* Someone may get burned because flames are not always easy to see.

- *Use a hotplate when heating flammable substances* (Figure 4).

- *Always clean your own equipment.* Although equipment may look clean, it usually is not!

- *To pick up chemicals, use a scoop or spatula that you have cleaned and dried.* Do not touch chemicals with your hands. They may hurt your skin.

- *After using a spatula with one chemical, always clean and dry the spatula before using it with another chemical.* If you do not clear the spatula, the second chemical will become contaminated with the first. The chemicals may react violently with each other.

- *If a chemical is stored in a container with a lid, you should always replace the lid properly after use.* Do not leave the container open for the second person. Replacing the lid avoids contamination of one chemical by another. It also prevents reaction of the chemical with air and water vapour.

- *Use a clean glass rod when pouring a liquid from one container into another.* This prevents splashing of the liquid.

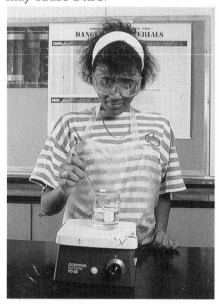

Fig. 4 *A hotplate should be used when heating flammable substances. Using the Bunsen burner may cause a fire.*

- *If you spill chemicals on your hands or clothes, rinse the chemicals off with water* (unless the instructions tell you not to use water). Water dilutes the chemicals and washes them off your skin or clothes.

- *Spilled chemicals should be cleaned up immediately.* Other people could get hurt by touching them.

- *Never try to push glass tubing through a hole in a stopper.* If the glass breaks, you may cut yourself. Your teacher will do this for you.

- *Do not add water to a chemical.* Always add the chemical to water. Many chemicals, especially concentrated acids, will react violently if water is added to them. Adding them to water reduces the violence of the reactions.

- *To smell a chemical, use your hand to wave some of the vapour toward your nose.* Partly fill your lungs with air and take a *short* sniff of the vapour.

- *Never taste a chemical* unless the instructions definitely tell you to. If you are required to taste a chemical, it should not be contained in equipment that is regularly used in the laboratory because it may be contaminated with poisonous chemicals. Use special or new equipment.

- *When using electrical equipment, make sure your hands are dry and there are no exposed wires.* Otherwise you may get an electrical shock.

- *Notify the teacher immediately if there has been an accident, or if any equipment is broken.*

- *If you burn yourself, immediately put the burned region under cold, running water.* Then notify your teacher. The cold water takes the heat away from the burn. Do not use ointments, which may cause problems.

- *Put any broken glass in the special "broken glass" container,* not in the regular paper garbage container.

To remind the class of the importance of laboratory safety, carry out the following:

1. Design a checklist or questionnaire on the safe operation of a school chemistry laboratory.

2. Design a campaign to promote safer procedures in a laboratory. This can be done in the form of a poster, a skit, a video, or a taped announcement.

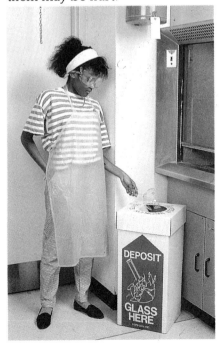

Fig. 5 *Dispose of your garbage properly. Don't put broken glass in the regular garbage containers; otherwise the people emptying them may be hurt.*

1.4 How Safe Are You?

Check your knowledge of the correct safety procedures and use of equipment by completing the crossword puzzle in Figure 6. Your teacher will give you a large puzzle to fill in.

Fig. 6 The safety crossword puzzle.

Fig. 6 The safety crossword puzzle.

Across

2. Heating equipment for flammable liquids
7. Worn at all times when doing an experiment
8. A flammable liquid that makes people drunk
9. A narrow piece of glassware that should never be more than one-third full when being heated
10. Equipment that must always be cleaned and dried before being used to transfer solids
13. A heating device used in the laboratory that should never be left unattended
15. A cone of _____ used to line a funnel
19. A piece of iron equipment attached to a retort stand to support a gauze or hold a funnel
20. _____ fool around in the laboratory
21. A box-like heating container used to heat materials over long periods
22. Dangerous to _____ glass tubing into a rubber stopper
24. A long piece of glass used to stir chemicals or to help when pouring liquids
25. Type of equipment which, if broken, must not be thrown in the regular garbage container
26. Equipment used to handle hot liquids in beakers

Down

1. Poisonous silvery liquid found in some thermometers
3. A device for measuring temperature
4. Cylinder to measure the volume of liquid
5. A device used to separate a liquid from an undissolved solid
6. A piece of glassware, with its top much narrower than its base, used to hold liquids
7. Metal mesh used to prevent glassware from cracking when heated with a Bunsen burner
8. A type of chemical which must be respected and handled carefully in the home and laboratory
11. A metal rod to which you attach clamps and other equipment
12. Fuel for the Bunsen burner
13. A piece of short glassware with no lid used to hold liquids and solids
14. A very expensive instrument used to weigh things (which must not be hot!)
16. A piece of glassware used when filtering a mixture
17. The way your laboratory equipment and work station should always be kept
18. A metallic piece of equipment used to attach other equipment to a retort stand
23. Metal instrument used to handle very hot items or to hold items in the Bunsen flame
24. For a series of weighings, use the _____ balance

1.5 Observations, Inferences, and Theories

In chemistry, we study many changes that occur around us. We try to understand these changes by performing experiments. During an experiment, we record what we observe. Then we try to explain our observations.

Observations are the most important part of any scientific investigation. Therefore, it is important that you make and record observations carefully.

To make observations you must use one or more of your senses.

Detecting	*Sense used*
shape, colour, shininess	sight
odour	smell
texture	touch
sound	hearing
taste (sweet, sour, salty, bitter)	taste

If you use your senses only, without any instruments, to make observations, the observations are **qualitative observations**. For example: "The watermelon has red flesh."

Sometimes you make observations using instruments, such as balances, graduated cylinders, thermometers, and rulers. Then the observations are **quantitative observations**. They are measured quantities, written as numbers and usually followed by units. For example: "The watermelon has a mass of 4.00 kg."

Fig. 7 *What qualitative and quantitative observations can you make?*

Fig. 8 *Observation or inference?*

If a guess is added to an observation, the statement is known as an **inference**. The inference may or may not be correct, depending on the correctness of the guess.

An example of an inference is: "The watermelon has a thick skin to protect it from insect attack." The observation is simply that the watermelon has a thick skin. By adding the reason (which is just a guess), we have turned the statement into an inference.

A **theory** is both an explanation for a number of observations and a way to predict things that have not yet been observed.

Even widely accepted theories may be proved wrong. An example is the Greek theory that the sun and the planets moved around the earth. This theory was accepted for over a thousand years.

If every week you observe a person buying cat litter, you would probably develop a theory that the person has a cat. If your theory were a good one, you might predict that the person would accept some free cat food samples. If the person were to say that cat food was of no use and turn down the free samples, you would need a new theory to match the old observations and include the latest piece of information or evidence. What could a new theory be?

Questions

1. Decide whether each of the following is an inference or an observation. Write in your notebook the letters (a) to (m). Beside each letter write *I* (inference) or *O* (observation).
   (a) When the candle burns, carbon dioxide is given off.
   (b) The candle is 10 cm long.
   (c) The candle has a diameter of 2.5 cm and is cylindrical.
   (d) A candle flame has three different colours.
   (e) The black smoke coming from the candle flame is carbon.
   (f) If oxygen is removed from around a burning candle, the flame is extinguished.
   (g) The length of the candle changes slowly as it burns.
   (h) The wick extends from the top of the candle to the bottom.
   (i) A burning candle makes no sound.
   (j) Carbon causes the yellow colour in the candle flame.
   (k) The candle flame has sharp sides and a ragged top.
   (l) In the candle flame, the wick is black except for the very tip, which glows red.
   (m) The candle flame gives off heat and light.

2. Note which of the above statements are quantitative observations. Write the letters in your notebook.

Fig. 9

(a)

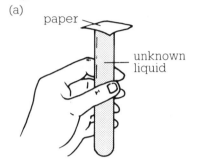

paper

unknown
liquid

(b)

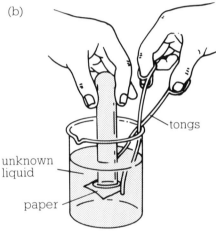

tongs

unknown
liquid

paper

(c)

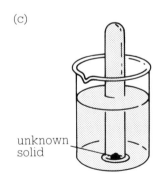

unknown
solid

Do not touch this chemical
with your hands. It may burn
your skin.

1.6 Testing Your Observational and Reporting Skills

In this experiment, you are supplied with unknown chemicals. Describe as fully as possible all the materials used, exactly what happens, and what the products look like. Organize your observations in a chart. There are many different methods of reporting information and you should design your own. At the end of the experiment, discuss the good points about all the reports.

Materials

safety goggles
3 small (18 × 150 mm) test tubes
250-mL beaker
unknown liquid
unknown solid
splints
matches or a lit Bunsen burner
tongs

Method

1. First read through the whole experiment, and decide how you intend to record your observations in your notebook. Remember to start making observations right from the start.

2. Pour the unknown liquid into three labelled test tubes, so that
   test tube 1 is one-tenth full,
   test tube 2 is half full, and
   test tube 3 is completely full.

3. Fill a 250-mL beaker about two-thirds full of the unknown liquid.

4. Cut out a 3-cm square of paper towel. Wet it with the liquid and slide it over the mouth of test tube 1 (Figure 9a). Invert the test tube slowly so that the liquid will not run out.

5. Place the mouth of the test tube under the unknown liquid in the beaker. Then use tongs to slide the paper away from the mouth of the test tube (Figure 9b).

6. Fold a piece of paper to form a cone (Figure 10). Use a clean, dry spatula to place a small piece of the unknown solid in the dry paper cone.

Fig. 10

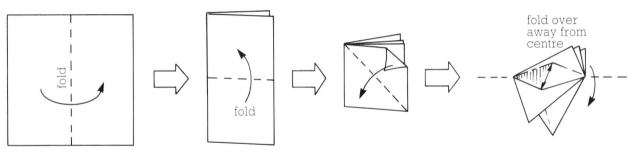

7. Drop this piece of unknown solid into the unknown liquid in the beaker. Immediately cover the solid with the mouth of the test tube (Figure 9c). Keep the test tube over the solid until the test tube has been emptied of liquid.

8. Light a splint with a match or a Bunsen flame. Lift the test tube straight up, holding it *mouth downwards*, and place the tip of the burning splint at the mouth of the test tube (Figure 11).

9. Repeat steps 3 to 8 for each of the other two test tubes.

Fig. 11

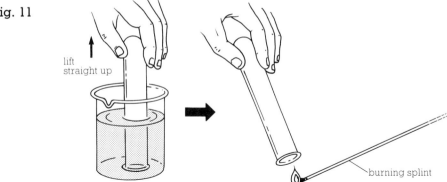

Follow-up

1. Share your observations and reports with the rest of the class. Pick out any inferences that your classmates have made.

2. Why was there a difference in behaviour between the three test tubes when the burning splint was applied? (This is how theories are developed.)

3. Why did different students make different observations even for the same test tube number?

4. As a class, discuss the different ways of reporting experimental observations. There is rarely only one way to do something. Which is the best way in this situation?

What Actually Happened?

The unknown solid in the experiment was calcium carbide, and the unknown liquid was water. The water had a mixture of dyes added to it so that it would change colour on reacting with calcium carbide. The reaction produced calcium hydroxide and a gas called acetylene (Figure 12). The cloudiness in the liquid was caused by the calcium hydroxide formed.

For acetylene to burn, it needs the oxygen in the air. Why were the changes in test tube 3 so different from those in test tube 1? In test tube 1, which contained the most air, the acetylene burned quickly with a loud explosion. In test tube 3, there was not enough air for all the acetylene to burn, so it burned slowly and a lot of black soot was formed.

Fig. 12 *Acetylene gas is a fuel. It is used in oxy-acetylene welding of metals.*

A CHANCE DISCOVERY

The first person to produce calcium carbide cheaply and on a large scale was a Canadian called "Carbide" Willson. He discovered his process by accident.

Thomas Leopold Willson was born in Princeton, near Woodstock, in Upper Canada in 1860, and was educated at Hamilton Collegiate Institute. As a young man he started experimenting in the basement of his home. He made all kinds of gadgets and a number of chemicals. With a blacksmith friend, he built one of the first electric dynamos in Canada. In 1880 he used the dynamo to run the first arc light in Hamilton. He became an electrical engineer and went to work in Spray in New Jersey. Here in 1892, in the Willson Aluminum Company, Willson tried to prepare calcium. He heated a mixture of lime (calcium oxide) and coal tar

1.7 Is the Lowest Price Always the Best Buy?

When you shop, you are constantly making observations. Frequently these observations are quantitative, involving checking and comparing prices of similar products. Many products, such as cleaning agents and processed foods, contain chemicals called **active ingredients**. Active ingredients are those that actually do the work in the product. For example, the active ingredients in a shampoo are a detergent and perhaps a conditioner. When comparing prices, you have to be aware that some products contain a larger percentage of active ingredient than others.

Which of the following products do you think is the better buy?

- 100 mL Brenstan with 10% active ingredient for $1.00, or

- 100 mL Tiapav with 20% of the same active ingredient for $1.50?

Tiapav appears to be the better buy because you are getting twice as much active ingredient for only one and a half times the price. But Tiapav is only a better buy if you use less Tiapav than Brenstan in the same situation.

A lot of products contain non-active ingredients, that is, ingredients that do not do the job for which the product is designed. These non-active ingredients are called **additives**.

in a high temperature electric furnace, and obtained a dark coloured molten mass. On cooling, the molten mass became a highly crystalline brittle solid. He threw some of the solid into a bucket of water. Calcium would have reacted with the water to form hydrogen gas. Instead of hydrogen, the reaction with water produced another gas, which started to burn because the top of the solid was still glowing. Unlike hydrogen, the gas burned with a smoky flame and gave off large quantities of black soot. The gas was acetylene, and the solid he had made was calcium carbide.

And so Thomas Willson was responsible for developing the commercial calcium carbide process for the manufacture of acetylene. He sold his American patents to the Union Carbide Company and moved to Merritton, Ontario, where he organized the Willson Carbide and Acetylene Works. In 1911, he sold all his Canadian manufacturing rights to the Canada Carbide Company.

Fig. 13 *"Carbide" Willson was the first person to produce acetylene in a cheap way.*

The following examples show the usefulness of additives.

Additive	Where used	Why used
vinegar	vegetables	pickling agent (preservative)
vitamin D	milk	dietary supplement
dextrose	salt	colour stabilizer
corn starch	aspirin tablets	supplier of bulk
fluorocarbons	hair spray	propellant
water	bleach	diluting agent
yellow dye	margarine	colouring agent
perfume	shampoos	fragrance

The reasons for using some additives are not very worthy ones. For example, foam-making additives make shampoos and detergents foam more than necessary, so that the consumer thinks the product is working very well. Similarly, thickening agents make liquid products look thicker, so that the consumer thinks the product is stronger or more powerful.

It is therefore up to you as a consumer to read labels to evaluate products. This is not always easy, as the information on the labels may not be very detailed.

Fig. 14 *What are the uses of the additives in this product?*

Fig. 15 *Additives in foods may add to consumer appeal (for example, the colour added to margarine).*

MARGARINE COLOUR—WHAT'S FAIR?

In 1949, the Canadian Supreme Court dropped the law banning the manufacture or sale of margarine. Ontario then passed the Oleomargarine Act, which legalized the sale of the butter substitute, so long as it was not the same colour as butter. The law was designed to protect both consumers and Ontario's dairy industry.

In 1987, Ontario's margarine manufacturers challenged the law, saying that it was against the Charter of Rights and Freedoms. They argued that almost all processed foods had some artificial colouring to make the product more appetizing. The manufacturers said that the law "discriminates against those who choose margarine over butter for health or economic or other reasons, but who object to its colour."

The Ontario government fears that if the colour controls on margarine are removed, consumers will switch from butter to margarine. This would hurt the dairy industry. The government also regards the law as protection for those who eat in restaurants. Restaurants may provide margarine instead of butter, and allowing butter and margarine to be the same colour may harm people who have to avoid certain foods.

What do you think?

1.8 Active Ingredients

In this experiment, you will estimate how much active ingredient is present in a liquid dishwashing detergent or shampoo. The method described is not always applicable to other types of products.

Materials

safety goggles
liquid dishwashing detergent or shampoo in a plastic dropper bottle
   with lid
oven pre-heated to about 105°C
petri dish with cover
tongs
balance that reads to 0.01 g

Method

1. Record all data in a chart. Draw up a new chart and perform two trials for each product. The following is a suggested chart:

Name of product/manufacturer: Size of product: Cost for this size of product:		
	Trial 1	Trial 2
Mass of petri dish	g	g
Mass of liquid dropper bottle with lid before squirt	g	g
Mass of liquid dropper bottle with lid after squirt	g	g
Mass of petri dish with solid after heating	g	g
Percent solid (after calculation)	%	%

2. Wash a petri dish with laboratory detergent and rinse it well. Dry the petri dish thoroughly with towels. Using a felt pen, label the underside of the dish with your name, product, and trial number.

3. Use the balance to carefully determine the mass of the petri dish and record the value.

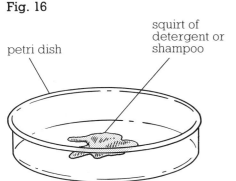

Fig. 16

petri dish

squirt of detergent or shampoo

4. Carefully determine the mass of the dropper bottle containing liquid detergent or shampoo. Be sure the dropper bottle is fitted with its lid.

5. Add a squirt (about 1 g) of the detergent or shampoo from the dropper bottle to the dish (Figure 16).

6. Immediately and carefully find the mass of the dropper bottle and its lid again. The decrease in mass is equal to the mass of the liquid in the petri dish.

7. Place the petri dish in the pre-heated oven to dry for at least 1 h. Remove the dish from the oven with tongs, place a cover over the dish, and allow the dish and the remaining material to cool.

8. When the dish is cool to the touch, remove the cover and carefully find the mass of the petri dish and its contents.

9. Calculate the percent by mass of solid as follows:

Mass of liquid dropper bottle with lid before squirt $= a$
Mass of liquid dropper bottle with lid after squirt $= b$
Mass of product used $= a - b$
Mass of petri dish $= c$
Mass of petri dish with solid after heating $= d$
Mass of dried product $= d - c$

$$\text{Percent solid} = \frac{\text{mass of dried product}}{\text{mass of product used}} \times 100\%$$
$$= \frac{d - c}{a - b} \times 100\%$$

The percent by mass of solid is an approximate measure of the percent by mass of active ingredients.

Follow-up

1. Based on the results of your class, which shampoo or detergent has the highest percent solid?

2. Does the highest percent solid necessarily mean that the product is the best? Explain your answer.

3. Which of the products do you think is the best buy? Explain your answer.

1.9 Laboratory Skills and Techniques

In this experiment, you will prepare lead(II) iodide and then purify it, changing it from a crude yellow solid into a beautiful shiny solid. The experiment will help you master many of the skills and techniques needed in a school chemistry laboratory, such as:

(a) pouring liquids
(b) decanting liquids
(c) filtering hot and cold liquids and solutions
(d) evaporating
(e) heating a liquid, or a liquid plus a solid, in a test tube
(f) recrystallizing a solid
(g) drawing diagrams

Materials

safety goggles
beaker tongs
two 100-mL beakers
two 250-mL beakers
short glass rod
125-mL evaporating dish
gauze
Bunsen burner
large ring clamp
small ring clamp
boiling chip
small vial
filter paper
filter funnel
medium size test tube
retort stand
0.12 mol/L (40 g/L) lead(II) nitrate solution
0.24 mol/L (40 g/L) potassium iodide solution
distilled (or demineralized) water in a wash bottle

Lead(II) nitrate solution is poisonous. Rinse your hands if you spill any on them.

Method

1. *Pouring liquids*
   Using a short glass rod, pour lead(II) nitrate solution into a clean 100-mL beaker to a depth of about 1 cm (Figure 17). Rinse the rod thoroughly with distilled water.

Now pour about the same volume of potassium iodide solution into the same beaker. Stir the contents of the beaker with the glass rod, and wash the rod with distilled water before putting it down.

Fig. 17

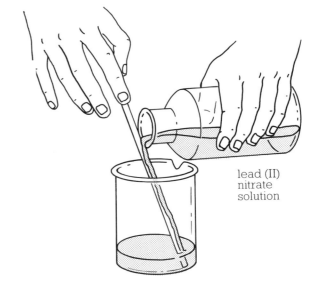

lead (II) nitrate solution

Allow the contents to sit so that they can settle somewhat.
The liquid layer is known as the **mother liquor**.
The solid formed when the two clear liquids react is called the **precipitate**.

2. *Preparing for filtration*
   Fix a small ring clamp to a retort stand. Place a clean glass funnel in the ring clamp.
   Fold a filter paper, open it out into a cone, and place the cone snugly in the funnel. Hold the filter paper in place while you wet it with distilled water. Wetting the paper holds it in position in the funnel.
   Adjust the end of the funnel over an evaporating dish, so that the end of the funnel is about 1 cm below the rim of the dish.

Fig. 18

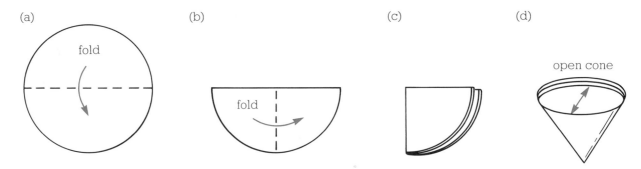

(a)   fold   (b)   fold   (c)   (d)   open cone

3. *Decanting and filtration*

When you decant, you pour off a liquid from a settled solid. Try not to disturb the solid.

Fig. 19

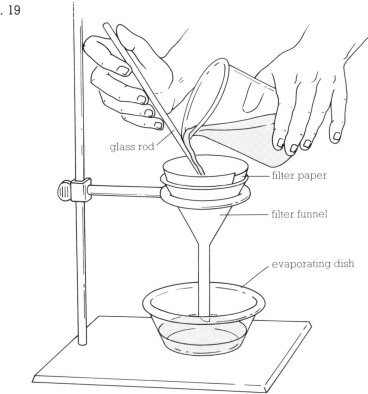

glass rod

filter paper

filter funnel

evaporating dish

Using a glass rod, decant the mother liquor from the beaker into the filter paper (Figure 19). Never allow the liquid level in the funnel to come within 5 mm of the top of the paper. This precaution prevents solid from slipping under the filter paper and spoiling your filtration. When most of the liquid has passed through the filter paper, swirl the remaining yellow mixture and pour it into the filter paper using the glass rod. Using your distilled water wash bottle, rinse any remaining solid into the filter paper. Use only a small volume of water at a time or the evaporating dish will overflow.

The liquid which comes through the filter paper is called the **filtrate**. The solid remaining in the filter paper is called the **residue**.

Save the residue in the filter paper and the filtrate in the evaporating dish.

If you decant the mother liquor first, the filtering process is speeded up because the solid cannot clog the filter paper.

Fig. 20 *Well-developed crystals (like these quartz crystals from British Columbia) have a regular shape and are often beautiful and shiny.*

The boiling chip helps to control the boiling action of the liquid. A fresh boiling chip must be used each time a cold liquid is heated to boiling.

4. *Recrystallization of a solid*

When the yellow solid first formed, it was a dull powder mixed with other chemicals. To make it into a beautiful, pure, shiny solid, you need to turn it into crystals. This is done by **recrystallization**. To recrystallize your yellow solid, you dissolve the solid in hot water, filter the solution to remove any unwanted solids, and allow the hot filtrate to cool. The shiny crystals appear as the filtrate cools.

Transfer the yellow solid to a 250-mL beaker, and add about 150 mL of distilled water and a boiling chip.

Set up a retort stand and fix two ring clamps onto it. The upper clamp should be just big enough for your beaker to pass through. The lower clamp should be about 3 cm above the top of the Bunsen burner. Place a gauze on the lower clamp and place your beaker through the upper clamp on the centre of the gauze (Figure 21).

Heat the contents of this beaker with a Bunsen burner until the liquid boils. Try to dissolve as much of the yellow solid as possible.

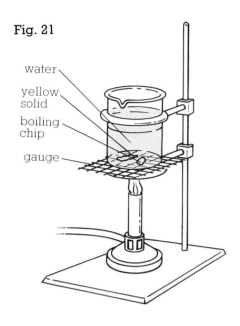

Fig. 21

water

yellow solid

boiling chip

gauge

The solvent is the liquid in which a solid is dissolved. In this experiment the solvent is water.

The evaporating dish must not be more than two-thirds full. Overfilling is dangerous as the liquid may boil over.

Meanwhile, set up your filtering equipment. Clean your funnel and warm it in a beaker of hot distilled water. Fold a fresh filter paper and use another clean 250-mL beaker to receive the hot filtrate.

Boil the mixture for about 5 min or until no further solid appears to be dissolving. Holding the hot beaker with beaker tongs, filter the hot liquid through the filter paper in your hot funnel into the clean beaker. Do this as quickly as possible. Cover the beaker with a watch glass or a piece of paper and allow its contents to cool slowly.

When the liquid is cold, filter the contents of the beaker through a fresh filter paper in a clean funnel.

Carefully remove the filter cone containing your crystals and place the cone on its side on some absorbent paper towel. (Put your name on the towel.) Allow your crystals to dry at least overnight in an undisturbed place.

Use a clean, dry spatula to transfer your dry sample to a vial and label it correctly. A label should show the following information:

- name of student(s)
- name of chemical in the sample
- number of recrystallizations and the solvent used

5. *Evaporation of a solution to dryness*

When lead(II) nitrate reacts with potassium iodide, two products are formed: one is the yellow precipitate, the other is dissolved in the filtrate.

Evaporation of the water from the filtrate enables you to recover the second product.

Fix a ring clamp to a retort stand and put a gauze on the clamp. Place the evaporating dish containing the filtrate on the gauze. Add a boiling chip to the contents and heat until the solution remaining is about 1 to 2 mm deep. Leave the contents to dry. The white solid left behind in the dish is your second product. It could be recrystallized (and freed from the boiling chip) like the yellow solid. However, because the white product is very soluble in water, the recrystallization is much more difficult.

Follow-up

1. In your notebook draw diagrams for each of the following procedures, using about a quarter of a page for each diagram.
   (a) evaporation
   (b) decanting a liquid from a solid
   (c) filtration

Fig. 22 *A student's diagram.*

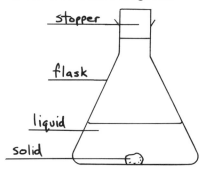

Some guidelines for drawing diagrams:

- No freehand drawing of equipment is acceptable in science diagrams.
- Draw in pencil using a ruler or a science stencil.
- Rule a horizontal line pointing to any item you label.
- Print in ink on this line the name of the item.

Figure 22 is an example of a student's diagram.

2. Write down what you now understand by each of the following terms:
   (a) precipitate
   (b) mother liquor
   (c) the process of decanting
   (d) the process of filtration
   (e) filtrate
   (f) residue
   (g) the process of dissolving
   (h) solute
   (i) solvent
   (j) process of evaporation
   (k) process of recrystallization

3. Why do you use a glass rod for pouring liquids?

4. Why must the outlet of the funnel be placed about 1 cm below the rim of the receiving vessel?

5. When filtering a precipitate, why do you decant the mother liquor first?

6. Why do you add a boiling chip to a liquid being heated in a beaker or dish?

7. Why do you recrystallize solids?

8. In recrystallization,
   (a) why do you filter the solution while it is hot,
   (b) why must you warm the funnel before you pour the hot liquid through the filter?

Changing Lead Into Gold—The Alchemists' Dream!

The beautiful gold crystals that you have prepared look just like flakes of gold metal. It isn't surprising then that alchemists, trying to change lead into gold many centuries ago, could be fooled into believing that they had indeed found the secret to great wealth.

The lead(II) nitrate solution could have been made by reacting lead with nitric acid. Potassium iodide solution could then have been mixed with the lead(II) nitrate solution to give lead(II) iodide —the "gold."

Lead(II) iodide has been used as a pigment in oil-based paints. Lead-containing paints are not used today because they are harmful to health.

Fig. 23 *Alchemists spent hundreds of years trying to turn cheap metals into gold.*

1.10 Preparing and Purifying a Painkiller

The drugs you find today in your medicine cabinet and in hospitals may have been discovered purely by chance. Some have been used for centuries and may have been extracted from materials found in nature. You can imagine that the active ingredients in these drugs were in a fairly crude form and were mixed with other chemicals. Nowadays, drugs have to be purified before they can be used. Purification is very important in chemical research and in drug production. Consumer products and drugs must contain no unwanted chemicals and should be packaged properly to prevent contamination (Figure 24).

An example of the discovery and purification of a lifesaving drug took place at the University of Toronto, starting in 1920. Two Canadians, Banting and Best (Figure 25), became famous for discovering the drug insulin. Insulin injections keep patients of severe diabetes alive. Insulin had to be isolated from the pancreas of domestic animals, such as cows, and purified.

A common drug, which you have probably taken to relieve a headache or fever, is aspirin. You are now going to prepare aspirin by reacting acetic anhydride with salicyclic acid. It is important that no water be present in the initial stages of the process. This reaction is usually very slow and can be speeded up by using concentrated sulfuric acid as a catalyst. (A **catalyst** is a chemical that speeds up a chemical reaction but does not get used up itself.)

Fig. 24 A "clean room" in a drug manufacturing plant.

Fig. 25 Frederick Banting (right) and Charles Best discovered insulin and were awarded the Nobel Prize in 1923. The picture shows the dog revived from diabetic coma with insulin.

Materials

safety goggles
glass stirring rod
large test tube, clean and dry
100-mL beaker
250-mL beaker
18 × 150 mm test tube
boiling chip
filter funnel
filter paper
balance
small ring clamp
hotplate
thermometer
crushed ice
salicyclic acid (solid)
cotton batting
concentrated sulphuric acid
acetic anhydride (kept in a burette in a fume hood)

Both sulphuric acid and acetic anhydride are highly corrosive. They will be given to you by your teacher.

Method

1. Prepare a hot water bath by filling the 250-mL beaker half full of water and heating it on a hotplate. Heat the water in the beaker to 70°C.

2. Find the mass of a piece of paper and then carefully weigh out 1 g of salicylic acid onto the paper.

3. Place the salicyclic acid in a *dry* 18 × 150 mm test tube.

4. Ask your teacher to add exactly 2 mL of acetic anhydride from the burette to your test tube. Your teacher will swirl the contents to mix the chemicals properly and to get any solid off the walls of the test tube. Your teacher will then add two drops of concentrated sulfuric acid.

5. Place the test tube and its contents in the hot water bath for about 10 min. Shake the contents. All the solid should dissolve.

6. Remove the test tube and allow the solution to cool for about 1 min.

7. Place about 10 mL of cold distilled water and about 20 mL of crushed ice in the 100-mL beaker. Pour the mixture from the test tube (in a thin stream) into this beaker (Figure 26a), and stir vigorously with a glass rod.

Fig. 26

(a)

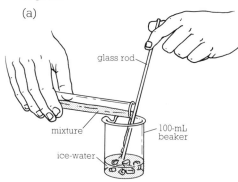

glass rod

mixture

ice-water

100-mL beaker

(b)

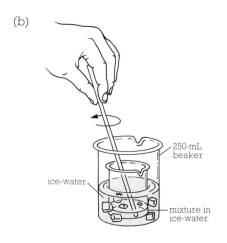

250-mL beaker

ice-water

mixture in ice-water

8. Empty the warm water out of the 250-mL beaker. Make a cold ice-water bath by placing some crushed ice in this beaker and adding about 50 mL of water. Place the smaller beaker into the larger beaker containing the ice-water (Figure 26b). Stir the mixture in the smaller beaker for about 10 min. A flaky white solid should form. Keep the ice-water bath cold by adding more ice if necessary.

9. Filter off the solid and wash with about 25 mL of ice-cold distilled water.

10. To recrystallize the white solid, place the solid in a clean test tube and add about 2 mL of distilled water. Place the test tube in a boiling water bath. Heat the contents of the test tube until all the solid is dissolved, adding a little more water to the test tube if necessary. Filter the hot solution through a hot funnel into a clean container, but use a small amount of fluffy cotton batting instead of a filter paper. Allow the contents of the container to cool slowly until no more crystals form. Filter off the crystals using a filter paper, and allow to dry. (An oven set at 100°C may be used to speed up the drying.) Transfer the dry sample to a vial and label it. Be sure to put your name on the vial, as you will need the sample for an activity in the next chapter.

11. To test your sample for purity, add a few drops of iron(III) chloride solution to a small portion of your sample. A purple colour would mean the presence of salicylic acid. If there is no purple colour, then your sample is ''pure.'' Record the result of this test on the label of the vial.

12. Hand in your sample of aspirin.

Do not use or taste your own aspirin!

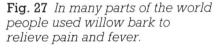

Fig. 27 *In many parts of the world people used willow bark to relieve pain and fever.*

The Aspirin Story

As early as 1763, it was reported that a brew made by boiling willow bark in water helped people who were in pain. The active ingredient in willow bark was later found to be salicylic acid. In some people salicylic acid had bad side effects, such as stomach pain and bleeding. In 1899, Felix Hoffman of the Bayer Company in Germany made a related chemical, acetyl salicylic acid (ASA). It was very successful in relieving pain and had fewer side effects. The company called it ''aspirin.''

The name aspirin comes from *a* in *acetyl*, and *spirin*, which was the common name for the ingredient in willow bark.

Aspirin is a most useful product. When you have a cold, the most common prescription is to go to bed, drink lots of fluids, and take an aspirin. Aspirin reduces fever, pain, and inflammation. It is used daily by people with bad arthritis and gout. It is also used by stroke victims because it reduces the clotting ability of blood and prevents strokes. However, this reduction in blood clotting could cause stomach bleeding in people who suffer from certain stomach ulcers. People who take too much aspirin experience buzzing or ringing in their ears and temporary hearing loss. An overdose can cause the death of a child or even an adult. Cats are poisoned by small amounts of aspirin and related chemicals.

Aspirin should never be stored in a humid place or for too long. Aspirin decomposes after a while to give salicylic acid, which is not very dangerous but does cause stomach irritation.

POINTS · TO · RECALL

- There are many chemicals in and around you.
- When you work with chemicals you must work safely so as to avoid hurting yourself and others.
- There are two types of observations: qualitative and quantitative.
- Qualitative observations are made using only your five senses.
- Quantitative observations are made using instruments; they are measurements involving numbers and units.
- If a guess is added to an observation, the observation becomes an inference.

- A theory is an explanation for certain observations and a way to predict things that have not yet been observed.
- You have practised: weighing, pouring liquids, decanting liquids, filtering mixtures, evaporating solutions, heating liquids, recrystallizing solids, and drawing scientific diagrams.
- The preparation of aspirin allows you to practise the knowledge and skills you have learned in this chapter.

1. List five items found in your bedroom that are made up of chemicals.
2. List three items that you find in the kitchen that contain colouring agents.
3. List three items that you find in the bathroom that contain perfume.
4. Some people feel that non-active ingredients in products should be banned. What do you think? Explain your answer.
5. Why is safety so important in the chemistry laboratory?
6. Give at least three safety precautions you would use when boiling a liquid in a beaker.
7. Pick out which of the following statements is a qualitative observation (*Qual*), a quantitative observation (*Quan*), or an inference (*Inf*). Write the letter of the statements in your note book and next to them the abbreviations: *Qual, Quan,* or *Inf.*
   (a) The strawberry is red.
   (b) The mass of 1 mL of water is 1 g.
   (c) The colour of butter is yellow because of the dyes in it.
8. Is it possible for two people doing the same experiment to observe different things? Explain your answer.
9. Why is it necessary to recrystallize solids? Why is this process so important in the drug industry?
10. What special precautions must you take when carrying out reactions that give out poisonous products?
11. Write down what you understand by:
    (a) decanting
    (b) precipitate
    (c) filtrate
    (d) ice-water bath
    (e) purification
    (f) recrystallization
12. Give two reasons why you should never weigh hot objects on a balance.
13. Find out as much as you can about a person, or persons, who discovered a new drug or chemical. Report your findings to the class. Your report may take any form. Be creative.
14. Discuss, as a class, the importance of the following to drugs and foods:
    (a) tamper-proof packaging.
    (b) product quality.
    How can society defend itself from unwanted chemicals in products?
    Consider the responsibilities of the public, the police, and the lawmakers.
15. Aspirin should always be used when it is as fresh as possible and should not be stored for long. (How does an old aspirin bottle smell?) Explain why.
16. Acetylsalicylic acid is one of many popular painkillers. List three other painkillers and indicate the products in which they are found. (Look in a book, or study medication labels.)
17. Choose five types of chemical products and briefly indicate how they are used in your daily life.

2

TYPES OF MATTER

What is the best way of classification here?

CONTENTS

Fig.1

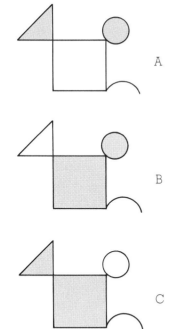

A

B

C

D

2.1 Classification

Millions and millions of different chemicals are known, and each day many more are discovered or made for the first time. How can a chemist hope to learn about so many chemicals? Fortunately, chemicals with similar properties can be categorized into groups. The group properties give the chemist some knowledge about the chemicals within the group.

Classification is the process of grouping things with common characteristics. It can, however, be difficult to decide on the common characteristic to use. For example, look at the objects in Figure 1.

Which characteristic would you use to group three of the objects together, leaving one out? There are several answers:

Answer 1: Group *A*, *B*, and *C* together because each has a solid tail
Answer 2: Group *A*, *B*, and *D* together because each has a coloured circle
Answer 3: Group *A*, *C*, and *D* together because each has a coloured triangle
Answer 4: Group *B*, *C*, and *D* together because each has a coloured square

Which answers are correct? All of them. How you classify depends largely on what you are interested in. A person interested in the shading of the triangle would choose answer 3. A person interested in the circle would choose answer 2.

Grouping the objects on the basis of two characteristics can be more complicated. For example, we could group *B* and *D* together because they have both a coloured square and a coloured circle.

In how many different ways can you group the following?

table salt   table sugar   orange juice   water   air

Members of the same group must have some characteristics in common. As an example, you can form three groups: solid, liquid, and gas.

Solid: table salt, table sugar
Liquid: water, orange juice
Gas: air

See how many other ways you can find. Then, as a class, decide on the "best" ways of grouping.

2.2 Classification of Matter

Matter is anything that has mass and occupies space.

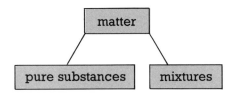

People are constantly classifying things. Can you imagine a library with the books not classified according to subject? The zoo classifies animals according to species; a department store classifies goods according to use; a record store classifies records according to type of music.

How then does a chemist classify matter? A study of the materials around us very quickly indicates that some are **pure substances** while many others are **mixtures**.

A pure substance contains only one type of matter. A mixture contains two or more pure substances. There are many different kinds of mixtures. One way in which chemists classify mixtures is according to the size of the particles present.

In **solutions**, the particles are too small to be seen with the naked eye or even under an optical microscope. All liquid and gaseous solutions are clear or transparent. Sugar dissolved in water is a good example of a solution (Figure 2).

Emulsions are mixtures of two liquids that do not dissolve in each other. One liquid is present in very small droplets that remain permanently suspended in the other liquid. Emulsions are never clear. Hand cream is a good example of an emulsion (Figure 3).

Foams are mixtures like emulsions but the suspended part is a gas. Examples of foams are shaving creams and beaten egg white (Figure 4).

Gels are mixtures that consist of liquid particles trapped within a network of solid particles. Examples of gels are Jello and some stick deodorants (Figure 5).

In **mechanical mixtures**, the particles are much larger than in the above mixtures and can usually be seen under an optical microscope or even with the naked eye. All mixtures that do not fall into the above categories are mechanical mixtures. An example is a mixture of salt and pepper (Figure 6).

Fig. 2 *Soft drink is a solution.*

Fig. 3 *What is the emulsion that is being used here?*

Fig. 4 *What is the use of foam in this photograph?*

Fig. 5 *Is this a gel that you enjoy?*

Fig. 6 *Concrete mix is a mechanical mixture.*

45

The following is an exercise in classification. The consumer products listed below will be displayed around the room. Look at them carefully.

Questions

aluminum foil	gold objects	shampoo
baking soda	hair gel	shaving foam
coffee (instant)	hair mousse	shoe polish
copper objects	Italian salad dressing	silver objects
dishwashing detergent	Jello pudding	soap flakes
dried vegetable mixture	ketchup	soup mix
eye shadow	laundry detergent	stick deodorant
face cream	lipstick	sugar
fruit drink crystals	mayonnaise	toothpaste
glass	Peptobismol	vinegar
glass cleaner	salt	water

1. Try to classify each product as a pure substance or as a mixture. If it is a mixture, try to indicate what kind.

2. In your list of pure substances, are there any products that you suspect of containing other substances? List these products.

3. Can you successfully classify materials on the basis of appearance alone?

2.3 Testing for Purity

It is very difficult to classify substances as pure substances or mixtures using appearance alone. Chemists must use other means of testing for purity.

In your preparation of aspirin, you used a chemical test to check the purity of your product. Chemical testing is a good method, except that it contaminates or destroys the product. An alternative method is to make certain quantitative observations of a given substance.

A pure substance has certain characteristic properties which are constant provided that the measuring conditions are kept constant. These properties include:

- the melting point (the temperature at which a substance changes from a solid into a liquid)
- the boiling point (the maximum temperature at which a substance changes from a liquid into a gas)
- the density (the ratio of the mass of a substance to its volume)
- the solubility in a certain solvent (the maximum amount of a substance that can be dissolved in a given quantity of the solvent)

Describing a liquid as clear and colourless does not necessarily identify the liquid. But a clear, colourless liquid melting at 0°C, boiling at approximately 100°C, and having a density of 1 g/mL is most probably water. An impure sample of water, however, will not have these exact characteristic properties. We can therefore tell if a given substance is pure by checking its characteristic properties.

In the following experiment you will test the purity of a given substance by finding its melting point. The technique uses only a small amount of material and is fairly accurate if the heating is done slowly. The term ''melting point'' suggests that a substance melts at a single temperature. For example, we might read that a substance has a melting point of 145°C. When we determine the melting point experimentally, however, we may find that the substance starts to melt at 144°C and finishes melting at 146°C. The temperature range, 144°C to 146°C, is called the **melting range** of the substance.

Materials

safety goggles
melting point tubes
thermometer
retort stand

ring and gauze
Bunsen burner
clamp
20 cm long glass tube
100-mL beaker
pestle and mortar
pure naphthalene
pure paradichlorobenzene
a sample of 90% naphthalene and 10% paradichlorobenzene by mass
a sample of 90% paradichlorobenzene and 10% naphthalene by mass

Method

1. Crush the solid naphthalene to a fine powder using the pestle and mortar (Figure 7a).

2. Gently tap the open end of a melting point tube into the powder until you have filled the tube with solid to a depth of about 2 mm (Figure 7b).

3. Turn over the melting point tube and gently tap the sealed end against the desk until all the solid in the tube has moved to the sealed end. If you cannot get the solid to the sealed end, try dropping the melting point tube, sealed end first, down a 20 cm long glass tube onto your desk (Figure 7c).

4. Use a thin rubber band to attach the melting point tube to a thermometer. The bottom of the thermometer bulb and the bottom of the melting point tube should be at the same level (Figure 7d).

For solids that melt below 100°C, water can be used as the heating liquid. For higher-melting solids, a higher-boiling liquid such as liquid paraffin should be used.

5. Clamp the thermometer to a retort stand so that the bulb of the thermometer and the bottom of the melting point tube are below the surface of water in a 100-mL beaker (Figure 7e).

6. Heat the liquid *slowly* with a Bunsen burner. As accurately as possible, record the temperatures at which the naphthalene begins to melt and finishes melting.

In melting point determinations, always start with cold water in the beaker.

7. Repeat the procedure to find the melting point of
   • a sample of pure paradichlorobenzene
   • a sample of 90% naphthalene and 10% paradichlorobenzene by mass
   • a sample of 90% paradichlorobenzene and 10% naphthalene by mass

8. Record your results in a suitable chart. Comparing your results with the rest of the class will give you some idea of the accuracy of your thermometer and your technique.

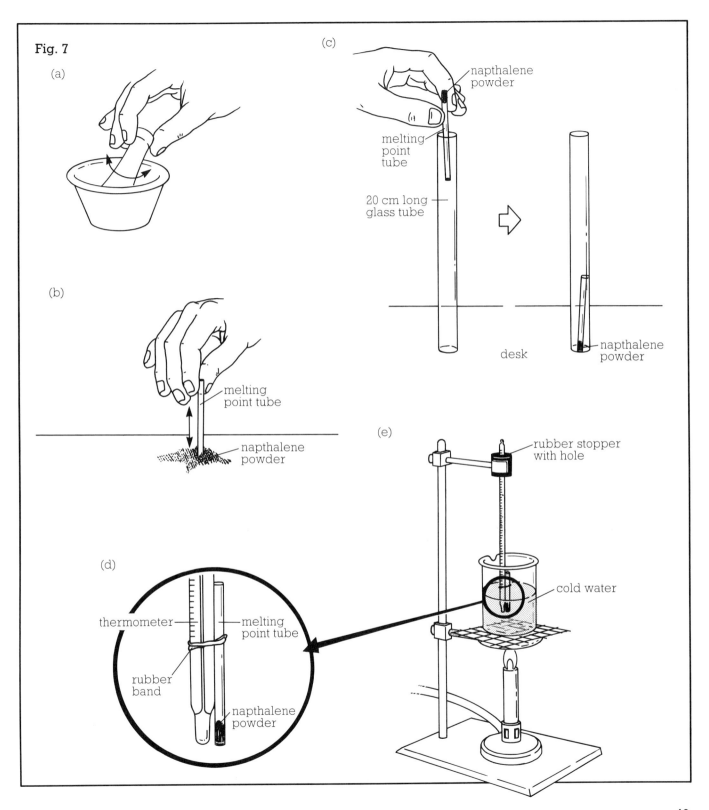

Fig. 7

(a)

(b)
melting
point tube
napthalene
powder

(c)
napthalene
powder
melting
point
tube
20 cm long
glass tube
desk
napthalene
powder

(d)
thermometer
melting
point tube
rubber
band
napthalene
powder

(e)
rubber stopper
with hole
cold water

49

1. Naphthalene and paradichlorobenzene are both pure substances. What did you notice about the temperatures at which these materials began to melt? What did you notice about their melting ranges?

2. What happened to the temperature at which melting started and the melting range when paradichlorobenzene was added to the naphthalene as an impurity?

3. What happened to the temperature at which melting started and the melting range when naphthalene was added to the paradichlorobenzene as an impurity?

4. An added impurity always lowers the temperature at which a pure substance begins to melt and usually also results in a wider melting range. Chemists use this to determine whether two samples with similar melting ranges are in fact the same substance or different substances. For example:

   Sample *A* melts at 95 to 97°C
   Sample *B* melts at 94 to 96°C

   The chemist mixes *A* and *B* and finds the melting range of the mixture. If the melting range of the mixture is lower than the melting range of *A* and *B*, then *A* and *B* cannot be the same substance. If the melting range of the mixture is approximately the same as the melting range of *A* and *B*, then *A* and *B* are samples of the same substance.

5. If you still have your sample of aspirin, find out if it is pure by determining its melting point. Pure aspirin melts at approximately 135°C, so you must use liquid paraffin in the beaker and a thermometer that can read temperatures up to and above 135°C. Even if your sample of aspirin begins to melt at approximately 135°C, it does not prove that you actually have aspirin. In making aspirin, you started with a substance called salicylic acid. Salicylic acid has a melting point of 159°C. Your "aspirin" sample may actually be an impure sample of salicylic acid. What could you do to check that your sample is aspirin?

6. In the above experiment, you were not measuring the temperature of the solid directly. You were actually measuring the temperature of the water that was being used to heat the solid. What precautions must be taken to ensure that the melting range is small and accurate?

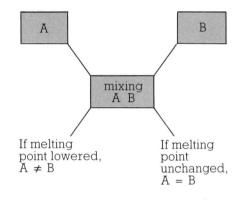

A   B

mixing
A B

If melting
point lowered,
A ≠ B

If melting
point
unchanged,
A = B

2.4 More About Melting

There are many examples of lowering melting points by forming mixtures. Motorists mix ethylene glycol (antifreeze) with water for their radiators. The antifreeze mixture has a lower melting temperature than water alone and can be cooled to below 0°C before the mixture begins to solidify or freeze. The more ethylene glycol that is added to the water, the lower the freezing temperature of the mixture. Motorists also mix isopropyl alcohol with water for use as windscreen washer fluid.

In some cities, the municipal authorities sprinkle salt on the roads as a form of snow clearing. The snow and salt mixture has a lower melting temperature than does pure water, and usually the air temperature is high enough to melt the mixture.

People who work in electronics often have to solder two pieces of wire together (Figure 9). The solder is usually a mixture of tin, lead, and bismuth.

Fig. 8 *These trucks are loaded with salt to be used for clearing snow.*

Fig. 9 *Solders made from different proportions of tin, lead, and bismuth have different melting points.*

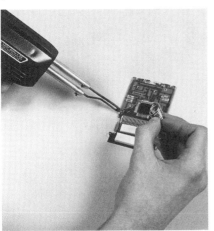

	Percentage by mass			Melting point
	tin	lead	bismuth	
Pure tin	100%	0%	0%	232°C
Pure lead	0%	100%	o%	328°C
Pure bismuth	0%	0%	100%	271°C
Solder 1	25%	25%	50%	130°C
Solder 2	38%	50%	12%	190°C
Solder 3	50%	25%	25%	169°C

Some magicians love to show how spoons can be bent by thought power alone. A spoon made from 45% bismuth, 23% lead, 8% tin, 5% cadmium, and 19% indium by mass melts at about 50°C. The friction of rubbing the middle of such a spoon between your fingers may release sufficient heat to soften the metal and allow the ends to bend downwards. Such a spoon completely melts in a hot cup of coffee.

The fabric softener for use in a clothes dryer is a mixture coated onto a suitable piece of material. In a clothes dryer, the temperature is high enough to melt the fabric softener mixture. The mixture then attaches to the clothes in the dryer. The fabric softener makes the clothes feel softer and reduces the build-up of static electricity.

Melting temperatures are also important in the manufacture of chocolate. Chocolate occurs in four different forms, each with a different melting temperature. Three of them have low melting points and are likely to melt in the hand. These three forms eventually change into the form with the highest melting point. Heat is released during this change. The heat melts parts of the chocolate. The fats in the chocolate then come to the surface and give the surface of the chocolate a dull grayish colour. The chocolate is still edible, only it does not look too appetizing.

Fig. 10 The form of chocolate with the highest melting point is desirable because it does not melt in the hand.

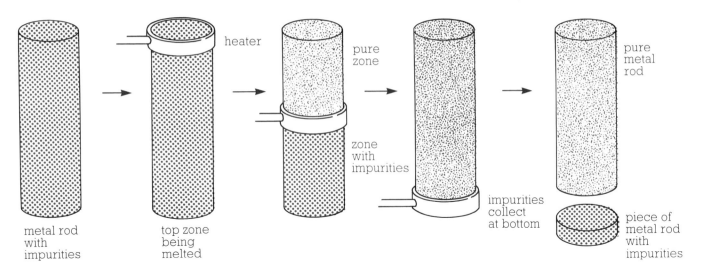

heater

pure zone

zone with impurities

pure metal rod

impurities collect at bottom

piece of metal rod with impurities

metal rod with impurities

top zone being melted

Fig. 11 *The various stages of zone melting.*

Fig. 12 *When you suck on a popsicle, the coloured material is pulled out, leaving colourless ice behind.*

Zone melting or **zone refining**, a technique to purify metals and other materials, is related to melting (Figure 11). One end of a metal rod is heated until this end is molten. The heater is then slowly moved towards the other end of the rod. Different zones of the metal melt and then resolidify as the heater moves on. As the molten zone moves, impurities collect in it. Eventually all the impurities are at the other end of the metal, where they can easily be removed. The remaining metal is purer. Metals can be zone refined so that there is no more than one part of impurity per ten billion parts of metal.

Zone refining is also used for the manufacture of semiconductors in the electronics industry. Materials such as germanium must first be made extremely pure. Strangely enough, once the germanium is pure, the same technique is then used to add minute quantities of a special impurity to the germanium. This turns the germanium into a semiconductor.

You may have noticed something very similar to this technique when sucking on a highly coloured popsicle (Figure 12). Similarly, the surface of an iceberg has melted and then refrozen over the years. In the process, many of the impurities have settled at the bottom of the iceberg, leaving the upper portion fairly pure.

2.5 Chromatography to Separate a Mixture

"Chromatography" comes from the Greek word *chroma*, which means colour.
There are various types of chromatography: paper, liquid column, thin layer, and gas chromatography.

Fig. 13 *The principle of chromatography is similar to a boat race.*

Very few materials found in nature are pure. Chemists have synthesized many chemicals but very few are used in a pure form. Most materials that we use every day are mixtures of two or more chemicals. Each part of the mixture is present for some definite purpose.

Identifying a sample of material in a chemical laboratory can be difficult if the sample is a mixture. Usually, the components of the mixture must first be separated. Recrystallization is one way of isolating a pure substance from a mixture. **Chromatography** is another method for separating the components of a mixture.

Imagine a boat race on a river between two points (Figure 13).

All the boats travel in the same direction. After some time, the boats will be located at different distances from the destination. Eventually, all the boats will reach the destination—at different times.

Chromatography is a technique that works in a similar way. Chromatography requires a fixed or stationary material (the river bed between the two points) and a solvent (water current and wind). The mixture (the boats) is added to one end of the fixed material. The solvent travels from that end of the fixed material to the other end. Components of the mixture travel along with the solvent at different speeds and are separated. Eventually all the components of the mixture reach the other end of the fixed material.

In the following experiment, you will use the technique called **paper chromatography** to separate the coloured dyes from a sample of fruit drink crystals.

Materials

safety goggles
1-cm wide chromatography paper or No. 1 filter paper cut into
    20-cm strips
250-mL Erlenmeyer flask
isopropanol/water mixture (2:1 ratio by volume)
micropipette
concentrated ethanol solutions of fruit drink crystals (for example,
    grape, lime, root beer, and tropical punch)

The micropipette can be made by warming a melting point tube in a Bunsen flame and then drawing out the hot glass.

Method

1. Write your name and flavour of fruit drink used in pencil at one end of three or four different filter paper strips (Figure 14a).

2. On each piece of filter paper, draw a pencil line about 1 cm from the other end (Figure 14b).

3. Dip the narrow end of the micropipette into a drink crystal solution. Carefully spot the paper at the centre of the pencil line (Figure 14c). Repeat the spotting two or three times on exactly the same spot, but allow it to dry between each spotting. Keep the spot as small as possible. Repeat with the other drink crystal solutions on your other paper strips.

4. Pour isopropanol/water mixture into the Erlenmeyer flask to a depth of about 0.5 cm.

5. Hang each paper strip in the Erlenmeyer flask so that the spotted end is just in the liquid. Make sure that the coloured spot is above the level of the liquid. Bend the top end over the top of the flask to keep each strip in place (Figure 14d).

Fig.14

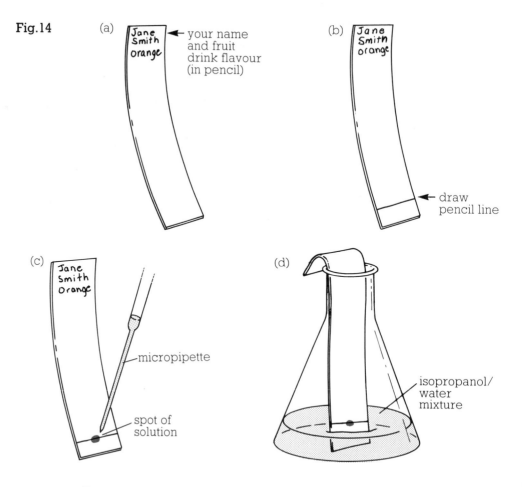

(a) your name and fruit drink flavour (in pencil)

(b) draw pencil line

(c) micropipette / spot of solution

(d) isopropanol/ water mixture

6. Allow the liquid to run up the paper for as long as you can or until the leading edge of the liquid has reached the top of the Erlenmeyer flask.

7. Remove the strips, mark the solvent edge with a pencil, and allow the strips to dry.

Follow-up

1. In this experiment, what is the stationary material and what is the solvent?

2. Why is the original spot kept as small as possible?

3. Do your paper strips show that the fruit drink crystals contain mixtures of dyes?

4. Which flavour of fruit drink crystals appeared to contain the greatest number of dyes? If you were asked to produce a pure sample of each of these dyes, how would you do it?

TESTING BLOOD FOR THE PRESENCE OF DRUGS

Chromatography is also used to identify the components of a mixture. If a suitable stationary material and solvent is chosen, the various components in the mixture will move at different speeds and separate. The distance travelled by each component in the mixture, compared to the distance travelled by the solvent, is then checked against the distance travelled by known substances. If there is a match, then there is an excellent chance that the known substances and the components in the mixture are identical.

Many laboratories use gas chromatography to identify unknown materials (Figure 15). A person suspected of having taken drugs has a blood sample tested in this way. A minute quantity of the blood is injected into the gas chromatograph at one end of a long and very thin glass tube (usually a coil about 25 m long). A gas is used to move the blood sample through the tube. A special detector, connected to a recorder, is placed at the other end of the tube. The recorder indicates both the time taken for the materials in the blood to move through the tube and the amount of each material in the blood. If a particular drug is indicated, a laboratory technician will confirm its presence with other tests.

Fig. 15 *Gas chromatography is used to identify unknown materials.*

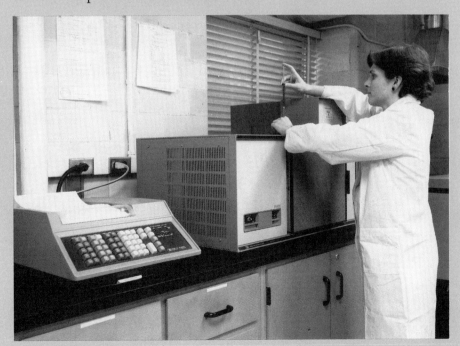

2.6 Types of Pure Substances

In your earlier science classes, you learned that all matter is made up of atoms and molecules. This means that pure substances and mixtures must be made up of atoms and molecules.

An **atom** is the smallest particle of matter than can take part in a chemical reaction. Atoms can join or bond with identical atoms or with other atoms to form molecules. A **molecule** is a particle consisting of two or more atoms held together. This bonding of atoms means that molecules are not just mixtures of atoms. The properties of a molecule are different from the properties of the atoms from which it is made.

In this chapter we have learned that mixtures are made up of pure substances. What then are pure substances? Chemists recognize two types of pure substances: elements and compounds.

An **element** is a pure substance containing atoms or molecules in which all the atoms are of the same type. There are about 108 different elements; about 91 exist naturally, and the rest are made by scientists using special equipment. An element is represented by a symbol of one or two letters. The first letter is always capitalized and the second letter is always lower case.

```
pure substances
   |
elements    compounds
```

An element is made up of only one type of atom, whether or not the atoms are joined to form molecules.

For example:　Au for gold　　C for carbon
　　　　　　　Na for sodium　Cl_2 for chlorine
　　　　　　　H_2 for hydrogen　O_2 for oxygen

Fig. 16 *Iron is a familiar element.*

Fig. 17 *A diamond is a pure form of the element carbon.*

Fig. 18
(a) *An element may be made up of individual atoms.*
(b) *An element may also be made up of molecules, not individual atoms.*
(c) *A compound is made up of identical molecules. Each molecule is made of two or more types of atoms.*
(d) *A mixture may contain various types of elements and compounds.*

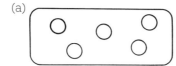
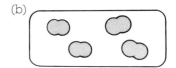
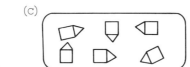
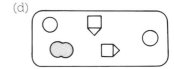

When numbers are used with the chemical symbol for the element, the numbers indicate how many atoms of that element make up a molecule of that element. Thus, H_2 indicates that a hydrogen molecule is made from two atoms of hydrogen.

A **compound** is a pure substance containing molecules made up of the atoms of two or more elements. We can also represent compounds using letters and numbers.

For example: H_2O for water C_2H_6O for alcohol
              $C_{12}H_{22}O_{11}$ for table sugar   NaCl for table salt

Fig. 19 *Water (or ice) is a compound made up of hydrogen and oxygen.*

Fig. 20 *A molecule of the compound called table sugar contains 12 carbon atoms, 22 hydrogen atoms, and 11 oxygen atoms. The picture shows sugar crystallized from the sugar sap concentrate of sugar cane.*

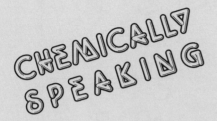

MORE ABOUT THE ELEMENTS

The known elements are not distributed evenly throughout the universe. Hydrogen is the most abundant element in the universe—about 90% of all the atoms are hydrogen atoms. Helium atoms make up most of the rest.

Twelve elements were known in ancient times (before the sixteenth century): antimony, arsenic, bismuth, carbon, copper, gold, iron, lead, mercury, silver, sulfur, and tin.

Some elements are named after people, for example, curium (Curie), and einsteinium (Einstein). Other elements are named after places, such as californium (California) and polonium (Poland). Four elements are named after Ytterby, a town in Sweden: erbium, terbium, ytterbium, and yttrium.

It is thought that the composition of the elements of the universe is constantly changing. Hydrogen is being changed into helium, and helium is being changed into the other elements.

About 70 elements have been identified in the sun. The element helium was discovered in the sun before it was discovered on the earth. In fact, the name "helium" comes from the Greek word *helios* meaning the sun.

The most abundant element found on the earth itself is oxygen (about 49% of all the atoms), followed by iron (17%) and silicon (14%). These three elements, together with magnesium, sulfur, nickel, aluminum, and calcium, make up about 99% of all the atoms found on the earth.

Fig. 21 *The most abundant elements on the earth.*

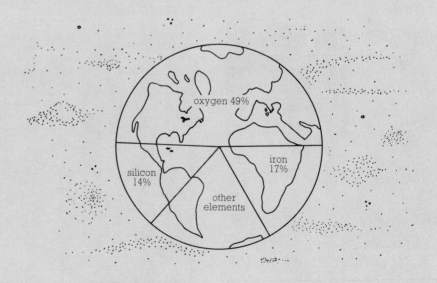

In the human body, 63.2% of the atoms are hydrogen, 25.6% oxygen, 9.5% carbon, 1.3% nitrogen, 0.2% phosphorus, and 0.2% all the rest.

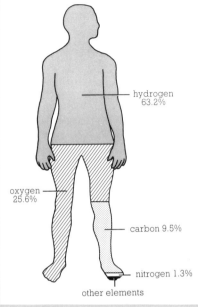

Fig. 22 *The elements making up the human body.*

By international agreement, each element has a unique symbol. It does not matter what language is spoken or what alphabet is used, everyone uses the same symbols for the elements.

Many of the symbols seem obvious when you consider the names of the elements. Some symbols, however, bear no resemblance to the corresponding name. The symbol, W, used for the element tungsten, comes from the German name *wolfram*. The symbols of other elements are related to their Latin names.

Element	Latin name	Symbol
Copper	Cuprum	Cu
Gold	Aurum	Au
Iron	Ferrum	Fe
Lead	Plumbum	Pb
Mercury	Hydrargyrum	Hg
Potassium	Kalium	K
Silver	Argentum	Ag
Sodium	Natrium	Na
Tin	Stannum	Sn

2.7 Physical Properties of Some Common Elements

You may have come across the **periodic table**, which is a method of grouping the elements. In this activity, you will observe the first 20 elements in the periodic table. They are:

Hydrogen	H
Helium	He
Lithium	Li
Beryllium	Be
Boron	B
Carbon	C
Nitrogen	N
Oxygen	O
Fluorine	F
Neon	Ne
Sodium	Na
Magnesium	Mg
Aluminum	Al
Silicon	Si
Phosphorus	P
Sulfur	S
Chlorine	Cl
Argon	Ar
Potassium	K
Calcium	Ca

Fig. 23 *A simple periodic table.*

1 H																	2 He
3 Li	4 Be											5 B	6 C	7 N	8 O	9 F	10 Ne
11 Na	12 Mg											13 Al	14 Si	15 P	16 S	17 Cl	18 Ar
19 K	20 Ca			23 V	24 Cr		26 Fe	27 Co	28 Ni	29 Cu	30 Zn		32 Ge	33 As		35 Br	
									48 Pd	47 Ag			50 Sn			53 I	
	56 Ba								78 Pt	79 Au	80 Hg		82 Pb				86 Rn

Do not touch the elements when trying to find out about their texture.

Find out more about each of these elements and write down its

(a) name

(b) symbol

(c) state (solid, liquid, or gas) at room temperature

(d) colour

(e) apparent texture if a solid

(f) lustre if a solid

(g) ability to conduct electricity—should already be noted on the sample

(h) ability to conduct heat—should already be noted on the sample

The following is an additional list of elements:

Vanadium   V
Chromium   Cr
Iron   Fe
Cobalt   Co
Nickel   Ni
Copper   Cu
Zinc   Zn
Germanium   Ge
Arsenic   As
Bromine   Br
Palladium   Pd
Silver   Ag
Tin   Sn
Iodine   I
Barium   Ba
Platinum   Pt
Gold   Au
Mercury   Hg
Lead   Pb
Radon   Rn

For each of these elements, write down its

(a) name

(b) symbol

(c) ability to conduct electricity

(d) ability to conduct heat

Graphite, a form of carbon, is a non-metal but it does conduct electricity.

1. Which of the 40 elements listed do you think are metals?

2. Many people think of metals as shiny solids. Do all the metals that you noted fit this description?

3. The only real test for a metal is whether it conducts electricity or not. List all the elements that conduct electricity. These are the metals and the rest are all non-metals.

4. Look at a periodic table. Where are the metals and where are the non-metals?

5. Of the first 20 elements, which are colourless gases?

6. Of the first 20 elements, which metals have a colour?

7. Of the first 20 elements, how many are liquids?

8. Of the first 20 elements, what are the colours of the non-metallic solids?

Fig. 24 *The only metal that is a liquid at room temperature is mercury.*

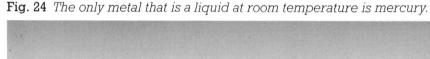

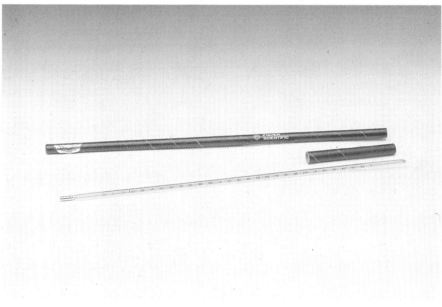

- Chemists classify the millions of chemicals into groups with common characteristics.
- The grouping used in classification depends upon the interest of the classifier.
- Matter may be classified as either a pure substance or as a mixture.
- Pure substances are either elements or compounds.
- An element contains atoms or molecules in which all the atoms are of the same type.
- A compound contains molecules made up of the atoms of two or more elements.
- Mixtures are classified, according to particle size, into solutions, emulsions, foams, gels, and mechanical mixtures.
- Melting point, boiling point, density, and solubility are characteristic properties used to identify a material.
- It is difficult to measure a single temperature for the melting point of a substance; the melting range is usually quoted.
- A pure substance melts at a constant temperature and has a narrow melting range.
- Added impurities lower the melting point of a pure substance.
- Adding impurities to lower the melting point of a substance explains why we mix metals to make solder, use salt for snow clearing in the winter, and add antifreeze to water in car radiators.
- Zone melting is used to purify metals and make semiconductor materials.
- Chromatography is used to separate the parts of a mixture.
- The periodic table is a method of grouping the elements.
- Appearance alone cannot be used to distinguish between metal and non-metal elements.

R E V I E W · Q U E S T I O N S

1. Classify the following materials in at least two different ways: milk, starch, nitrogen gas, salt water, flour.

2. Classify the following materials as emulsions, foams, gels, mechanical mixtures, or solutions:

   (a) homogenized milk
   (b) ketchup
   (c) shaving cream
   (d) gelatin dessert
   (e) air
   (f) cake mix
   (g) beaten egg white
   (h) "flat" pop
   (i) chicken noodle soup mix
   (j) black tea made from a tea bag

3. Why is it difficult to classify materials on the basis of appearance alone?

4. Which of the following represent elements and which represent compounds?

   (a) O_2
   (b) Co
   (c) CO
   (d) Fe
   (e) $Al_2(SO_4)_3$
   (f) NO
   (g) Xe
   (h) P_4
   (i) SO_2
   (j) C_8H_{18}

5. If two solids both melt at 55°C, what other properties can you measure in order to distinguish between the two solids?

6. Substance A melts at 110°C to 112°C. Substance B melts at 111°C to 112°C. How can you decide whether or not the two substances are the same material?

7. When is water not useful as the heating liquid to find the melting point of a solid?

8. When should a hotplate be used instead of a Bunsen burner to carry out a melting point determination?

9. Pure substance A melts at 120°C and pure substance B melts at 80°C. A 50:50 mixture of A and B melts at about 40°C.

   (a) Sketch a graph of temperature (vertical axis) versus percentage of A in the mixture. Plot the three points shown in the following chart. Join the three points with straight lines to get a V-shape graph.

% A	0	50	100
Melting temperature	80°C	40°C	120°C

   (b) Use the graph to predict the melting point of a mixture which has 25% A in it.

10. The table below shows the freezing points of different strengths of antifreeze/water mixture. If you live in a place where the coldest recorded temperature in winter is −30°C, what strength of antifreeze would you use in your radiator?

Antifreeze %	40	50	55	60	70
Water %	60	50	45	40	30
Freezing point	−24°C	−37°C	−44°C	−52°C	−64°C

11. Some motorists fill their car radiators with fresh water during the summer. Why can this be a dangerous practice?

12. Briefly explain how zone melting works.

13. How would you use zone melting to add an even distribution of impurity to a pure metal?

14. A little research for you to carry out. Adding an impurity to a metal lowers the melting point of the metal. Does the added impurity cause the metal to become softer or harder? If you like jewellery, you may already know the answer.

15. Since icebergs usually form in sea water, why do they mostly contain fresh water?

16. Explain why we are able to separate mixtures using chromatography?

17. In paper chromatography two measurements are important: the distance moved by the spot (D_{spot}), and the distance moved by the solvent (D_{solv}) over the same time period (Figure 25).

Fig. 25

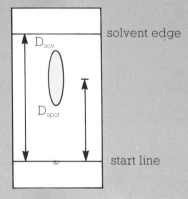
solvent edge
D_{sov}
D_{spot}
start line

The ratio $\dfrac{D_{spot}}{D_{solv}}$ is used to match the identity of two materials. If the two materials do not have the identical ratio, measured under the same conditions, then the two materials are unlikely to be the same.

Measure the $\dfrac{D_{spot}}{D_{solv}}$ ratio for each substance A and substance B in Figure 26. Are they the same material?

Fig. 26

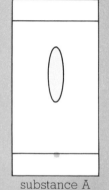
substance A

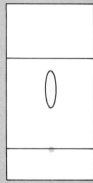
substance B

18. The following values for D_{spot} and D_{solv} were found for different coloured dyes in fruit drink crystals using the same solvent.

Flavour	Colour of dye	D_{spot}	D_{solv}
Rainbow punch	purple orange	13 mm 29 mm	49 mm 49 mm
Strawberry punch	purple orange	20 mm 43 mm	70 mm 70 mm
Lemon-lime	yellow blue	19 mm 47 mm	67 mm 67 mm
Grape	purple blue	19 mm 50 mm	70 mm 70 mm

(a) Calculate the $\dfrac{D_{spot}}{D_{solv}}$ ratio for each dye present in each flavour.

(b) Is there any evidence that the same dye is used in the different flavours?

19. Without referring to the periodic table, give the symbols used for the following elements:

(a) helium
(b) beryllium
(c) boron
(d) chlorine
(e) iodine

(f) calcium
(g) potassium
(h) iron
(i) lead
(j) gold

20. Without referring to the periodic table, give the name of each of the following elements:

(a) Hg
(b) Na
(c) Br
(d) Mg
(e) Si

(f) P
(g) S
(h) Cu
(i) Sn
(j) Ag

21. How can the periodic table be used to indicate which elements are metals and which are non-metals?

22. List the first 20 elements in the periodic table under the headings *solid*, *liquid*, or *gas*. Write down the symbol and colour of each element.

3

CHEMICAL CHANGES

Fire is an indication that a chemical change is taking place.

CONTENTS

3.1 A Burning Sensation

Have you ever been advised by a fire safety officer on how to keep your home safe from fire? If so, the officer might have told you that the three requirements for a fire to occur are:

- fuel
- oxygen
- a sufficiently high temperature

In groups of four, discuss the following questions:

1. How would you light a campfire or a fire in your fireplace? Write down each step and why you would do it.

2. Based on the requirements for a fire listed above, discuss how you would put out a fire.

3. What would you do if you were in a house that was on fire?

4. Develop a set of fire safety rules for your own home.

When you are finished, post your group summary. The whole class can then discuss the questions.

Your fire safety officer might also have told you not to accumulate rubbish, old newspapers, and junk in your home or garage. Oil, paint, or polish on cleaning rags slowly reacts with oxygen to produce heat, and the heat may build up sufficiently to set the rags on fire. This is an example of **spontaneous combustion**, or burning that starts by itself.

Fig. 1 *Learn how to keep fire out of your home and how to put out a fire.*

Sometimes, burning can occur explosively or in a flash of flame (Figure 2). If you have a cloud of powder (such as sawdust, grain dust, coal dust, or flour), a spark can set the whole cloud on fire almost at once. This is because the fuel in powdered form has a large surface area exposed to oxygen. If the fire occurs in an enclosed space, like a grain elevator, an explosion may occur.

3.2 Chemical and Physical Changes

When wood is burned, water vapour (steam), gases, and charcoal are produced. You cannot put these materials together to obtain wood again. Burning is an example of a chemical change.

A **chemical change** is a change that produces new substances with different physical and chemical properties from the original substances. The production of acetylene from calcium carbide, in Chapter 1, is another example of a chemical change.

In some other changes, known as physical changes, matter only changes its form. Examples of physical changes are melting, freezing, dissolving, and recrystallizing.

A **physical change** is a change in which the chemical composition of the original substances remains the same.

Observations during a chemical change may include:

- gas bubbles being formed
- the formation or disappearance of a solid
- a permanent colour change
- heat or light being given off or taken in
- electricity being produced (Figure 3)

Fig. 2 *The fire in this grain elevator could have been caused by a dust explosion.*

Fig. 3 *Stick a piece of zinc and a penny into the flesh of a lemon about 1 cm apart. The voltmeter will show you that electricity is produced. Hook up several "lemon cells" in series. See who can get the most electricity!*

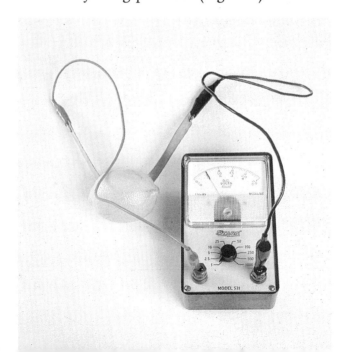

Fig. 4 *Barbecuing—a chemical change or a physical change?*

Questions

1. What is a chemical change?

2. What is a physical change?

3. Decide whether each of the following is a chemical change or a physical change. Write in your notebook the letters (a) to (p). Beside each letter write *Ch* (chemical change) or *Ph* (physical change).

(a) iron rusting
(b) dynamite exploding
(c) a cigarette burning
(d) water boiling
(e) meat barbecuing
(f) stone being crushed
(g) sulfur melting
(h) silver tarnishing
(i) an egg frying
(j) sugar dissolving in water
(k) a cake baking
(l) leaves changing colour in the fall
(m) freezing food
(n) sulfur burning
(o) paint discolouring
(p) glass breaking

3.3 Types of Chemical Changes

In a chemical change, the chemicals we start off with are called **reactants**, and the chemicals we end up with or produce are called **products**.

$$\text{reactant(s)} \rightarrow \text{product(s)}$$

A chemical reaction can be represented by a **word equation**. A word equation names all the reactants and all the products. For example, in Chapter 1, you added solid calcium carbide to water and produced acetylene gas and calcium hydroxide. The word equation for this reaction is:

calcium carbide + water → acetylene + calcium hydroxide

You will now do experiments involving the four main types of chemical changes:

(a) synthesis A + B → AB

(b) decomposition AB → A + B

(c) single displacement A + BC → B + AC

(d) double displacement AB + CD → AD + CB

71

3.4 Heating Magnesium in Air

Materials

safety goggles
1.5-cm piece of magnesium ribbon
tongs
Bunsen burner

Do not look directly at the reaction! You could damage your eyes. Look through cobalt blue glass.

Method

1. Obtain a piece of magnesium ribbon (about 1.5 cm long).

2. Describe its appearance.

3. Using a pair of tongs, place the magnesium in a Bunsen flame until the magnesium starts to react. Describe what happens during the reaction and describe the product.

Synthesis

When magnesium is heated in air, the reaction is a **synthesis**. In this reaction, the reactants are both elements (magnesium and oxygen), and the product is a compound (magnesium oxide) formed from the two elements.

In a synthesis reaction, if one of the elements is a metal and the other a non-metal, then the compound formed is named by:

- writing the name of the metallic element first (and unchanged)
- modifying the name of the non-metallic element to end in *-ide*

The word equation for the reaction you just did is:

$$\text{magnesium} + \text{oxygen} \rightarrow \text{magnesium oxide}$$

metallic element   non-metallic element   compound

If calcium (metal) reacts with carbon (non-metal), the word equation is

$$\text{calcium} + \text{carbon} \rightarrow \text{calcium carbide}$$

A reaction between two chemicals, not necessarily elements, to form one compound may also be called synthesis. For example, the following is also a synthesis:

$$\text{calcium oxide} + \text{water} \rightarrow \text{calcium hydroxide}$$

Fig. 5 *The reaction when a non-electronic flashbulb goes off is the same as heating magnesium.*

CHEMICAL TIDBITS

CUTTING DOWN ON THE HOUSEWORK!

Many homes now have windows with aluminum frames (Figure 6). The surface of the aluminum looks dull. This is because the following synthesis reaction takes place as soon as you shine the aluminum:

aluminum + oxygen → aluminum oxide

The aluminum oxide coating prevents further corrosion, or destruction, of the aluminum surface beneath. So do not waste your time trying to shine up aluminum frames.

Aluminum oxide is very different from the destructive iron oxide, **rust**. Rust is called a destructive oxide because it falls off the surface of iron and does not protect the metal underneath.

iron + oxygen → iron(III) oxide

Fig. 6 *It is all right for aluminum window frames to look dull!*

3.5 Heating Zinc and Sulfur (Demonstration)

Materials

safety goggles
retort stand
Bunsen burner
spatula
clamp
fume hood
20 × 150 mm test tube
sulfur powder
zinc powder

Method

1. Describe the appearance of the zinc powder.

2. Describe the appearance of the sulfur powder.

3. Make a 50:50 mixture (by mass) of zinc and sulfur. Mix thoroughly. Place enough of this mixture in a 20 × 150 mm test tube to barely cover the bottom of the test tube. Fix one end of a clamp near the top of the test tube and fix the other end onto a retort stand at a 45° angle (Figure 7).

4. Place the whole assembly in the fume hood or in a well ventilated spot. Your teacher will carefully heat the mixture with a Bunsen flame until the reaction starts.

5. Describe the reaction and the products formed.

Follow-up

1. How many substances are there in the test tube after the reaction? What are they?

2. Using the synthesis of magnesium oxide as an example, write a word equation for the reaction between zinc and sulfur.

3. Complete the word equations for the following synthesis reactions:

   (a) aluminum + sulfur →
   (b) zinc + oxygen →

Fig. 7

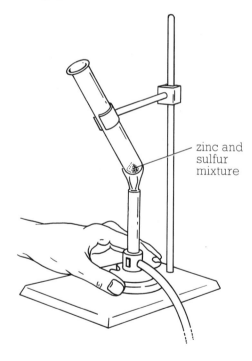

zinc and
sulfur
mixture

3.6 Decomposition of Hydrogen Peroxide

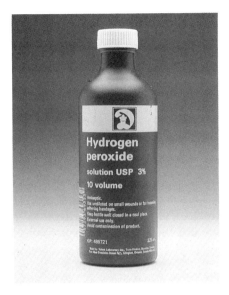

Fig. 8 *Solutions containing 3% to 6% hydrogen peroxide are used as antiseptics. A strong hydrogen peroxide solution may damage your skin. If it gets on your skin, wash it off with water.*

The glowing splint test is a test for oxygen gas.

Manganese dioxide is a catalyst in this reaction. It is *not* used up in the reaction and is *not* shown in the word equation.

Materials

safety goggles
wooden splints
Bunsen burner
spatula
test tube
matches
test tube rack
hydrogen peroxide solution (30 volume)
manganese dioxide

Method

1. Place a 1 cm depth of hydrogen peroxide solution in a clean test tube.

2. Using a dry spatula, measure out enough manganese dioxide powder to thinly cover a dime. Add this to the solution in the test tube. What do you observe?

3. When the reaction is occurring fairly vigorously, bring a glowing splint up to, and just inside, the mouth of the test tube. Do not place the splint too far into the tube. What happened when the gas produced came in contact with the glowing splint?

Decomposition

The word equation for the reaction of hydrogen peroxide is:

$$\text{hydrogen peroxide} \rightarrow \text{water} + \text{oxygen}$$

      compound   simpler   element
                       compound

The reaction is a **decomposition**, which can be considered as the opposite of synthesis.

In a decomposition reaction, the reactant is a single compound, and the products are elements or simpler compounds formed when the original compound breaks apart.

It is sometimes difficult to predict what the products of a decomposition will be. The word equation below represents the simplest example of decomposition:

calcium oxide → calcium + oxygen

Calcium oxide is made of only two elements, and it breaks apart into its two parent elements. The name of the non-metallic part of the compound (oxide) changes back to the name of the element (oxygen) after decomposition.

Write the word equations for the decomposition of the following two compounds. Each compound contains only two elements and the products formed are elements.

(a) hydrogen oxide (more commonly known as water)
(b) barium phosphide

If a decomposition reaction produces heat and gases very rapidly, an explosion may result. For example, when nitroglycerin decomposes, the products are all in the gaseous form, and a lot of heat is released. The hot gases expand quickly and blow apart everything in their path.

nitroglycerin → carbon dioxide + oxygen + nitrogen + water

Dynamite contains nitroglycerin. Other chemicals are added to make the dynamite safer to handle.

Fig. 9 *Alfred Nobel invented dynamite in 1867 by combining nitroglycerin with an absorbent substance. The fortune he made from manufacturing explosives funds the Nobel Prizes.*

3.7 Reacting Calcium With Water

Do not touch the calcium with your hands. It may burn your skin.

Fig. 10

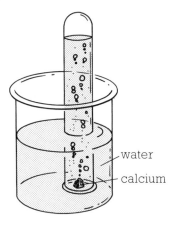

water

calcium

The burning splint test is a test for hydrogen gas.

Materials

safety goggles
test tube with stopper
test tube rack
600-mL beaker
spatula
matches
Bunsen burner
wooden splints
calcium chunks
hydrogen hydroxide (water)

Method

1. Half fill a 600-mL beaker with water. Fill a test tube all the way to the top with water. Place your thumb over the mouth of the test tube. Turn the test tube upside down into the water before removing your thumb.

2. Obtain a piece of calcium in a paper cone. Drop the piece of calcium from the cone into the water in the beaker. The calcium will sink at first. Before it can rise to the surface, place the mouth of the test tube over the calcium to trap it (Figure 10).

3. Repeat step 2 if necessary until the test tube no longer contains water. Describe what happens.

4. When there is no further reaction in the beaker, place a stopper in the mouth of the test tube while it is still under the water. Remove the stoppered test tube from the beaker and place it upright in a test tube rack.

5. Light a wooden splint and bring the burning splint near to the mouth of the test tube. Remove the stopper, and your hand, just before placing the splint over the mouth of the test tube. Describe what happens.

Single Displacement

The reaction between calcium and water is a **single displacement** reaction. In a single displacement reaction, the reactants are an element and a compound, and the products are a new element and a new compound.

If the element is a metal, it will displace the first part of the compound. The metal uses its original name in the new compound formed. This can be seen in the word equation for the reaction between calcium and water:

calcium + **hydrogen** hydroxide → **hydrogen** + calcium hydroxide

metallic
element

If the element is a non-metal, it displaces the last part of the compound. An example of this is:

chlorine + sodium **bromide** → sodium chloride + **bromine**

non-metallic
element

Note that the name of non-metal in the compound is changed: bromide becomes bromine.

| *Investigation* | # 3.8 Reacting Iron With Copper(II) Sulfate |

Materials

safety goggles	steel wool
3 test tubes	0.1 mol/L copper(II) sulfate solution
test tube rack	iron nails (each student to supply)

Method

1. Place water in a test tube to a depth of about 4 cm, and place an equal volume of copper(II) sulfate solution into each of two other test tubes. What is the colour of the copper(II) sulfate solution? This colour is usually present when simple copper(II) compounds are dissolved in water.

2. Clean two iron nails by rubbing them with steel wool. Place one iron nail into the water, and another into one of the two copper(II) sulfate solutions (Figure 11).

3. Allow the three test tubes to stand for as long as possible (at least 30 min).

4. Compare and describe the contents of the test tubes with nails in them.

5. Pour off the water from the nail, and slide the nail out of the test tube. Describe the appearance of the nail.

Fig. 11

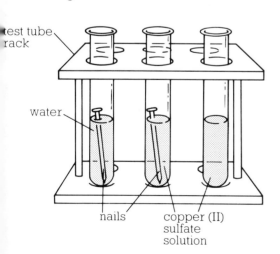

test tube rack

water

nails   copper (II) sulfate solution

6. Carefully decant the copper(II) sulfate solution from the nail and then gently slide the nail and any other solid onto some white paper. Describe the appearance of the nail and of any solid residue.

Follow-up

1. Has the nail reacted with the water?
   Has the nail reacted with the copper(II) sulfate solution?
   With which part of the solution does the iron react — with the copper(II) sulfate, or with the water?

2. Copper(II) sulfate is blue because of the presence of a dissolved copper(II) part of the compound.
   Compare the colour of the two copper(II) sulfate solutions. Which, if any, is lighter in colour? Does this give you a clue as to whether the iron is reacting with the copper(II) or with the sulfate? Explain.

3. Write a word equation for the reaction between iron and copper(II) sulfate. Is this a single displacement reaction?

4. Write word equations for the following single displacement reactions:

   (a) sodium + hydrogen hydroxide →

   (b) zinc + mercury(II) sulfate →

   (c) fluorine + potassium iodide →

Fig. 12 *The reaction between iron and copper(II) sulfate is important industrially. The picture shows a copper recovery plant where scrap iron is added to copper(II) sulfate solution to recover the more valuable copper metal.*

THE STEEL INDUSTRY

Iron ores used in iron and steel production are mainly iron oxides. Small pieces of iron ores, some anthracite or coke (sources of carbon), and some lime are mixed together. The carbon is there to remove the oxygen from the iron oxides. The lime is there to help melt some of the unwanted, valueless parts of the ore. The mixture of iron oxides, carbon, and lime is loaded into giant ovens, which can withstand very high temperatures. Then the mixture is heated from below with hot air. The following single displacement reaction occurs:

iron oxide + carbon → iron + carbon oxide

(Note that these are not the correct chemical names of the compounds.)

The molten iron is poured off and the wastes, called slag, are drawn off and discarded.

Fig. 13 *A single displacement reaction between oxides of iron and carbon in the production of iron or steel.*

3.9 Reacting Lead(II) Nitrate with Hydrochloric Acid

Materials

safety goggles
2 test tubes
test tube rack
0.1 mol/L hydrogen chloride solution (hydrochloric acid)
0.1 mol/L lead(II) nitrate solution

Method

1. Pour lead(II) nitrate solution into a clean test tube to a depth of about 1 cm. Describe the appearance of the solution.

2. Pour hydrogen chloride solution into another clean test tube to a depth of about 2 cm. Describe the appearance of the solution.

3. Mix the two solutions by pouring one into the other and shaking. Describe what happens.

Double Displacement

The reaction between lead(II) nitrate and hydrogen chloride (hydrochloric acid) is a **double displacement** reaction. The products formed are lead(II) chloride and hydrogen nitrate (nitric acid). In a double displacement reaction, the reactants are two compounds, and the products are two new compounds.

The word equation for the reaction is:

lead(II) nitrate + hydrogen chloride →
lead(II) chloride + hydrogen nitrate

This type of reaction is like switching partners. The first part of each reactant compound joins up with the second part of the other reactant compound to form the two new products. Notice that the names of the parts of the compounds do not change.

Another example of double displacement is:

silver nitrate + sodium chloride → silver chloride + sodium nitrate

Avoid contact with the potassium chromate solution. Wash any spills off your skin with water.

3.10 Reacting Lead(II) Nitrate With Potassium Chromate

Materials

safety goggles
2 test tubes
test tube rack

0.1 mol/L potassium chromate solution
0.1 mol/L lead(II) nitrate solution

Method

1. Pour lead(II) nitrate solution into one test tube to a depth of about 1 cm. Describe its appearance.

Fig. 14 *The chemicals that pollute lakes and rivers are often removed by double displacement reactions.*

COMMON DOUBLE DISPLACEMENT REACTIONS

Hard water contains dissolved calcium, magnesium and iron compounds. When the chemicals in hard water undergo a double displacement reaction with soap, a precipitate forms and "scum," or bathtub ring, results.

sodium stearate + calcium chloride →
  (a soap)   calcium stearate + sodium chloride
                                     (precipitate)

Some soap is wasted when it reacts with calcium and magnesium compounds instead of cleaning. This wastage can be reduced if sodium carbonate (washing soda) is first added to the hard water. The sodium carbonate precipitates the unwanted calcium and magnesium from their compounds. When the water is "softened," the soap is used solely for cleaning purposes. The word equation for chemically softening hard water is:

sodium carbonate + calcium chloride →
 (washing soda)   calcium carbonate + sodium chloride
                                  (precipitate)

There is no need to soften hard water if detergents are used instead of soap. Detergents contain chemicals which avoid precipitate formation. This is a benefit because there are now no scummy precipitates sticking to the clothes.

2. Pour an equal volume of potassium chromate solution into a second test tube. Describe its appearance.

3. Carefully, add the contents of one test tube to the other test tube. Describe what happens.

Follow-up

1. Write a word equation for the double displacement reaction between lead(II) nitrate and potassium chromate.

2. Complete the word equations for the following double displacement reactions:

   (a) potassium hydroxide + hydrogen chloride →
   (b) sodium phosphate + barium chloride →

Industrial pollution has resulted in a build-up of metal-containing compounds in our lakes and rivers. Double displacement reactions could be used to remove poisonous metal compounds by precipitation.

Double displacement reactions are also used to recover silver from the wastes of photographic processing solutions.

You may have seen some naturally dyed yarns. Yarns can be dyed by boiling them with plant material. If the yarns have been pretreated with different metal-containing compounds (called mordants), different colours result.

The mordants are absorbed by the fibres. When the yarn attached to a metal-containing compound is heated with a natural dye (a second compound), a double displacement reaction takes place. The colour-giving part of the natural dye becomes fixed to the metal attached to the yarn (Figure 16). Different metals give different dye-metal combinations, and therefore different colours.

Fig. 15 *This person recovers silver from used film and film processing solutions by means of double displacement reactions.*

Fig. 16

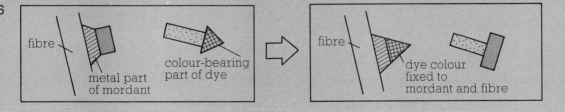

3.11 Energy and Chemical Reactions

Place solid barium hydroxide into a 18 × 150 mm test tube to a depth of about 2 cm. Add a similar volume of solid ammonium thiocyanate and place the stopper in the test tube. Shake the contents and note what happens. Feel the outside of the test tube. What is in fact going on?

During the reaction between barium hydroxide and ammonium thiocyanate, heat is being taken in. That is why the test tube and its contents get so cold. The reaction is grabbing heat from the test tube, your hand, and the surroundings. This type of chemical reaction is said to be **endothermic**.

endo means going to

exo means going out

thermic means heat

Fig. 17 *The "cold pack" used by athletes contains ammonium nitrate and water in two separate compartments. When the barrier between them is broken, an endothermic process occurs.*

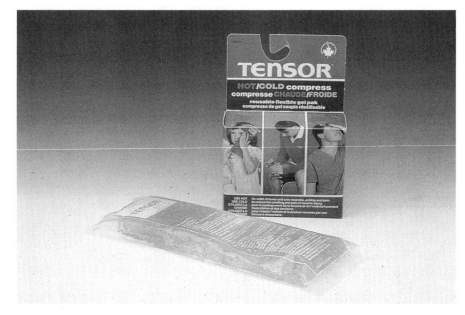

In your previous experiments, you will have noticed several reactions that produced heat. These reactions give out energy and are said to be **exothermic**.

Combustion reactions are exothermic. When you use the Bunsen burner, you are burning hydrocarbon gases in oxygen. **Hydrocarbons** are compounds that contain the elements carbon and hydrogen. Examples of hydrocarbons used in homes and schools are methane (natural gas), propane, and butane (Figure 18).

The burning of compounds containing carbon, hydrogen, and perhaps oxygen always produces carbon dioxide and water if sufficient oxygen is available. A typical word equation for such a combustion reaction is:

methane + oxygen → carbon dioxide + water

Fig. 18 *Propane is a hydrocarbon often used as a fuel.*

84

However, if the oxygen supply is insufficient, the combustion reaction may produce **carbon monoxide**, which is a highly poisonous gas.

Some reactions give off energy in the form of light. Such a reaction occurs in tubes known as "light sticks." The light stick contains two compartments of chemicals. When you break the barrier between the chemicals, they react and produce a coloured light. **Chemiluminescence** is the name given to this type of light. Chemiluminescence occurs naturally in fireflies.

Fig. 19 *The female glow worm has a tail that can give a bright green light—an example of chemiluminescence.*

P O I N T S · T O · R E C A L L

- Fuel, oxygen, and a sufficiently high temperature are needed for burning to occur.
- In a physical change, the chemical composition of the original substances remains unchanged, and no new substances are formed.
- In a chemical change, new substances are formed.
- The four main types of chemical reactions are:
    synthesis
    decomposition
    single displacement
    double displacement

- A word equation uses words to describe the chemicals used (reactants) and the chemicals produced (products) in a chemical reaction.
- An endothermic reaction takes in heat from the surroundings.
- An exothermic reaction releases heat.
- When a compound containing carbon, hydrogen, and perhaps oxygen, burns in sufficient oxygen, carbon dioxide and water are produced.

1. Write down all the steps you would take if you woke up and smelled smoke in your bedroom. Give a reason for each step.
2. List three safety precautions you would take in your home to prevent a fire starting. Give a reason for each of the precautions.
3. What is spontaneous combustion? Give an example of situations which could result in spontaneous combustion.
4. What is the main difference between a chemical change and a physical change?
5. List at least four observations which would tell you that a chemical change was occurring.
6. Decide whether each of the following is a chemical change or a physical change.
   (a) a match burning
   (b) freezing popsicles
   (c) food rotting
   (d) ice melting
   (e) Jello dissolving
   (f) toasting bread
7. What is a word equation?
8. Why is it not safe to look directly at the flame of burning magnesium? Why should you avoid exposing your eyes to non-electronic flashbulbs for too long?
9. What are the four types of chemical reactions you studied in this chapter? Give an example of each type.
10. Why is it a waste of time to polish aluminum window frames to make them shiny?
11. What is a catalyst? Why is the catalyst for a reaction not included in the word equation for that reaction?
12. Describe a chemical test for:
    (a) oxygen gas
    (b) hydrogen gas
13. What is hard water? How can hard water be softened chemically?
14. Why do people prefer laundry detergents to soaps?

15. In each of the following, indicate what type of chemical reaction is represented (synthesis, decomposition, single displacement, double displacement, or combustion):
    (a) sodium nitrate → sodium nitrite + oxygen
    (b) calcium + oxygen → calcium oxide
    (c) propane + oxygen →
            carbon dioxide + water
    (d) zinc chloride + ammonium hydroxide →
        zinc hydroxide + ammonium chloride
    (e) aluminum + hydrogen chloride →
         aluminum chloride + hydrogen
    (f) potassium + water →
         potassium hydroxide + hydrogen
    (g) hydrogen + chlorine → hydrogen chloride
    (h) hydrogen oxide → hydrogen + oxygen
        (Hydrogen oxide is water.)
    (i) silver nitrate + hydrogen phosphate →
        silver phosphate + hydrogen nitrate
    (j) aluminum hydroxide →
          aluminum oxide + water
16. Complete the following word equations.
    (Please do not write in this textbook.)
    (a) aluminum + oxygen →
    (b) silver nitrate + magnesium bromide →
    (c) zinc + silver sulfate →
    (d) sodium chloride →
    (e) ammonium sulfate + barium nitrate →
    (f) octane + oxgygen
        (Octane is a hydrocarbon.) →
    (g) zinc oxide + calcium →
    (h) silver nitrate + sodium chloride →
    (i) zinc + bromine →
    (j) aluminum + zinc chloride →
    (k) ethanol + oxygen →
        (Ethanol molecules contain carbon, hydrogen, and oxygen.)
    (l) magnesium + aluminum chloride →
    (m) chlorine + sodium iodide →
    (n) potassium + water →
        (Water may be called hydrogen hydroxide.)

CHEMICAL CHANGE
new substances produced

PHYSICAL CHANGE
no new substances produced

TYPES

SYNTHESIS

two chemicals react to produce a new chemical

DECOMPOSITION

a compound breaks apart to produce elements or simpler compounds

SINGLE DISPLACEMENT

element reacts with compound to form a new element and new compound

DOUBLE DISPLACEMENT

two compounds react to form two new compounds

COMBUSTION

a fuel burns in oxygen to produce carbon dioxide and water

DUST EXPLOSIONS

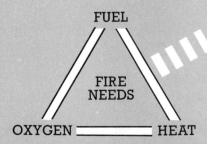

FUEL

FIRE NEEDS

OXYGEN — HEAT

SPONTANEOUS COMBUSTION

Korey Wallace works as a Quality Control laboratory Technician for a major steel company. This job is concerned primarily with testing the physical properties of her company's sheet steel. Korey has the last word on the quality of the steel. If she says "no" to a sample, it does not leave the plant. This is an important responsibility of any person who works in a quality control laboratory.

Korey's chief tool is a new elasticity testing machine which tests the tensile strength of steel by pulling a sample until it breaks. The machine is linked to a computer which analyzes and prints the results.

Korey also carries out the chemical analysis of steel to ensure that impurities such as silicon and zinc do not exceed the limits set for high quality steels. In order to do this, Korey uses a highly sensitive method of detecting impurities called atomic absorption analysis. This type of analysis also involves the use of a computer which the technician must load and program appropriately.

Korey first started working at the steel company as a summer student during high school. A love of science prompted her to enter Mohawk College's two-year Chemical Technician program. Although the company hires new employees directly from high school and trains them, Korey felt that formal laboratory training would give her an advantage in the highly competitive steel industry. In fact, she had to apply several times before getting the job.

Korey's desire to work in research led her to upgrade her skills by attending another

Instron tensile test machine— measures tensile strength of steel samples

year at college. Korey hopes to further her knowledge of the steel industry by continuing her education through correspondence courses. A strict schedule of shiftwork does not allow very much flexibility, but Korey is confident that her determination to learn about the steel industry will help her to get ahead.

Korey is proud to be part of an industry as important as steelmaking. She recognizes that her company's products play an important role in all of our lives.

A major steel plant is a complex operation. Many activities go on which, to the outsider, do not seem to be related to steel produc-

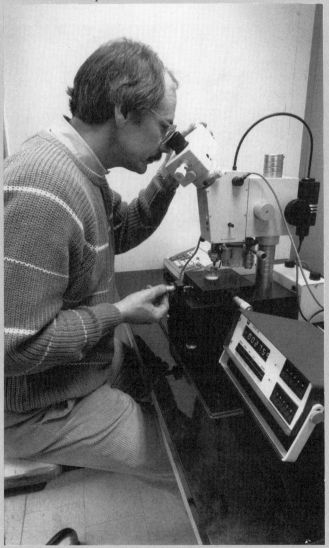

Micro Hardness Tester—measures hardness of small steel samples

tion at all. There are both chemical as well as metallurgical support functions. For instance, steel must be "pickled" in hydrochloric acid to remove surface impurities. Titration is used constantly as a method of testing the acid for such impurities.

Titration is only one of the many tasks performed by Vince Rossi, a technician in the "sheet laboratory" of a steel company. The primary function of the lab is to maintain the high quality of the plant's sheet steel product. Vince's many skills allow him to do more than just his own job. Sometimes he performs hardness and tensile strength tests on the steel. Hardness tests are used to examine the hardness of samples by comparing them to other standard samples. Tensile testing (strength against pulling) is a more involved process. The tensile testing machine pulls on a piece of steel and records how it stretches and breaks. Vince then sets up a computer which is interfaced to the tensile tester. The computer analyzes the results and prints a report of the test.

Although Vince Rossi did not initially have his mind set on this kind of career, jobs were hard to find in the early 1980s, so he decided to enroll in the three-year Metallurgical Technology program at Mohawk College. Upon graduation, Vince had to take a less satisfactory job tending furnaces for a small firm in Mississauga, Ontario. The better pay, benefits and home town location of the position at the steel company induced Vince to change jobs. This change was a good career choice for Vince who now considers himself a member of a steel team in Canada's Steel City.

4 ATOMIC STRUCTURE

Colourful fireworks are related to the energy of electrons in atoms.

CONTENTS

| **Investigation** | ## 4.1 *What Puts the Spark in Our Lives?* |

Fig. 1

(a)

(b)

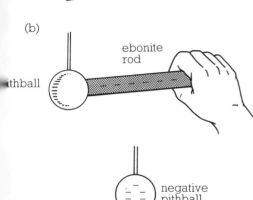

Have you ever touched a metal door knob after walking across a carpet in nylon socks on a cold, dry day? Then you know it can be a "shocking" experience! When you comb or brush your hair and it gets the fly-away look, are you thinking about chemistry? You should be!

These observations can be explained in terms of electrically charged particles. The following experiment will help you understand how charged particles behave.

Materials

ebonite rod
lucite rod
fur
plastic bag
pithball apparatus

Method

1. Rub an ebonite rod on some fur. The rod becomes negatively charged (Figure 1a).

2. Touch a hanging pithball with the tip of the ebonite rod. The charge on the ebonite rod is transferred to the pithball which becomes negatively charged (Figure 1b).

Fig. 1 *(continued)*

(c)

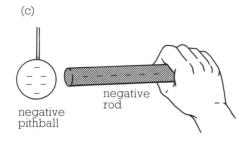

negative
pithball

3. Recharge the ebonite rod by rubbing it on some fur. Move the tip of the negatively charged rod toward the suspended negatively charged pithball (Figure 1c). What do you observe?

4. Rub a lucite rod with some plastic. The rod becomes positively charged (Figure 1d).

5. Make the pithball positively charged by touching it with the positively charged rod. Recharge the lucite rod and move this positive rod toward the positively charged pithball (Figure 1e). What do you notice?

6. Make a pithball positively charged. Rub the ebonite rod with the fur to make it negatively charged.

7. Move the tip of the negatively charged ebonite rod toward the positively charged pithball (Figure 1f). What do you notice?

(d)

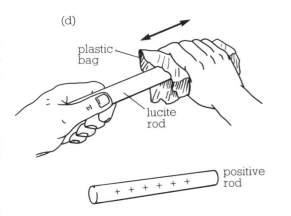

(e)

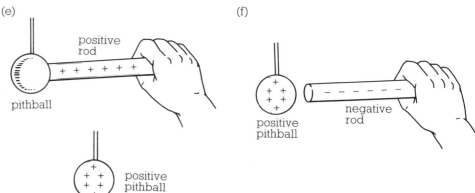

(f)

Fig. 2 *Lightning is caused by the movement of positive and negative charges.*

Behaviour of Charged Particles

Your experiment should have shown you the rules for the behaviour of charged particles: *Like charges repel each other, while unlike charges attract.*

An **atom**, the smallest building block of an element, is made up of

- positively charged particles called **protons** (p)
- negatively charged particles called **electrons** (e)
- neutral particles called **neutrons** (n)

Most materials are neutral because they have equal numbers of protons and electrons. The only particles that can be dislodged by friction (rubbing) are the negative electrons.

The ebonite rod becomes negatively charged because it picks up extra electrons from the fur, and the fur becomes positively charged after losing electrons to the ebonite rod. The lucite rod becomes positively charged because the plastic picks up electrons from the lucite.

Sliding across a car seat and touching another person often gives you a shock because of electron movement from the person with the greater negative charge.

The fly-away look of your hair is due to electron movement between your hair and the comb.

4.2 Structure of an Atom

The existence of a dense nucleus at the centre of an atom was first proposed by Ernest Rutherford in 1907.

Think of an atom as a ball. The atom has a dense central core called the **nucleus**. The nucleus contains the protons and the neutrons and has an overall positive charge. The electrons constantly move about the positively charged nucleus forming a negatively charged

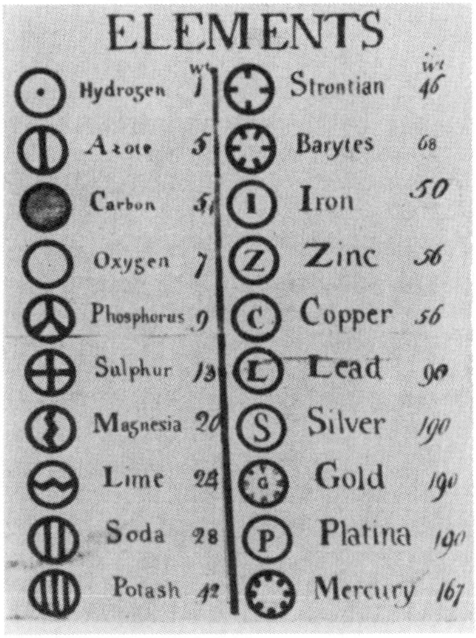

Fig. 3 *John Dalton (1766–1844) was the first person to develop a model of the atom, but his idea that the atom was a solid sphere has now been disproved. The picture shows Dalton's list of elements.*

Fig. 4 *The atom can be considered as a dense nucleus surrounded by an electron cloud.*

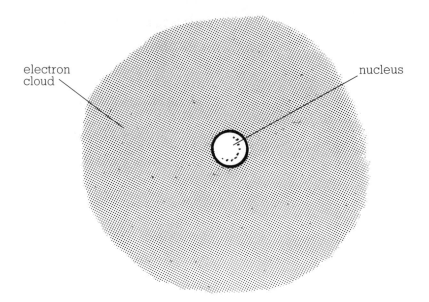

If the nucleus was the size of a baseball, the outer edge of the atom would be 3 km away, and an electron would be the size of a pea!

electron cloud (Figure 4). The radius of an atom is the distance from the centre of the nucleus to the edge of the electron cloud, and is about 100 000 times longer than the radius of the nucleus.

Scientists have developed a method of showing how many protons, neutrons, and electrons there are in one atom of an element. An example, using the element fluorine, is given below.

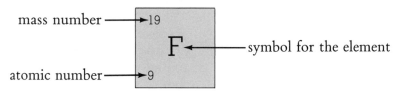

The **atomic number** (the bottom number on the left) of an element is the number of protons found in the nucleus of an atom of that element.

The **mass number** (the top number on the left) of an element is the total number of protons and neutrons found in the nucleus of the atom.

Since an atom, as a whole, is electrically neutral, the number of protons is equal to the number of electrons. Therefore the atomic number is also the number of electrons found in the atom.

In an atom of the element fluorine:

- the number of protons = the atomic number = 9
- the number of electrons = the atomic number = 9
- the number of neutrons = mass number − atomic number
  = 19 − 9 = 10

The mass of a proton is about the same as that of a neutron, but is about 2000 times the mass of an electron. The mass of an atom is largely determined by the total number of protons and neutrons in its nucleus.

Another way of showing the mass number is to write the name of the element followed by the mass number of the atom. For example, fluorine-19 tells you the atom is fluorine and its mass number is 19.

Another example is hydrogen-3. From the periodic table you can find that the atomic number of hydrogen is 1. Therefore this hydrogen atom can be shown as:

3	the number of protons = 1
H	the number of electrons = 1
1	the number of neutrons = 3 − 1 = 2

The term "mass number" refers to the number of protons and neutrons that determine the mass of an atom.

The atomic number of an element is unique.

Questions

1. Draw up a chart with the following headings:

Element	Number of protons	Number of electrons	Number of neutrons
$^1_1$H	1	1	0

Fill out the chart for

$^1_1$H, $^2_1$H, $^3_1$H, $^4_2$He, $^7_3$Li, $^{35}_{17}$Cl, $^{37}_{17}$Cl, $^{80}_{35}$Br, $^{32}_{16}$S, $^9_4$Be, $^{24}_{12}$Mg, $^{131}_{53}$I.

The first one is done for you.

2. Is it possible that the atoms of an element have different atomic numbers?

3. Is it possible that the atoms of an element have different mass numbers?

4.3 Isotopes and Atomic Mass

You will notice that some of the atoms in your chart have the same number of protons but a different number of neutrons. These atoms are called isotopes of the same element.

Isotopes of an element are atoms that have the same number of protons and electrons, but different numbers of neutrons. Because of the different numbers of neutrons, isotopes of the same element have different masses.

The chemical behaviour of isotopes of an atom depends on the number of electrons only. Therefore all the isotopes of an element have the same chemical properties.

In nature, the isotopes of an element occur in a fairly constant proportion. Scientists calculate the "average" mass of the isotopes of an element and call it the **atomic mass** of that element.

The unit for atomic mass is the **atomic mass unit** (symbol u). The mass of a proton or neutron is approximately 1 u. You can find the values of the atomic masses of elements in the periodic table.

Chlorine has two main isotopes, chlorine-35 and chlorine-37. In a natural sample of chlorine, three quarters of the atoms have a mass of 35 u each, and one-quarter of the atoms have a mass of 37 u each. The average mass of a chlorine atom is then 35.5 u.

Therefore the atomic mass of chlorine is 35.5 u.

The atomic mass of an atom is approximately equal to the mass number of the atom.

By definition, 1 u is equal to $\frac{1}{12}$ of the mass of a carbon-12 atom.

Questions

1. Look in your periodic table to find the atomic masses of: copper, oxygen, hydrogen, uranium, and gold.

2. The atomic mass of magnesium is not a whole number. Why?

4.4 Coloured Lights and Chemistry

Neon lights and fireworks—so bright, colourful, and exciting! Strangely enough, these effects can give us clues about the inside structure of the atom.

In the following "flame tests," you will see how different elements produce different colours.

Fig. 5 *Why are these lights different in colour?*

Fig. 6 *What is the metal that is now being tested?*

Fig. 7 *What metal would produce the colour of this flare?*

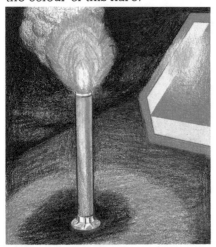

Materials

Bunsen burner
wooden splints
0.1 mol/L solutions of metal compounds in dropper bottles:
   sodium nitrate, potassium nitrate, strontium nitrate, barium
   nitrate, calcium nitrate, copper(II) nitrate, and an "unknown"

Method

1. Light the Bunsen burner and produce an almost colourless flame.

2. Place a drop of the solution on the tip of a wooden splint.

3. Place the tip, with the drop of the solution, into the hottest part of the Bunsen flame. (This is just above the pale blue zone of the flame.)

4. Note the first flare of colour that is different from the colour of the Bunsen flame. Do not hold the splint in the flame after the flare as you will only see the orange flame of burning wood.

5. Clean the wire and repeat the process for each of the given solutions. Record your observations in a chart, as shown below.

Name of compound	Metal in compound	Colour of flare
sodium nitrate	sodium	

6. Carry out the flame test with the "unknown" sample. See if you can tell which metal is present.

Follow-up

1. Were all the flare colours different? Which part of the compound causes the colour in the flame? (Look at the names of the compounds.)

2. Could you tell the difference between strontium and calcium? Explain.

3. What chemical would you use if you were making a green flare?

4.5 Using a Spectroscope

Where does the colour come from in flame tests, fireworks, and neon tubes? To answer this question, you should first try to analyze coloured lights using an instrument called the **spectroscope** (Figure 8).

Fig. 8 *A spectroscope.*

Fig. 9 *The rainbow is similar to the continuous spectrum that you see through a spectroscope.*

Fig. 10 *The line spectrum of hydrogen gas.*

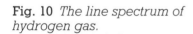

The line spectrum of an element is unique. Spectra analysis led to the discovery of the element helium in the sun in 1868. Helium was found on the earth later—in 1895.

Look through the spectroscope at natural daylight. What you observe is a full continuous series of colours like that seen in a rainbow. A series of colours like this is called a continuous spectrum. In this **continuous spectrum**, all possible energies of visible light are coming to your eyes.

Your teacher will use electricity to energize or excite a sample of hydrogen gas contained in a glass tube. In a darkened room, view the light coming from the excited hydrogen gas through your spectroscope.

An excited atom is one that has absorbed additional energy. It is not possible for an atom to stay excited. As the excited atom "relaxes," it loses energy in the form of light. Different coloured lights correspond to different energies. When an atom of hydrogen "relaxes," it gives out only red, green, and purple visible light. You will see three vertical, brightly coloured lines separated by blackness in the hydrogen spectrum (Figure 10). Because these colours appear as sharp lines, this kind of spectrum is called a **line spectrum**.

4.6 The Bohr Atom

How does an energized element produce a unique line spectrum? Niels Bohr, a Danish scientist, came up with an explanation in 1913.

Bohr said that the electrons in an atom travel around the nucleus at fixed distances. Imagine a series of spherical shells at greater and greater distances from the nucleus. As long as an electron moves around on one of these shells or levels, it does not gain or lose any energy.

An electron is excited when it is given additional energy (Figure 11a). The excited electron can jump to a higher level further away from the nucleus (Figure 11b).

When the electron loses the extra energy, the electron falls to a lower shell or energy level (Figure 11c). The energy released gives rise to certain colours of light (the coloured lines in a line spectrum).

The colours that we see in fireworks, flames, and neon lights are a result of the energy given out when excited electrons in these materials "relax."

Bohr said that an atom in an unexcited state has its electrons in the shells with the lowest possible energy. Each shell can only hold so many electrons before it is "full." The following table shows the maximum number of electrons allowed in each energy level.

Energy level	Maximum number of electrons
1	2
2	8
3	18
4	32

Fig. 11

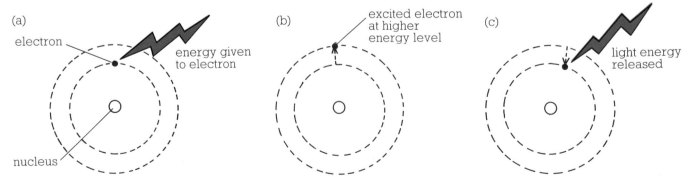

(a) electron / nucleus / energy given to electron

(b) excited electron at higher energy level

(c) light energy released

Such a diagram is called the Bohr-Rutherford diagram because Rutherford proposed the existence of the nucleus and Bohr proposed the ways in which electrons are arranged around the nucleus.

As an example, let us draw a diagram for an atom of chlorine-35. It has 17 protons, 17 electrons, and 18 neutrons.

(a) Draw a small circle to represent the nucleus (Figure 12a). Inside this there are 17 protons and 18 neutrons.

(b) Draw a circle outside the nucleus to represent the first shell (energy level 1). Place two electrons in this shell (Figure 12b). It is now full. There are still 15 more electrons.

(c) Draw a larger circle to represent the second shell (energy level 2). Place 8 electrons here (Figure 12c). This is the maximum number of electrons possible in this shell. You have located 10 of the 17 electrons.

(d) Draw the third shell. The maximum number of electrons in this shell is 18, but you only have 7 electrons left. Place all your 7 electrons here (Figure 12d). You have now located all the electrons.

Bohr's model of the atom is useful in explaining a lot of chemical behaviour. Let us see how the model is related to the arrangement of elements in the periodic table.

(a) Draw the outline of the periodic table to show just the first 20 elements (Figure 13). Use a whole page.

Fig. 12

(a)

chlorine nucleus (17 protons 18 neutrons)

(b)

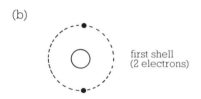
first shell (2 electrons)

(c)

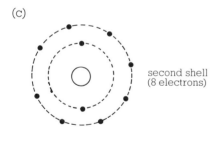
second shell (8 electrons)

(d)

third shell (remaining 7 electrons)

Fig. 13 *Draw the atoms of the first 20 elements in a simplified periodic table like this one.*

1								2
3	4		5	6	7	8	9	10
11	12		13	14	15	16	17	18
19	20							

(b) Put the appropriate symbol and atomic number in the top left corner of each square.

(c) In each square, draw a Bohr-Rutherford diagram of the atom of the element, like the one you did for chlorine.

(d) Write the numerals 1 to 8 at the top of the columns starting from the left.

(e) What do you notice about the outermost shell of the elements in a vertical column?

(f) As you look across a horizontal row, what do you notice about the location of the electrons?

(g) What do you think happens to the sizes of the atoms starting at the top of a column and moving down?

As you go down a vertical column of the periodic table, the size of the atom increases because the electrons are filling shells further and further away from the nucleus. Going across a row, the size of the atom varies little because you are filling the same shell. The slight contraction is caused by the increased charge and pull of the positive nucleus on the negative electrons.

Fig. 14 *The relative sizes of atoms.*

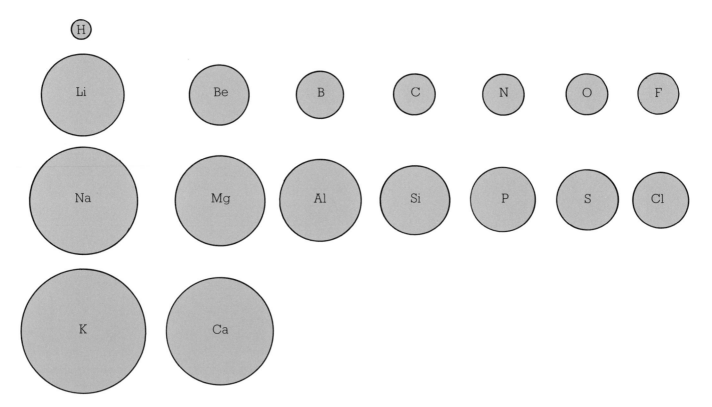

DETECTION USING A SPECTROSCOPE

A tourist bought a ruby for $10 000. On returning home, an appraiser discovered that the stone was a red spinel, a far less valuable stone than a ruby. In fact the "Black Prince's ruby" in the English state crown has been found to be a red spinel and not a ruby, so the mistake is easy to make.

Fig. 15 *There is a great variety of gemstones.*

Fig. 16 *The line spectra of ruby, red spinel, and emerald.*

Fig. 17 *The spectroscope is also used in crime detection.*

Each gem has its own spectrum, like its fingerprint (Figure 16). However, good synthetic gems have the same spectra as their natural counterparts. There is nothing wrong with buying a synthetic gem as long as someone is not over-charging you or claiming that the stone is a natural one.

Sometimes coloured glass is sold by fraudulent salespeople in place of a real gem. Using a spectroscope, a gem expert can certainly tell if the "gem" is glass.

The spectroscope is also used in crime detection. In a hit and run case, some paint from the car involved in the accident was found on the victim's bicycle. Police used a sophisticated spectroscope (Figure 17) to analyze the paint. Since the spectrum matched that of the paint on a suspected person's car, this helped to convict the person.

- All matter is made up of atoms, the smallest building block of an element.
- Positive charges attract negative charges, but charges of the same kind repel each other.
- Positive particles (called protons) and neutral particles (called neutrons) are located in the nucleus of an atom. Most of the mass of an atom is located in the nucleus.
- Negative particles called electrons surround the nucleus of an atom.
- The atomic number of an atom is the number of protons in the nucleus.
- In a neutral atom, the number of protons is equal to that of electrons.
- The mass number of an atom is the total number of protons and neutrons in the nucleus.
- The number of neutrons in the nucleus = mass number − atomic number.
- Isotopes of an element are atoms that have the same number of protons, but different numbers of neutrons.
- The atomic mass of an element is the average mass of its neutral isotopes.
- A study of spectra led to the Bohr theory of electron arrangement in atoms.
- Electrons exist in shells surrounding the nucleus. The maximum number of electrons in the first shell is 2, in the second shell 8, and in the third shell 18.

1. Explain why you can pick up little bits of paper with a plastic comb that has been rubbed on your clothing.
2. Copy the following chart in your notebook and complete it.

Element	Number of protons	Number of electrons	Number of neutrons
$_1^1H$			0
	19		20
$_{92}^{238}U$			
	82		126
		13	14

3. In what way(s) are isotopes of an element
   (a) the same,
   (b) different?
4. Give an example of a pair of isotopes of the same element.
5. Will different isotopes of an element behave in the same way in chemical reactions? Explain.
6. The following is a box from a typical periodic table.

| 17 |
| Cl |
| 35.5u |

   (a) List three pieces of information you can obtain from this box.
   (b) Can you tell how many isotopes this element has?

7. In carrying out a flame test on a sample, you obtain the following results. Write down the metal atom responsible for the flame colour in each case.

Colour of flame	Metal present
emerald green	
orange-red	
scarlet	
pale purple (mauve)	

8. What metal compound could be used to make a firecracker with a bright orange-yellow colour?
9. What is the difference between a continuous spectrum and a line spectrum?
10. Draw diagrams to show the electron arrangement of the following atoms:
    (a) neon-20
    (b) argon-40
    List two similarities you notice about these two diagrams.
11. What happens to the size of atoms as you go down a vertical column of the periodic table? Explain.
12. (a) How is a synthetic emerald different from a natural emerald?
    (b) How is a synthetic emerald the same as a natural emerald?
    (c) Would you buy a synthetic emerald? Explain.
    (d) How can you avoid gem fraud?

Combining the roles of wife, mother and chemical laboratory technician makes life busy for Anna-Maria Randazzo, but the variety of responsibilities keeps things interesting for her.

As a student, Anna-Maria had always been interested in science. A presentation to her high school class by the Canadian Centre for Inland Waters, which tests lakes and rivers for impurities, helped her make a decision. She decided that chemistry plays an important role in today's society, and as a result she enrolled in Mohawk College's Chemical Technician program after she completed Grade 12. Upon graduating from the two-year program at Mohawk, Anna-Maria took a job at M&T Chemical, a firm in the electroplating business. Electroplating is used to make the shiny chrome plate on car bumpers, or gold and silver plate on jewellery and cutlery. It involves the careful control of chemical baths to ensure smooth and even plating. M&T's lab staff analyze the outgoing chemicals, as well as samples from the customers' plating baths.

Anna-Maria spent three years at M&T and then took some time off to be at home with her family. But the lure of the lab was too strong and she decided to return to Mohawk College as the Chemistry Department's laboratory technician.

Her new job involves restocking chemicals, setting up equipment, preparing solutions, such as acids and bases, and assembling "kits" for all student experiments. As a laboratory technician, Anna-Maria sometimes acts as an assistant teacher by helping students to perform experiments.

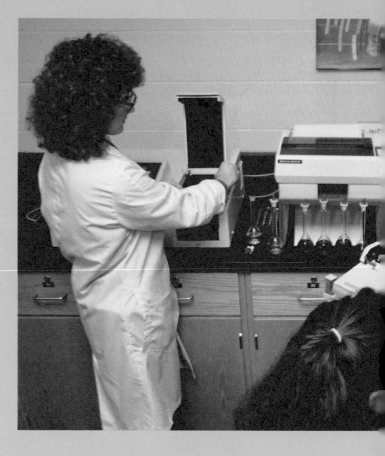

Anna-Maria's role in chemical education has allowed her to have much more contact with people than her career in industry allowed. This ability to work well with other people, along with her interest in chemistry have helped to make her career very satisfying. Anna-Maria feels that her choice of career has given her potential flexibility to work in industry, education or government. As well, she has the option to work part-time which would allow her to spend more time with her family.

FORENSIC LABORATORY TECHNICIAN

Sherlock Holmes may be a fictional detective, but his scientific methods of crime detection bear more than a slight resemblance to modern criminology.

In a forensic laboratory, scientific techniques are used to analyze blood stains, hair samples, paint scrapings, etc. Such chemical analysis is a valuable and important tool in the fight against crime.

Mary Svaluto is a real-life member of a chemical crime solving team: she works as a forensic laboratory technician in the Ontario Government's Centre for Forensic Science laboratories in Toronto. Mary's main responsibility is the operation of a sensitive and sophisticated machine called a mass spectrometer. This machine analyzes drugs in the blood samples of crime victims or suspects. To prepare a chemical sample, the lab technician must filter, adjust the acidity, and "wash" away any chemicals that might interfere with the analysis. Such preparation takes a good deal of time and skill, but is necessary before the sample can be injected into the machine. Finally, a computer which is linked to the mass spectrometer stores and analyzes the results and produces a printed report.

Mary first became interested in forensics while working at a drug store during her high school years. Helping to dispense pharmaceuticals led to an interest in the effects of drugs on the body. Mid-way through high school, Mary was intrigued by a career in forensics and enquired at the city morgue to find out about the kinds of jobs available. After high school, Mary completed a three-year program in Chemical Technology at Ryerson Polytechnical Institute which prepared her for her career in the lab. With further training, Mary's job has the potential of becoming even more varied, adding to its already high level of interest and importance to the detection of crime.

Without people like Mary Svaluto and her co-workers, there would be no modern "Sherlocks"!

Helium gas, often used to fill balloons and airships, belongs to a group of unreactive elements. This group is an important link in the periodic arrangement of elements.

1046
2

1046
2

HELIUM

T189 T189

CONTENTS

5.1 A Tale of the Future

You are the science officer on the first space ship to explore the universe beyond our solar system. Unfortunately your space ship is relatively small and your equipment is very limited. You have:

- a science kit containing a set of chemicals marked C1, C2, C3, and C4
- an instrument for measuring the atomic mass of an element
- an instrument for measuring the melting point of a solid
- an instrument for measuring the density of a substance

After a long journey, your crew finally lands on a large planet. Although the temperature on this planet is about the same as that on the earth, there is no atmosphere and there are no living organisms.

You search the planet and bring back "rocks" and "minerals" for analysis. After an extended study, you think that all substances on this planet are made from only 12 different elements. After further work, you isolate and purify 11 of these elements. The elements are completely different from those found on earth. (Remember this is a science fiction story.)

As you isolate each element, you assign it a name and a symbol based on a sign of the zodiac. You then determine the atomic mass, melting point, and density of each of the 11 elements. Each element is tested with the chemicals in your science kit. You also try to burn each element in oxygen to produce its oxide. Not all the elements react with oxygen, but the oxides of those that do are analyzed. All the results of these experiments are shown in Figure 1.

Fig. 1 *Data on the 11 elements.*

Aquarius

Symbol: Aq
Atomic mass = 9.4 u
Density = 3.1 g/cm³
A yellow solid
Melting point = 250°C
Formula of oxide = Aq_2O_3

Reacts only with C3 to form a yellow-red solution

Aries
Symbol: Ai
Atomic mass = 11.8 u
Density = 4.0 g/cm³
A black solid
Melting point = 290°C
Does not form an oxide

Does not react with C1, C2, C3, or C4

Cancer
Symbol: Cn
Atomic mass = 32.3 u
Density = 6.1 g/cm³
A silver solid
Melting point = 400°C
Does not form an oxide

Does not react with C1, C2, C3, or C4

Gemini
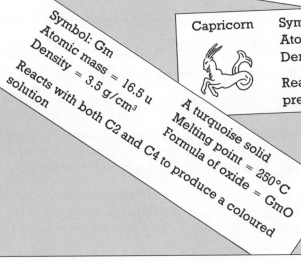
Symbol: Gm
Atomic mass = 16.5 u
Density = 3.5 g/cm³
A turquoise solid
Melting point = 250°C
Formula of oxide = GmO

Reacts with both C2 and C4 to produce a coloured solution

Capricorn
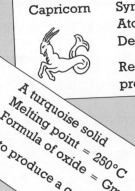
Symbol: Cp
Atomic mass = 3.1 u
Density = 2.5 g/cm³
A white solid
Melting point = 100°C
Formula of oxide = Cp_2O

Reacts with both C1 and C2 to produce a white precipitate

Leo

Symbol: Le
Atomic mass = 29.1 u
Density = 5.0 g/cm³
A red solid
Melting point = 380°C
Formula of oxide = Le_2O_3

Reacts only with C3 to form a yellow-red solution

Pisces

Symbol: Pi
Atomic mass =
Density = 2.7 g
Reacts with bo
solution

Libra

Symbol: Lb
Atomic mass = 27.2 u
Density = 4.5 g/cm³
A green solid
Melting point = 320°C
Formula of oxide = LbO

Reacts with both C2 and C4 to produce a coloured solution

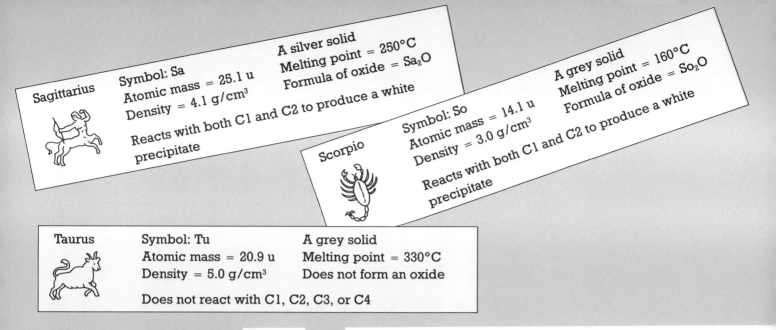

Sagittarius

Symbol: Sa
Atomic mass = 25.1 u
Density = 4.1 g/cm³

A silver solid
Melting point = 250°C
Formula of oxide = Sa_2O

Reacts with both C1 and C2 to produce a white precipitate

Scorpio

Symbol: So
Atomic mass = 14.1 u
Density = 3.0 g/cm³

A grey solid
Melting point = 160°C
Formula of oxide = So_2O

Reacts with both C1 and C2 to produce a white precipitate

Taurus

Symbol: Tu
Atomic mass = 20.9 u
Density = 5.0 g/cm³

A grey solid
Melting point = 330°C
Does not form an oxide

Does not react with C1, C2, C3, or C4

blue solid
.elting point = 200°C
ormula of oxide = PiO
4 to produce a coloured

Questions

1. Of the properties listed for each element, which are physical properties and which are chemical properties?

2. If you look closely at the chemical properties, you will find that certain elements are very similar chemically. Organize the elements into groups containing similar chemical properties.

3. You should have four groups of elements. Arrange all the elements into a chart consisting of three rows and four columns.

1	2	3	4
5	6	7	8
9	10	11	12

Place the 11 elements into the chart in order of their atomic mass. The element with the lowest atomic mass should be placed in box 1. Continue with the other elements but only place them in a particular column if they have the same chemical properties. Leave a space if necessary. When you are finished you will have a chart of the elements found on this planet.

111

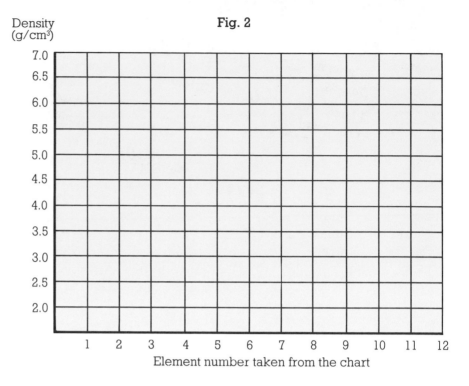

Density (g/cm³)   Fig. 2

Element number taken from the chart

4. Copy Figure 2 onto a piece of graph paper. Plot the density values for each of the elements. Connect the point for element 1 to element 2, and from element 2 to element 3, and so on. Leave a gap where you have missing data.
   (a) What do you notice about the pattern of your graph?
   (b) Use the graph to predict the density of the missing element.

5. Draw a similar graph for the melting points of the elements.
   (a) What do you notice about the pattern of your graph?
   (b) Use the graph to predict the melting point of the missing element.

6. Use the atomic masses of the elements surrounding the blank box in your chart to predict the atomic mass of the missing element.

7. What do you think is the colour of the missing element? Give reasons for your answer.

8. What do you think is the formula of the oxide of the missing element?

9. How will the missing element react with your chemicals C1, C2, C3, and C4?

10. Without having actually isolated and purified the missing element, you can predict many of its properties. Complete the following summary chart for the missing element. You can use a name and symbol of your choice:

Name of element	
Symbol	
Atomic mass	
Density	
Colour	
Melting point	
Formula of oxide	
Reaction with C1	
Reaction with C2	
Reaction with C3	
Reaction with C4	

11. You have now predicted quite a bit about the element you were not able to isolate. As the science officer on the space ship, what should be your next investigation before you radio home the good news?

5.2 A Brief History of the Periodic Table

Around 1860, scientists were quite preoccupied with the 60 or so elements that were then known. They were attempting to further purify the elements so that accurate measurements could be made on the elements. Many of the scientists tried to find some sort of pattern in the properties of the elements.

In 1872, Mendeleev (Figure 3) published a chart of the then known elements. In this chart the elements were arranged in order of their atomic masses. Elements with similar properties were grouped together. Because some of the properties were seen to repeat on a regular or periodic basis, this chart became known as a **periodic table of the elements**. A great deal of the data of those days was inaccurate and this led to some inconsistencies in Mendeleev's periodic table. Mendeleev, however, was so convinced that he was correct that he used his periodic table to predict which

Several chemists around 1860 proposed that the properties of elements followed periodic trends. They included John Newlands from England, Dmitri Mendeleev from Russia, and Lothar Meyer from Germany. Only Mendeleev is now widely remembered for this idea.

Fig. 3 *Dmitri Mendeleev's theory of periodic trends in the properties of elements (1872) is the basis of our modern periodic table.*

of the elements had incorrect data. He also predicted properties of elements that had not yet been discovered. He did this by using the properties of "surrounding" elements. This is similar to what you did in the previous exercise.

At first, few scientists agreed with Mendeleev's idea. When the elements Mendeleev had predicted were later discovered and shown to have properties close to those predicted, scientists became more convinced of the usefulness of the periodic table.

Mendeleev's arrangement of the elements according to their atomic masses led to some inconsistencies. After the discovery of protons, neutrons, and electrons, the order of some of the elements was changed. Scientists realized that an atom of each element is distinguished by the number of protons in its nucleus. In today's version of the periodic table, the elements are arranged in order of *increasing atomic numbers*, not atomic masses.

Questions

1. At the time of Mendeleev, the element uranium was thought to have an atomic mass of about 116 u. Today we believe the correct value should be about 238 u. Why do you think these values are so different?

2. One whole family of elements was not known at the time of Mendeleev. The first member of this group of elements was found on the sun. This was done by viewing the sun with a spectrometer attached to a telescope during a solar eclipse. Analysis of the line spectrum suggested the presence of an unknown element. The element was named helium after the Greek word *helios*, meaning sun. Once it was discovered, why would scientists believe that other elements with similar chemical properties existed?

5.3 The Modern Periodic Table

The modern periodic table (Figure 4) is arranged in horizontal rows (called **periods**) and vertical columns (called **groups** or **families**). The eight longer columns (two on the left-hand side and six on the right-hand side) are called Groups 1 to 8. All the elements in the middle of the table, between Groups 2 and 3, are called **transition metals**.

Fig. 4 *The modern periodic table.*

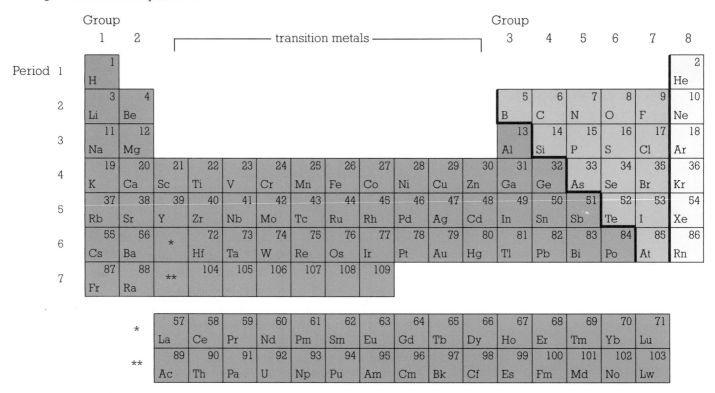

There are several ways for numbering the groups in the periodic table. They are shown in the more detailed periodic table at the back of this book.

There are seven periods. To make the size of the periodic table more manageable, Periods 6 and 7 are shortened by removing 14 elements. These 14 elements are shown separately below the main table.

Elements within a group are often referred to as a chemical family of elements. They have similar chemical properties.

The periodic table also indicates metallic elements and non-metallic elements (Figure 6). Refer to the staggered line which starts with element 5, boron. Elements to the left of this line are metals; those to the right of the line are non-metals.

Fig. 5 *Hydrogen, used as a fuel for the space shuttle, is not a metal. You will learn later why hydrogen is placed in Group 1 even though its chemical properties are different from the other Group 1 elements.*

Fig. 6 *The division into metals and non-metals in the periodic table.*

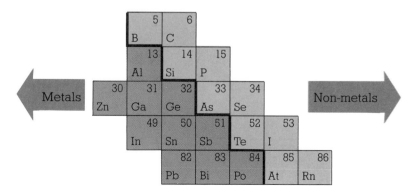

Fig. 7 *The noble gases (Group 8) were not yet discovered when Mendeleev drew up his periodic table.*

	2
	He
9	10
	Ne
17	18
	Ar
35	36
	Kr
53	54
	Xe
85	86
	Rn

The last group of elements to be discovered were Group 8 — the **noble gases**, helium through to radon (Figure 7). These elements did not at first appear to react with any other element, making it difficult to detect their presence. However, in 1962, Neil Bartlett (Figure 8) at the University of British Columbia formed the first compound of xenon. Today, other xenon compounds and some krypton compounds are known.

Fig. 8 *Neil Bartlett showed in 1962 at the University of British Columbia that the noble gas xenon could react to form a compound. In the photograph he is holding the apparatus in which the original reaction took place.*

Questions

1. Which of the following elements are metals and which are non-metals?

oxygen (O)	tin (Sn)	bismuth (Bi)
gold (Au)	tungsten (W)	radium (Ra)
radon (Rn)	chlorine (Cl)	hydrogen (H)

2. Which elements form a family of elements with the element iodine?

5.4 Reactivity of the Elements in the Periodic Table

In this experiment, you will be looking at the reactions of three metals in Group 1 (lithium, sodium, and potassium), two metals in Group 2 (magnesium and calcium), and three non-metals in Group 7 (chlorine, bromine, and iodine).

Chlorine, bromine and iodine are dangerous elements in their pure forms, so you will use compounds of these elements and water solutions of chlorine and bromine.

Fig. 9 *Chlorine, a poisonous yellowish green gas, has many industrial uses. For example, it is used to kill bacteria in swimming pools. It was also used in World War I as a deadly weapon.*

Only displacement reactions will be used in this investigation:

$$A \;+\; BC \;\rightarrow\; AC \;+\; B$$

Element A can displace element B from the compound BC only if element A is more reactive than element B. If A is less reactive than B, then no reaction occurs.

Materials

safety goggles
250-mL beaker
three 18 × 100 mm test tubes
ceramic gauze pad
glass rod
1-cm strip of magnesium ribbon
lump of calcium metal
1-mm^3 piece of sodium metal
1-mm^3 piece of potassium metal
1-mm^3 piece of lithium metal
0.1 mol/L sodium chloride solution
0.1 mol/L sodium bromide solution
0.1 mol/L sodium iodide solution
saturated chlorine water
saturated bromine water

Method

1. Draw a suitable chart to record all your observations.

2. Obtain a small piece of potassium, sodium, and lithium from the teacher. In turn, use the dry glass rod to add each metal to about 150 mL of fresh water in a clean 250-mL beaker. Immediately cover the beaker with the ceramic gauze and observe from a distance of about 1 m. See Figure 10.

3. Repeat step 2 using a small piece of magnesium and calcium instead of the potassium, sodium, and lithium.

4. Number three small test tubes, 1, 2, and 3. Place about 3 mL of sodium chloride solution in test tube 1, 3 mL of sodium bromide solution in test tube 2, and 3 mL of sodium iodide solution in test tube 3. Add about 1 mL of chlorine water to each test tube, mix well, and observe any colour change. See Figure 11.

5. Repeat step 4 but this time use bromine water instead of chlorine water.

Do not touch the metals used in this experiment because they are extremely reactive with moisture. Use a large sheet of clean paper to transfer the metals. Wear safety goggles at all times.

Fig. 10 *Potassium, sodium, and lithium — which is the most reactive with water?*

Fig. 11

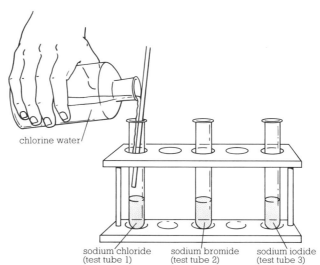

chlorine water

sodium chloride (test tube 1) sodium bromide (test tube 2) sodium iodide (test tube 3)

Follow-up

Remember the chemical name for water is hydrogen oxide.

1. Potassium, sodium, and lithium are members of Group 1 of the periodic table. What evidence suggests that the Group 1 metals react with water in the same way? Did all three metals of Group 1 react with water at the same speed?

2. Complete the following word equations for the reactions of the metals with water. Place a slash through the arrow (↛) if there is no reaction. (Please do not write in the textbook.)

lithium + water →
sodium + water →
potassium + water →
magnesium + water →
calcium + water →

3. Based on your observations, arrange lithium, sodium, and potassium in order from most reactive to least reactive. If this list could be extended to all the metals in Group 1, what do you think the order would be, from most reactive to least reactive?

Fig. 12 *Compare potassium to calcium and sodium to magnesium. Which group is more reactive, Group 1 or Group 2?*

Group 1

Group 1	Group 2
1 H	
3 Li	4 Be
11 Na	12 Mg
19 K	20 Ca
37 Rb	38 Sr
55 Cs	56 Ba
87 Fr	88 Ra

4. Based on your observations for magnesium and calcium, place all the metals in Group 2 in order from most reactive to least reactive.

5. Compare potassium to calcium, and sodium to magnesium. Which group of metals is more reactive, Group 1 or Group 2 (Figure 12)?

6. Which do you think is the most reactive metal in the periodic table? Explain your answer.

7. Based on your observations of the displacement reactions for the Group 7 elements, complete the following word equations. Place a slash through the arrow ($\nrightarrow$) if there is no reaction. (Please do not write in the textbook.)

chlorine + sodium chloride →
chlorine + sodium bromide →
chlorine + sodium iodide →
bromine + sodium chloride →
bromine + sodium bromide →
bromine + sodium iodide →

8. In a single displacement reaction, the single element can "kick out" the element in the compound only if the single element is more reactive than the element in the compound. Otherwise, there is no reaction. Use this information and your result from question 7 to list the three non-metals, iodine, bromine, and chlorine, in order from most reactive to least reactive.
Can you extend this list to cover all the non-metals in Group 7?

9. Is the order of reactivity for the non-metals the same as that for the metals?

10. Based on your answer to question 9 and knowing how the metals in Group 1 and Group 2 behave, predict which group of non-metals would be more reactive, Group 6 or Group 7.

11. Which do you think is the most reactive non-metal in the periodic table? Remember helium is a member of the noble gases and should not be considered.

12. Draw an outline of the periodic table. On your diagram indicate where the noble gases are located. Show the dividing line between metals and non-metals. Summarize your findings from this experiment by labelling the diagram with the following terms:
   (a) metals
   (b) non-metals
   (c) the general direction, both horizontal and vertical, in which metals become more reactive
   (d) the general direction, both horizontal and vertical, in which non-metals become more reactive.

13. Based only on the results from this investigation, select the more reactive element from each pair of elements below:

Li or Be   Zn or Al   F or S   He or F   C or Si
Rb or Ca   Pt or Au   Pb or Sn   Sr or Sc   As or Se

To simplify this exercise, some of the names of the compounds in question 14 are not the proper ones.

14. From your knowledge of the periodic table, decide whether each of the following reactions should or should not occur. If the reaction should occur, complete the word equation. If the reaction should not occur, put a slash through the arrow ($\nrightarrow$). (Please do not write in the textbook.)

(a) magnesium + sodium chloride →
(b) chromium + nickel oxide →
(c) barium + calcium chloride →
(d) bromine + sodium chloride →
(e) argon + water →
(f) lead + tin sulfate →
(g) iron + silver nitrate →
(h) silver + copper sulfate →
(i) arsenic + phosphorus sulfide →
(j) magnesium + hydrogen sulfate (sulfuric acid) →

Investigation

5.5 Some Metal Displacement Reactions

We have seen that in single displacement reactions, only a more reactive element is able to displace a less reactive element. In this experiment you will study this idea a little further.

Materials

safety goggles
spot plate
0.1 mol/L copper(II) nitrate solution
0.1 mol/L zinc nitrate solution
0.1 mol/L aluminum nitrate solution
0.1 mol/L lead(II) nitrate solution
0.1 mol/L tin(II) nitrate solution
0.1 mol/L nickel(II) nitrate solution
0.1 mol/L magnesium nitrate solution
strip of copper metal
strip of zinc metal
strip of aluminum metal
strip of lead metal
strip of tin metal
strip of nickel metal
strip of magnesium metal

Fig. 13

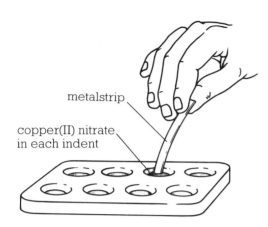

metalstrip

copper(II) nitrate
in each indent

Method

1. Use a piece of fine steel wool or emery paper to thoroughly clean the surface at one end of each metal strip.

2. Almost fill each of seven indents on the spot plate with copper(II) nitrate solution.

3. Dip each metal strip into a different sample of the copper(II) nitrate solution on the spot plate. Observe any signs of a chemical reaction. See Figure 13.

4. Clean the spot plate and the metal strips. Repeat steps 1 to 3 for each of the other solutions.

5. Record all your observations in a chart such as the following:

	Copper	Zinc	Aluminum	Lead	Tin	Nickel	Magnesium
copper(II) nitrate	no reaction	reaction					
zinc nitrate							
aluminum nitrate							
lead(II) nitrate							
tin(II) nitrate							
nickel(II) nitrate							
magnesium nitrate							

Remember that single displacement reaction occurs because the free element is more reactive than one of the metallic elements that is part of the compound.

Follow-up

1. Choose a metallic element used in this experiment and list all the metals that are less reactive than it. Repeat for each of the other metals.

2. Use your lists to place the metals in order from most reactive to least reactive.

3. Does your order agree with that predicted by the periodic table? In fact, it should not. The periodic table is a powerful predicting device, but chemists know that the only way to be certain is to check the prediction with an experiment.

4. Can you use the periodic table to predict which metals are the least reactive (Figure 14)?

Fig. 14 *Gold and platinum are unreactive metals. They do not tarnish and can remain shiny for a long time.*

To simplify this exercise, some of the names of the compounds in question 5 are not the proper ones.

5. Based only on the following reactions, place the elements iron, copper, zinc, silver, and lead in order from most reactive to least reactive. Briefly explain your order.

(a) iron + copper oxide → iron oxide + copper
(b) copper + zinc oxide ↛
(c) silver + copper sulfate ↛
(d) zinc + iron oxide → zinc oxide + iron
(e) copper + lead oxide ↛
(f) lead + iron oxide ↛

5.6 A Periodic Table Project

To do the following project, you will make use of what you have learned about the periodic table:

- It is called a periodic table because it is arranged such that elements within the same group show similar chemical properties. A periodic repetition of properties of the elements occurs with every new row.
- The elements in the periodic table are divided into two categories —metals and non-metals. Within the non-metals there is also a group of elements which rarely react with other elements. This group contains the noble gases.
- The atoms of the elements get bigger as we move down a group.
- Metals become more reactive as we move to the left and down the periodic table.
- Non-metals (not the noble gases) become more reactive as we move up and to the right in the periodic table.

Now design your own special periodic table:

1. Select a subject for your periodic table. It does not have to be chemistry. You can choose almost any topic in which you have an interest. Food would be a good topic.

2. Your periodic table need not even be the same shape as the chemical one, but should be divided into three categories: ''metals,'' ''non-metals,'' and ''noble gases.''

3. Each category should have at least one group but it would be nice if there were more.

4. Choose ''elements'' for each group. The elements within the group should also be similar in some way. Remember the atoms of elements become bigger down a group.

5. In our food example, we could choose ''junk'' food as our ''metals,'' ''healthy'' food as our ''non-metals,'' and ''exotic'' foods as our ''noble gases.'' A group within the junk foods could be hamburgers. You could start with a simple hamburger and build up to a triple decker with cheese, bacon, and so on.

6. Each of the ''elements'' that you use in your periodic table should have a name and a symbol.

7. This is your chance to be creative. Get pictures of all your elements. Use a big piece of paper to set out your periodic table. Have fun!

- The periodic table is divided into horizontal rows called periods and vertical columns called groups.
- Elements within a group are often called a chemical family of elements and have similar chemical properties.
- Within a group, the atoms of the elements get larger as we move down the group.
- The periodic table divides elements into metals and non-metals.
- Within the non-metals, there is a group of elements called the noble gases. Only xenon and krypton within this family are known to form compounds with other elements.
- Metals and non-metals react differently.
- The metals generally become more reactive as we move down a particular group and as we move from right to left within the periodic table.

- The non-metals generally become more reactive as we move up a particular group and as we move from left to right within the periodic table.
- Francium is the most reactive metal and fluorine is the most reactive non-metal.
- The periodic table can be used to predict chemical and physical properties of elements that have not yet been discovered. These properties should, however, always be confirmed with an experiment.
- In single displacement reactions, only a more reactive element can displace another element that is part of a compound.

1. If a new element, with atomic number 118, was to be discovered, to which group of elements in the periodic table would this new element belong?
2. Magnesium reacts with oxygen to form a compound with the chemical formula MgO. Write the formula of the compound formed between calcium and oxygen.
3. The elements carbon and chlorine form a compound with the chemical formula CCl_4. What would be the formula of the compound formed between carbon and bromine?
4. Potassium nitride has the chemical formula K_3N. What is the chemical formula of the compound formed from sodium and phosphorus?
5. Scientists have made estimates of the size of the atoms of the different elements. The bar graph in Figure 15 shows the atomic radii of the first 20 elements in the periodic table. The values for two of the elements are missing.
   (a) What evidence suggests that the atomic radii of the elements follow a periodic trend?
   (b) Use the graph to estimate the atomic radius of each of the two missing elements.

Fig. 15 *The atomic radii of the first 20 elements.*

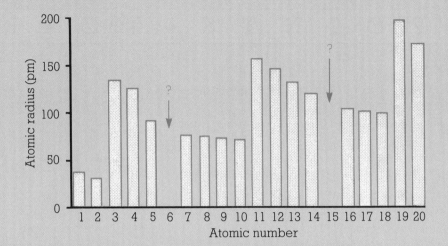

Fig. 16 *The ionization energies of the first 20 elements.*

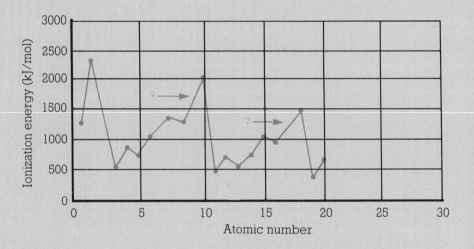

6. The term ionization energy is used to describe how much energy is needed to completely remove an electron from an electrically neutral atom. The line graph in Figure 16 shows the values of the ionization energies for the first 20 elements in the periodic table. The values for two of the elements are missing.
   (a) What evidence suggests that ionization energy values for the elements form a periodic trend?
   (b) Use the graph to estimate the ionization energy of each of the two missing elements.

7. Chlorine is used as a purifying agent in drinking water and for swimming pools. The following equation represents the reaction between chlorine and water:

$$Cl_2 + H_2O \rightarrow HCl + HOCl$$

Scientists believe that the chemical HOCl (hypochlorous acid) is largely responsible for the purification properties of chlorine. More recently, bromine has been used as a purifying agent. Write a chemical equation to show what happens when bromine reacts with water. How would you name the chemical HOBr?

8. Which of the following elements are metals and which are non-metals?

titanium (Ti)   silicon (Si)   iodine (I)
lead (Pb)   mercury (Hg)   sulfur (S)
aluminum (Al)   hydrogen (H)   uranium (U)

9. Which elements form a family of elements with arsenic?

10. Using only the general trends for reactivity in the periodic table, select the less reactive element from each pair of elements below:

C or N   Cs or Sr   Fe or Cu
Cl or F   Ca or Zn   Ba or Mg
S or Si   Ne or F   Se or T
Au or Cu

11. The answers you gave in question 10 are only predictions. As a scientist, what would you have to do in order to check your prediction?

12. The following are a set of experimental results:

copper + silver nitrate → copper nitrate + silver
gold + silver nitrate ↛

(a) Use these results to place the metals, copper, gold, and silver, in order from least reactive to most reactive.
(b) Does the order agree with the general rule in the periodic table?
(c) Which is correct, the general rule or your answer in (a)? Explain.

6

IONIC BONDING

A familiar ionic compound — salt.

CONTENTS

6.1 Ion Formation

You learned in Chapter 4 that in an electrically neutral atom, the number of electrons is equal to the number of protons. When an atom gains or loses one or more electrons, it becomes charged. The charged atom produced in this way is called an **ion**.

Since the noble gases are so non-reactive, chemists believe that there is something special about the way in which their electrons are arranged.

A neutral atom of sodium has one electron in its outermost occupied energy level. If that electron is lost, the electronic structure of the resulting sodium ion resembles that of a neon atom (Figure 2a). The sodium ion has a positive one charge, $1+$, because it now has 11 protons and 10 electrons.

Magnesium also forms a positive ion. In order to resemble the noble gas neon, a magnesium atom loses two electrons from the outermost occupied energy level (Figure 2b).

What about non-metals? When an oxygen atom gains two extra electrons, it becomes an ion with a negative two charge, $2-$ (Figure 2c). By gaining one extra electron, a fluorine atom becomes an ion with a negative one charge, $1-$ (Figure 2d). Both ions are similar to a neon atom in electronic structure.

The electrons in the outermost occupied energy level of an atom are called **valence electrons**. The outermost occupied energy level is called the **valence shell**. In the examples above, we saw that only the valence electrons of the atoms are involved in ion formation. Gilbert Lewis therefore suggested that we simply represent an atom by its symbol and a set of dots around the

Fig. 1 *In 1916, Gilbert Lewis devised a simple way of representing the valence electrons of atoms.*

symbol to indicate the valence electrons of that atom. This type of representation, known as the **Lewis diagram**, is much easier to use than the Bohr-Rutherford diagram (Figure 3).

Some examples of Lewis diagrams are:

Li· ·Be· $\dot{\text{B}}$: ·$\dot{\text{C}}$· ·$\ddot{\text{N}}$: :$\ddot{\text{O}}$: :$\ddot{\text{F}}$: :$\ddot{\text{Ne}}$:

Fig. 2 *The ions formed from sodium, magnesium, oxygen, and fluorine are similar to the atom of the noble gas neon in electronic structure.*

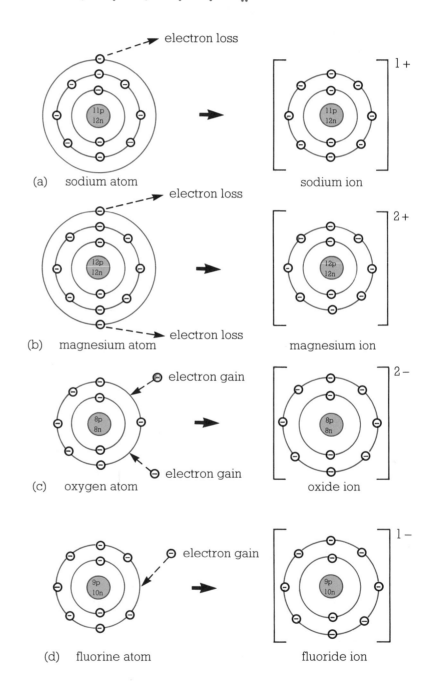

(a) sodium atom — sodium ion

(b) magnesium atom — magnesium ion

(c) oxygen atom — oxide ion

(d) fluorine atom — fluoride ion

Fig. 3 *The Lewis diagram is much simpler than the Bohr-Rutherford diagram.*

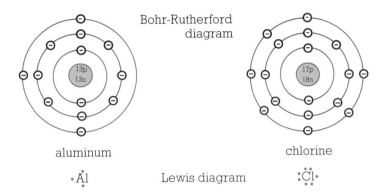

Bohr-Rutherford diagram

aluminum

·A̤l

Lewis diagram

:C̤l·

chlorine

Groups 1 to 8 are called the "long groups" in the periodic table.

Questions

1. The number of valence electrons of lithium is 1; that of fluorine is 7. Look at the elements in Groups 1 to 8 of the periodic table. How is the group number related to the number of valence electrons of the elements?

2. Draw the Lewis diagram for an atom of each of the following elements:

Na	Sr	Cs	He	H	Al	P	I	Br	Rn
Mg	Si	S	Cl	As	Xe	Ca	K	Ba	

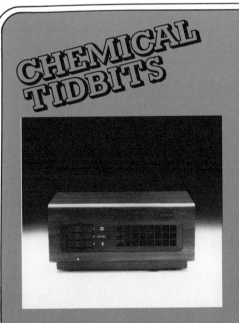

CHEMICAL TIDBITS

DO IONS AFFECT PEOPLE?

Different atmospheric conditions can lead to a build-up of positive or negative ions in the air. On humid days there tend to be more positive ions and some people think that this is why some of us feel down. Clinical studies have also shown that with a build-up of positive ions in the air, some people have more headaches, others feel more fatigued, and others suffer more from sinus and asthma conditions. The air immediately after a thunderstorm tends to contain more negative ions. Some people have said that they feel better after a storm. Today you can actually buy a negative ion generator to place in your home (Figure 4).

Fig. 4 *Can commercially produced negative ion generators improve your health and mood?*

6.2 Ionic Bonding

We described above that when a metal atom loses all its valence electrons, it has an electronic structure similar to the nearest noble gas. With a non-metal, the atom gains one or more electrons to form an electronic structure similar to the nearest noble gas. Because most of the noble gases have eight electrons in their valence shell, this idea became known as the **octet rule**.

Using a Lewis diagram to represent an ion then becomes a much easier task. With metal atoms, we simply remove all the valence electrons. The ion is then shown with just the symbol and the charge.

Mg: loses two electrons to become $[Mg]^{2+}$

Ål: loses three electrons to become $[Al]^{3+}$

With non-metal atoms, we add sufficient electrons to make a total of eight. The ion is then shown with the symbol and eight dots around the symbol plus the charge.

:S̈:   gains two extra electrons to become $[\,:\!\ddot{S}\!:\,]^{2-}$

:P̈·   gains three electrons to become $[\,:\!\ddot{P}\!:\,]^{3-}$

The only exception to the rule is a hydrogen atom. It gains one electron to resemble the noble gas helium.

H·   gains one extra electron to become $[\,\cdot H\cdot\,]^{1-}$

In some cases, a hydrogen atom can also lose its valence electron and become a $[H]^{1+}$ ion.

Ion formation is used to explain how a metal and a non-metal join (or **bond**) together to form a compound. The metal atom loses all its valence electrons to become a positive ion. The non-metal atom gains sufficient electrons to form eight electrons in its valence shell and forms a negative ion. The positive and negative ions then attract each other. The attraction is called an **ionic bond**.

Let us use the compound lithium fluoride, LiF, as an example.

$$\text{Li·} \longrightarrow \cdot\ddot{F}\!: \quad \text{becomes} \quad [Li]^{1+}\ [\,:\!\ddot{F}\!:\,]^{1-}$$

lithium fluoride

The lithium atom only has one valence electron and loses this one electron. The fluorine atom has seven valence electrons and needs one more to fill its valence shell with eight electrons. When lithium bonds with fluorine, the valence electron from a lithium atom is donated to a fluorine atom. In this way, a positive lithium

"Oct" means eight. Octet means a group of eight.

When we write the formula of the compound, we must leave out the ion charges. For example, we write LiF for lithium fluoride, not $Li^{1+}F^{1-}$.

ion and a negative fluoride ion are formed. These two ions have opposite charges. They therefore attract each other to form an ionic bond.

Some atoms lose or gain more than one electron.

$$\text{Na}\cdot\!\!\searrow\!\!\underset{\displaystyle \ddot{\text{O}}:}{} \quad \text{becomes} \quad \begin{matrix}[\text{Na}]^{1+}\\ \\ [\text{Na}]^{1+}\end{matrix} \quad [:\ddot{\text{O}}:]^{2-} \quad \text{or} \quad [\text{Na}]_2^{1+}[:\ddot{\text{O}}:]^{2-}$$

$$\text{Na}\cdot\!\!\nearrow$$

sodium oxide

In this example, the oxygen atom gains two electrons. Since each sodium atom only loses one electron, the oxygen atom takes one electron from each sodium atom. The compound, sodium oxide, therefore consists of two positive sodium ions bonded to one negative oxide ion.

We can consider a third example.

$$\begin{matrix}\text{Mg}:\rightarrow\ddot{\text{P}}:\\ \\ \text{Mg}:\searrow\ddot{\text{P}}:\\ \\ \text{Mg}:\nearrow\end{matrix} \quad \text{becomes} \quad \begin{matrix}[\text{Mg}]^{2+}\ [:\ddot{\text{P}}:]^{3-}\\ \\ [\text{Mg}]^{2+}\ [:\ddot{\text{P}}:]^{3-}\\ \\ [\text{Mg}]^{2+}\end{matrix} \quad \text{or} \quad [\text{Mg}]_3^{2+}\ [:\ddot{\text{P}}:]_2^{3-}$$

magnesium phosphide

This example is more complicated. Each of the magnesium atoms loses two electrons and each of the phosphorus atoms gains three electrons. Magnesium phosphide is therefore a compound made up of three positive magnesium ions and two negative phosphide ions.

Questions

1. Use a Lewis diagram to represent the ion formed from each of the following atoms:

   N   O   Na   Be   Cl   K   Ca   Br   Li   Ga

2. Use a Lewis diagram to show the ionic bonding in each of the following pairs of elements:

Li and Cl	K and Br	Ca and O	Na and S
Li and S	Mg and Cl	Al and O	Ca and P
Al and Cl	Cs and P	Ga and As	Ba and Cl
Be and Br	Rb and F	Mg and N	Al and N
Sn and As	Al and I	Ga and Se	Ba and N

6.3 Writing Chemical Formulas

Chemists obviously did not want to go through the above exercise every time they wanted to know what the chemical formula would be when a metal atom combined with a non-metal atom. So they looked for a short cut.

The term **valence value** means the number of electrons an atom loses or gains when it bonds with another atom.

Recall the three examples in the previous section: lithium has a valence value of 1, sodium has a valence value of 1, and magnesium has a valence value of 2. Fluorine gains one electron and has a valence value of 1. Oxygen gains two electrons and has a valence value of 2. Phosphorus gains three electrons and has a valence value of 3. Look closely at the example for sodium and oxygen. Sodium with valence value 1 and oxygen with valence value 2 form a compound called sodium oxide with the formula Na_2O. It seems as if the valence values were simply switched to give the formula. This is also true with magnesium phosphide, Mg_3P_2. This switching of valence values in formula writing is known as the **crossover rule**.

Using the crossover rule to write the formula of a compound requires six steps:

		Lithium fluoride	Sodium oxide	Magnesium oxide
Step 1	Write down the symbol in the order given in the name	Li F	Na O	Mg O
Step 2	Record the valence value for each element given	$1 \diagdown 1$ Li ⤬ F	$1 \diagdown 2$ Na ⤬ O	$2 \diagdown 2$ Mg ⤬ O
Step 3	Crossover the valence values	Li_1 F_1	Na_2 O_1	Mg_2 O_2
Step 4	Find the highest factor common to the two valence values	1	1	2
Step 5	Divide the two valence values by this highest factor	Li_1 F_1	Na_2 O_1	Mg_1 O_1
Step 6	Drop any "1" in the formula	LiF	Na_2O	MgO

"Binary" means two.

The examples in the chart contain only two elements. Such compounds are referred to as **binary compounds**. By international agreement, the English names of these compounds all end with *-ide*.

136

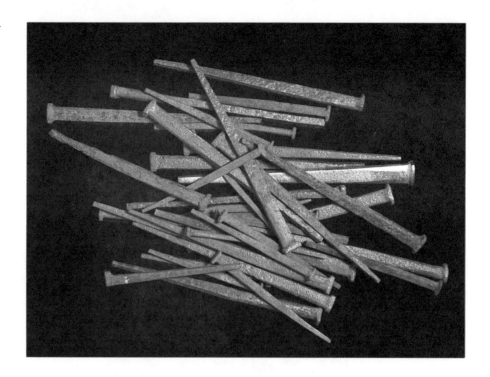

Fig. 5 *Iron oxide (rust) is a binary compound.*

Questions

It is not intended that you memorize the valence values and the symbols of the elements. You will get to know them after frequent use.

1. You can look up the valence values of the elements from the periodic table at the back of this book. How is the group number related to the valence values of the elements in Groups 1 to 8?

2. Consider the electronic arrangements of lithium, sodium, and potassium. What do they have in common? Do the elements magnesium and calcium have a similar relationship? What about chlorine, bromine and iodine?

3. Give the correct formula for:

sodium sulfide	potassium oxide
calcium chloride	aluminum hydride
calcium phosphide	barium chloride
silver bromide	cadmium oxide
hydrogen iodide	aluminum oxide
beryllium fluoride	silver sulfide
magnesium hydride	strontium nitride
lithium bromide	zinc chloride
barium oxide	cadmium bromide
potassium phosphide	calcium iodide

6.4 Naming Multivalent Elements

Many elements have more than one valence value. Most transition metals in the periodic table are multivalent (Figure 6).

Fig. 6 *The transition metals.*

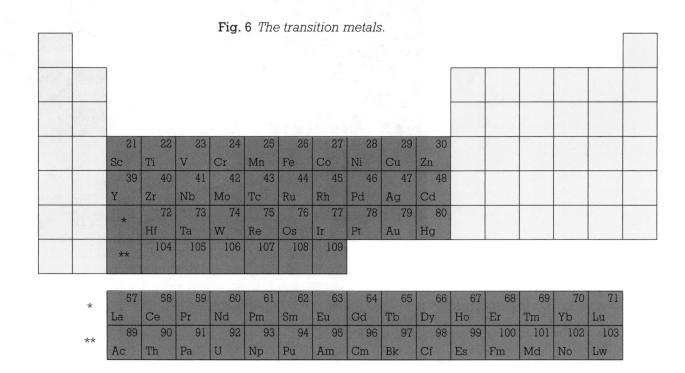

In naming a compound containing a multivalent metal, the valence value of the metal in that compound is given in Roman numerals. Some examples are shown in the chart below:

An old system (still found on the labels of bottles of chemicals) to name multivalent elements uses the Latin name of the element with *-ous* and *-ic* endings. For example, cuprous for copper(I), cupric for copper(II), ferrous for iron(II), ferric for iron(III).

Compound	Valence value of metal
mercury(I) nitride	1
copper(II) chloride	2
gold(III) oxide	3
lead(IV) oxide	4
bismuth(V) sulfide	5
uranium(VI) fluoride	6

Questions

1. Give the correct formula for:

mercury(II) bromide
copper(I) sulfide
gold(I) fluoride
cobalt(II) hydride
iron(II) phosphide
tin(IV) oxide
copper(I) nitride
tin(II) fluoride
chromium(II) sulfide
manganese(II) chloride

uranium(VI) oxide
copper(II) nitride
gold(III) chloride
nickel(II) bromide
iron(III) sulfide
chromium(III) oxide
lead(II) fluoride
lead(IV) phosphide
mercury(I) hydride
cobalt(III) oxide

2. Name the following compounds using Roman numerals:
$FeCl_2$ $FeCl_3$ Cu_2S CuS

Investigation

6.5 Chemistry of Some Multivalent Elements

You learned earlier that the chemical properties of an element can be explained by considering only the valence electrons in the atoms of that element. Different elements with different valence values have different chemical behaviour. But what about the chemical behaviour of an element that has more than one valence value? In this experiment you will investigate some chemical reactions involving such multivalent elements.

Materials

Ammonium sulfide solution has an unpleasant rotten egg smell. It should be used in a fume hood. At the end of the experiment, the contents of the test tube should be discarded into a large beaker in the fume hood.

safety goggles
spatula
3 to 4 small test tubes
tin(II) chloride
tin(IV) chloride
iron(II) sulfate
iron(III) chloride
sodium sulfite
distilled water
3 mol/L ammonium
  sulfide solution

5 mol/L sodium hydroxide solution
3% hydrogen peroxide solution
5 mol/L ammonium hydroxide
  solution
0.15 mol/L potassium ferrocyanide
  solution
0.5 mol/L copper(II) sulfate solution
0.5 mol/L ammonium thiocyanate
  solution
5 mol/L ammonium chloride
  solution

Method

All your observations should be recorded in a suitable chart. In this experiment, a small quantity of material means about 1 mm³ in size.

1. *Reactions of tin(II) and tin(IV) compounds*
   (a) Place a small quantity of tin(II) chloride in a clean, small test tube. Dissolve it in about 2 mL of distilled water. Carefully add a few drops of ammonium sulfide solution and mix well. Record your observations.
   (b) Repeat step 1a using tin(IV) chloride instead of the tin(II) chloride.

2. *Reactions of iron(II) and iron(III) compounds*
   (a) Place a small quantity of iron(III) chloride in a clean, small test tube. Dissolve it in about 2 mL of distilled water. Add about 2 mL of sodium hydroxide solution and mix well. Record your observations. Keep this test tube with its contents. Label it as test tube 1.
   (b) Repeat step 2a using iron(II) sulfate instead of the iron(III) chloride. Record your observations. Keep this test tube for the next step. Label it as test tube 2.
   (c) Carefully add a few drops of hydrogen peroxide solution into test tube 2. Record your observations. Compare the colour now found with that in test tube 1.
   (d) Dissolve a small quantity of iron(III) chloride in about 2 mL of distilled water in a test tube. Add 2 mL of ammonium chloride solution, followed by 2 mL of ammonium hydroxide solution. Mix well and record your observations. Keep this test tube with its contents. Label it as test tube 3.
   (e) Repeat step 2d using iron(II) sulfate instead of the iron(III) chloride. Record your observations and once again add hydrogen peroxide solution. Compare the colour now found with that in test tube 3.
   (f) Dissolve a small quantity of iron(III) chloride in about 2 mL of distilled water in a test tube. Add three drops of potassium ferricyanide solution and mix well.
   (g) Repeat step 2f using iron(II) sulfate instead of the iron(III) chloride.

3. *Converting a copper(II) compound into a copper(I) compound*
   (a) Place 2 mL of copper(II) sulfate solution in a test tube and add an equal amount of ammonium thiocyanate solution. Mix well. Record your observations. The product that forms is called copper(II) thiocyanate.

Hydrogen peroxide is a bleaching agent that works on coloured clothing as well as skin. Do not spill it!

(b) Add a small scoop full of solid sodium sulfite to the test tube in step 3a. Mix well. Record your observations. The product that forms is copper(I) thiocyanate.

Follow-up

1. When tin(II) chloride or tin(IV) chloride reacts with ammonium sulfide, a tin sulfide is formed. What evidence suggests that the tin sulfides produced from tin(II) chloride and tin(IV) chloride are actually different substances?

2. Complete the following word equations. (Please do not write in the textbook.)
   (a) tin(II) chloride + ammonium sulfide →
   (b) tin(IV) chloride + ammonium sulfide →

These are double displacement reactions.

3. When iron(II) sulfate or iron(III) chloride reacts with sodium hydroxide, an iron hydroxide is formed. What evidence suggests that the iron hydroxides produced from iron(II) sulfate and iron(III) chloride are actually different substances?

4. Complete the following word equations. (Please do not write in the textbook.)
   (a) iron(III) chloride + sodium hydroxide →
   (b) iron(II) sulfate + sodium hydroxide →

5. Hydrogen peroxide was added to a test tube containing iron(II) hydroxide. Looking at your results, what do you think is formed when hydrogen peroxide is added to iron(II) hydroxide? It is not iron(II) peroxide.

6. How can potassium ferricyanide be used to tell the difference between an iron(II) and an iron(III) compound?

7. What observation suggests that copper(II) thiocyanate could have been converted into copper(I) thiocyanate?

8. You should now be able to write the formula of a binary ionic compound when you are given the name of the compound.
   In the following exercise, you are to do the reverse. Give the correct name for each substance. Remember, if the metal is multivalent, use Roman numerals to indicate its valence value in a particular compound.

$FeBr_2$	Mg_3P_2	$PbCl_4$	Bi_2S_5	SnO_2
Hg_2O	UO_3	Cu_2S	CaO	Zn_3N_2

6.6 Preparing a Ternary Compound

A binary ionic compound contains only two elements. A **ternary compound** contains three elements. In the last experiment, you used chemicals such as copper(II) sulfate, iron(II) sulfate, and sodium sulfite. The names of these ternary compounds do not end in -*ide*, but in -*ate* or -*ite*. The -*ate* or -*ite* ending in a name indicates that the compound contains oxygen. The rest of the name identifies the other elements present. For example,

copper(II) sulfate	$CuSO_4$
iron(II) sulfate	$FeSO_4$
sodium sulfite	Na_2SO_3

You will see later that the crossover rule is also used to write the formula of ternary compounds.

In the experiment below, you are going to prepare a ternary compound — potassium nitrate. This can be done by mixing a solution of sodium nitrate with a solution of potassium chloride. If you apply the rules for double displacement reactions, then the word equation is

potassium chloride + sodium nitrate →

potassium nitrate + sodium chloride

Making potassium nitrate, however, is not as simple as suggested by the word equation. All four compounds mentioned are soluble in water and it can be difficult to obtain pure potassium nitrate. To do so we must use the fact that the four substances are not equally soluble in water at all temperatures.

Materials

safety goggles	400-mL beaker
stemless funnel	250-mL beaker
filter paper	100-mL beaker
stirring rod	boiling chips
thermometer	ice
balance	0.1 mol/L silver nitrate solution
2 medium-sized test tubes	distilled water
tongs	sodium nitrate
oven	potassium chloride
hotplate	

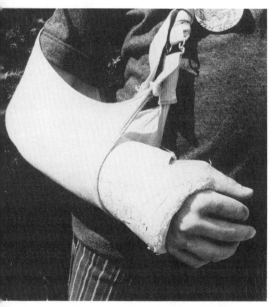

Fig. 7 *Calcium sulfate, used to make plaster casts, is a ternary compound.*

Method

1. Mix together 27.2 g of sodium nitrate, 18.6 g of potassium chloride, 40 mL of distilled water, and two boiling chips in a 250-mL beaker.

If a hotplate is not available, the mixture can be heated over a Bunsen burner. Make sure the beaker is stable by putting it through a ring clamp, then on a wire gauze supported by another clamp.

2. Heat the mixture (with stirring) on a hotplate to 100°C. Keep the mixture at a low simmer for about 5 min (Figure 8a). You do not want to evaporate the liquid to dryness.

3. Filter the mixture through a hot, stemless funnel and filter paper into a 100-mL beaker (Figure 8b). (Think about ways that you can preheat the funnel and filter paper.)

4. The residue on the filter paper will be largely sodium chloride and possibly a little potassium chloride. It can be thrown away.

5. Cool the filtrate to 5°C by placing the 100-mL beaker into a 400-mL beaker containing ice and water (Figure 8c).

6. Filter while cold. Wash the residue (mostly potassium nitrate) with about 2 mL of ice-cold distilled water.

7. Purify the potassium nitrate by adding it to about 5 mL of distilled water in a medium-sized test tube. Heat the test tube in a 250-mL beaker containing boiling water. While heating, add distilled water, a few drops at a time, to the test tube until all of the solid just dissolves (Figure 8d). Filter through a hot funnel and filter paper into a second test tube. Allow the filtrate to cool to 5°C by placing it in an ice/water bath. Filter off the crystals that form. Dry the crystals by placing them in the oven at 100°C for about 30 min.

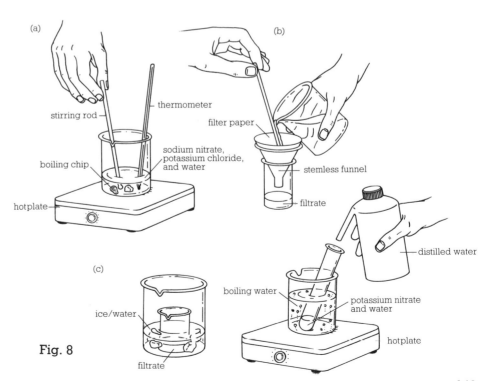

(a) stirring rod — thermometer — boiling chip — sodium nitrate, potassium chloride, and water — hotplate

(b) filter paper — stemless funnel — filtrate

(c) ice/water — filtrate — boiling water — potassium nitrate and water — distilled water — hotplate

Fig. 8

143

Handle silver nitrate solution carefully, as it can stain your skin and clothing.

8. Repeat the recrystallization procedure in step 7.

9. Test the potassium nitrate for purity by adding a few crystals of the potassium nitrate to about 2 mL of distilled water in a test tube. Add a few drops of silver nitrate solution. If a cloudy, white substance forms, then the potassium nitrate crystals are still impure. Recrystallize one more time if necessary.

10. Place your potassium nitrate crystals in a labelled vial and hand them in to your teacher.

Follow-up

Figure 9 shows the approximate solubility of sodium nitrate, potassium nitrate, sodium chloride, and potassium chloride in 20 mL of sodium nitrate solution.

Fig. 9 *The approximate solubility in water of sodium nitrate, potassium nitrate, potassium chloride, and sodium chloride.*

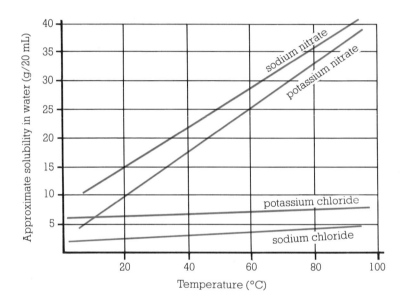

1. Look at the word equation for the reaction in this experiment. What are the two products formed?

2. One way to obtain the desired potassium nitrate is to remove the unwanted sodium chloride. What does the graph indicate about the solubility of these two products in hot solution?

3. When a hot solution containing the two products is filtered, which of the two products would be largely dissolved in the filtrate?

4. When the filtrate is cooled, what is the name of the crystals that begin to form?

144

6.7 What Are Radicals?

A **radical** is a group of atoms of different elements bonded together to form a **polyatomic** ion. In formula writing the radical is used as if it were a single element. The sulfate radical consists of one sulfur atom and four oxygen atoms (SO_4) and behaves as if it was an element with a valence value equal to 2.

The crossover rule is also used when writing the formula of a compound containing a radical.

		Lithium nitrate	Iron(III) sulfate	Magnesium carbonate
Step 1	Write down the symbols in the order given in the name	Li NO_3	Fe SO_4	Mg CO_3
Step 2	Record the valence value for each element or radical given	$\overset{1}{Li}\diagdown\overset{1}{NO_3}$	$\overset{3}{Fe}\diagdown\overset{2}{SO_4}$	$\overset{2}{Mg}\diagdown\overset{2}{CO_3}$
Step 3	Crossover the valence values	$Li_1(NO_3)_1$	$Fe_2(SO_4)_3$	$Mg_2(CO_3)_2$
Step 4	Find the highest factor common to the two valence values	1	1	2
Step 5	Divide the two valence values by this highest factor	$Li_1(NO_3)_1$	$Fe_2(SO_4)_3$	$Mg_1(CO_3)_1$
Step 6	Drop any "1" in the formula	$LiNO_3$	$Fe_2(SO_4)_3$	$MgCO_3$

In step 3, brackets were used to make sure that the whole radical was kept together. The "3" in NO_3 and the "4" in SO_4 are not part of the crossover rule and are not to be divided or dropped in steps 5 and 6.

The brackets are only kept around the radical if, after you have applied the crossover rule, the number outside the bracket is 2 or more.

Questions

1. Use the symbols and valence values of the elements and radicals given at the back of this textbook to write the correct formulas for the following:

sodium nitrate
copper(II) sulfate
ammonium bromide
aluminum carbonate
zinc phosphate
iron(II) sulfate
iron(III) sulfide
magnesium carbonate
calcium hydrogen carbonate
nickel(II) nitrate
sodium hydride
manganese(II) nitrate
potassium chloride
potassium carbonate
tin(IV) carbonate
mercury(II) sulfate
copper(I) phosphate
barium nitrate
mercury (I) nitride
gold(I) fluoride
strontium fluoride

aluminum hydrogen carbonate
strontium bromide
lithium iodide
chromium (VI) oxide
lead(IV) chloride
lead(II) nitrate
lead(II) nitride
manganese(IV) oxide
silver nitrate
sodium hydrogen carbonate
cobalt(III) sulfide
cobalt(II) sulfate
cadmium bromide
zinc nitrate
aluminum phosphate
aluminum sulfite
gold(III) oxide
nickel(II) chloride
gold(III) bromide
sodium chlorate
tin(IV) oxide

Fig. 10 *The compound sodium hydrogen carbonate is the baking soda used to make dough rise.*

The -ide ending in hydroxide and cyanide does not mean that the compound is binary.

2. You have learned that a compound with the ending *-ate* or *-ite* always contains a radical. Exceptions are compounds containing the ammonium radical (NH_4, valence = 1), the hydroxide radical (OH, valence = 1), and the cyanide radical (CN, valence = 1).

Write the correct formulas for the following:

calcium hydroxide   ammonium sulfide
magnesium cyanide   potassium cyanide

Fig. 11 *Silver nitrate has been used in the photographic industry since the early days of glass plates.*

- Ions form when atoms lose or gain electrons.
- The electronic structure of an ion resembles that of the nearest noble gas in the periodic table.
- Ions usually have eight electrons in the outermost shell.
- Electrons in the outermost occupied energy level are referred to as valence electrons.
- Lewis diagrams represent only the valence electrons.
- Metals form positive ions by losing all their valence electrons.
- Non-metals form negative ions by gaining sufficient electrons to obtain eight electrons in their valence shell.
- According to the octet rule, an atom loses or gains enough electrons so that there are eight electrons in the outermost shell.
- Hydrogen is an exception. It usually reacts by gaining only one more electron into its valence shell.

- Ionic bonding occurs when a positive ion is attracted to a negative ion.
- The crossover rule is used to write the formula of an ionic compound.
- Binary compounds contain only two elements and the name ends in *-ide*.
- Ternary compounds contain three elements.
- Compounds whose names end in *-ate* or *-ite* contain oxygen.
- The term valence value refers to the number of electrons an atom of an element loses or gains when it reacts to form a compound.
- Roman numerals are used to indicate the valence value of a multivalent element in a particular compound.
- Atoms of the same element but with different valence values have different chemical properties.
- A radical is a group of atoms which bond to form a polyatomic ion.

1. What is the relationship between ion formation and the electronic structure of the atom of the nearest noble gas?
2. What type of ion forms when a neutral atom gains an electron?
3. What type of ion forms when a neutral atom loses an electron?
4. What is a binary compound?
5. What is a ternary compound?
6. What information is given when the name of a compound ends in -ide?
7. What information is given when the name of a compound ends in -ate or -ite?
8. Give three examples of multivalent elements.
9. Give an example of a positively charged radical.
10. Give two examples of negatively charged radicals.
11. Draw the Lewis diagram for an atom of each of the following elements:

   K   Ba   Li   Ne   B   F   Pb   C
   N   O   S   Se   I   Kr   He   H

12. Use a Lewis diagram to represent the ions formed from each of the following atoms:

   P   Na   Mg   Al   N   S   Cl   P

13. Use a Lewis diagram to show the ionic bonding in each of the following pairs of elements:

   Na and Cl   Mg and S   Al and P
   Ga and O   K and N   Ca and Br
   Li and O   Ca and N   Cs and F
   Sr and P

14. Use the crossover rule to write the correct formula for each of the following:

   barium phosphate   manganese(IV) oxide
   beryllium sulfide   nickel(II) sulfate
   calcium sulfate   silver nitrate
   chromium(III) carbonate   tin(IV) oxide
   iron(II) fluoride   zinc hydroxide
   lithium nitride   ammonium carbonate
   magnesium phosphide   calcium hydroxide
   potassium oxide   gold(I) hydride
   sodium chloride   gold(III) fluoride
   strontium nitrate   lead(II) nitrate
   aluminum sulfate   manganese(II) sulfate
   ammonium nitrate   mercury(II) phosphate
   cobalt(III) chlorate   potassium hydroxide
   copper(I) chloride   tin(II) bromide
   copper(II) sulfate   uranium(VI) fluoride

15. Give the correct name for each of the following:

   K_3PO_4 $CuCl_2$
   SnO_2 $NiSO_4$
   $Ba(OH)_2$ $Fe_2(SO_3)_3$
   SnF_2 $Al(NO_3)_3$
   $SrBr_2$ $Ca_3(PO_4)_2$

7 COVALENT BONDING

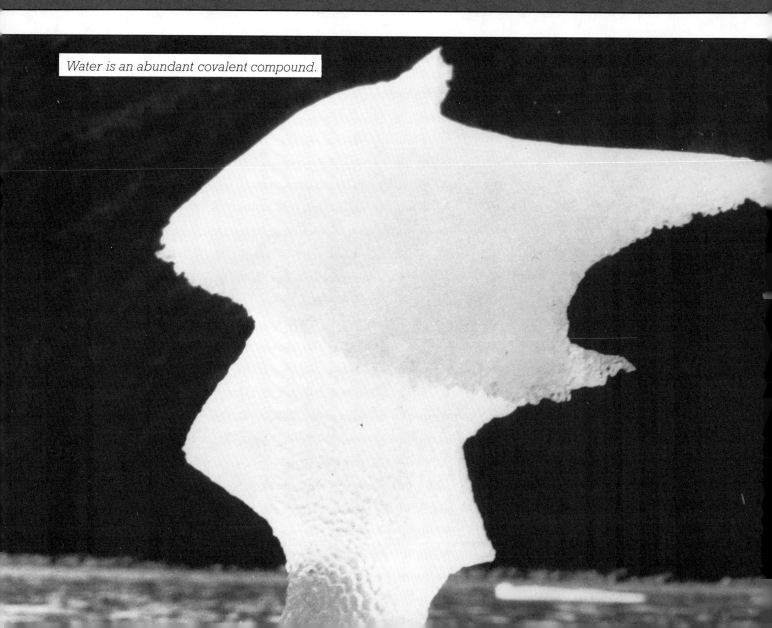

Water is an abundant covalent compound.

CONTENTS

7.1 Covalent Bonding

In Chapter 6 we learned how a metal atom and a non-metal atom are held together by an ionic bond. The metal atom donates its valence electrons to the non-metal atom, and both become ions which resemble a noble gas in electronic structure.

What happens if the two atoms are non-metal atoms? In this case, both atoms need to gain electrons. The non-metal atoms can both gain electrons at the same time only by *sharing* their valence electrons. This sharing of electrons is called a **covalent bond**.

Hydrogen fluoride is a covalent compound. If a hydrogen atom has an extra electron, its electronic structure will resemble that of the noble gas helium. If a fluorine atom has an extra electron, its electronic structure will resemble that of the noble gas neon. When a hydrogen atom and a fluorine atom share their valence electrons, they will both have stable noble gas electronic structures. A covalent bond results and a hydrogen fluoride molecule forms.

$$\text{H}\cdot \quad + \quad {}^{xx}_{x}\text{F}^{x}_{xx} \quad \rightarrow \quad \text{H}{}^{x}_{\cdot}\text{F}^{x}_{xx}{}^{xx}$$

| hydrogen atom | fluorine atom | hydrogen fluoride molecule |

Questions

1. Indicate which type of bond—ionic or covalent—will form between each of the following pairs of atoms:

H and Cl	K and S	S and O	Li and O	N and O
C and S	Si and O	Mg and Cl	Fe and Cl	I and Cl
Sr and Br	K and N	P and O	Cu and I	Al and N
Ca and F	Cr and O	O and O	C and Cl	Ba and P

2. A molecule of hydrogen is made up of two hydrogen atoms held together by a covalent bond. A molecule of chlorine is made up of two chlorine atoms in the same way. Draw Lewis diagrams to represent a hydrogen molecule and a chlorine molecule.

7.2 Physical Properties of Ionic and Covalent Compounds

You have just learned that ionic compounds are made up of ions, and covalent compounds are made up of molecules. In this experiment, you will look at differences in physical properties between an ionic compound (potassium chloride) and a covalent compound (paradichlorobenzene).

Fig. 1 *Paradichlorobenzene is the major ingredient in many solid air fresheners. Exposure to a large amount of the vapour can be dangerous.*

A polar substance is attracted to a charged object. A non-polar substance is not.

Materials

safety goggles
Bunsen burner
spatula
2 small test tubes
2 evaporating dishes
2 burettes
2 100-mL beakers
conductivity apparatus
distilled water
cyclohexane
potassium chloride
paradichlorobenzene

Method

1. *Test the given solvents for polarity.* Rub a plastic rule with a synthetic material, or an ebonite rod with some fur, to produce a charge on the plastic rule or ebonite rod. Allow water to run very slowly but continuously from the tap or from a burette.

Place the charged rule or rod alongside the stream of water. Describe what happens to the stream. Repeat with cyclohexane in a burette. Which solvent is affected more by the charged rule or rod? This solvent is said to be **polar** (Figure 2). The other solvent can be considered to be **non-polar**.

Fig. 2 *The flow of a polar solvent is affected by charged rods.*

(a) Molecules in a polar solvent re-align themselves and are attracted by a charged rod.

(b) A non-polar solvent is unaffected by a charged rod.

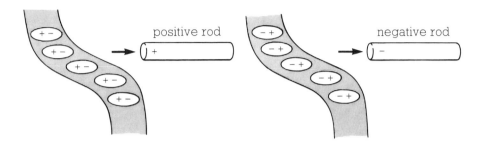

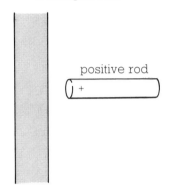

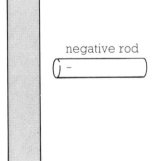

2. Copy the following chart into your notebook and use it to record your results.

Test	Potassium chloride	Paradichlorobenzene
Is the substance volatile?		
Is it hard and granular, or soft and waxy?		
Which has the lower, and which the higher melting point?		
Does it conduct electricity as a liquid?		
Does it dissolve in water?		
Does it conduct electricity when dissolved in water?		
Does it dissolve in a non-polar solvent?		

The term volatile describes
solids and liquids which are
easily vapourized.

"Hard and granular" and
"soft and waxy" are not really
opposite properties. Scientists
simply use these terms to
describe ionic and covalent
substances.

After touching the chemicals,
wash your hands immediately.

The conductivity test should
be done by the teacher as a
demonstration.

3. *Test for volatility*. If a substance is volatile, you may be able to detect an odour easily. Place a little potassium chloride on a piece of paper. Smell it carefully. Does it have any odour? Repeat with the paradichlorobenzene.

4. *Check the texture*. Rub a little potassium chloride and then a little paradichlorobenzene in your fingers for 2 to 3 s. You do not want the materials to dissolve in any moisture or oil on your skin as this makes it difficult to accurately describe the texture. Indicate whether the material feels hard and granular, or soft and waxy.

5. *Compare the melting points*. Place sufficient potassium chloride in a small test tube to just cover the bottom. Place a similar amount of paradichlorobenzene in another test tube. Holding the two test tubes alongside each other, pass the test tubes through a very low Bunsen flame. Continue to do so until one of the solids begins to melt. Which solid has the lower melting point?

6. *Test for conductivity*. Place potassium chloride in an evaporating dish to a depth of about 2 mm. Place the same amount of paradichlorobenzene in another evaporating dish. Using the conductivity apparatus, check whether the solids conduct electricity.
Place the evaporating dishes on a gauze and heat each with a Bunsen burner until the materials are molten. Do not overheat the paradichlorobenzene. Check whether the molten materials conduct electricity.

Fig. 3 *The conductivity apparatus.*

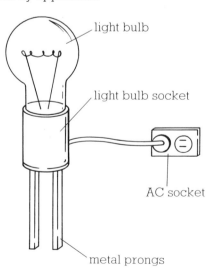

154

Check whether distilled water conducts electricity. Add a small scoop of each material to about 25 mL of distilled water in a 100-mL beaker. Does each material dissolve in water? Check whether the mixture conducts electricity.

7. *Examine the solubility in a non-polar solvent.* Place about 5 mL of cyclohexane in each of two test tubes. Add a small scoop of potassium chloride to one test tube and the same quantity of paradichlorobenzene to the other. Shake each test tube. Record whether each material dissolves in the cyclohexane.

Follow-up

1. Which is a better solvent for an ionic substance, a polar or a non-polar solvent?

2. Consider a yellow crystalline solid that melts at a high temperature and feels hard and granular. Is this substance likely to be ionic or covalent?

3. You learned earlier that ionic substances contain positive and negative ions. A substance will conduct electricity if it contains charged particles that can move freely. Explain why a solid ionic substance does not conduct electricity but a molten ionic substance does.

4. What do you think happens to ionic materials when they dissolve in water? Does your answer explain why the solution becomes a good conductor of electricity?

7.3 I Love Water, I Love Oil

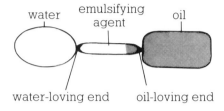

Fig. 4 *An emulsifying agent can break up an oil film by holding water and oil molecules together.*

In the previous experiment, you learned that some materials dissolve quite readily in polar solvents such as water. These substances are said to be **water-loving**. Other materials only dissolve in non-polar solvents; they are **oil-loving**.

Oil and water do not mix (Figure 4). If the two are well shaken together, the oil breaks up into small droplets that stay suspended in the water for a short time. Eventually, however, the oil droplets once again form a large "blob" of oil and float to the surface of the water.

To keep oil and water mixed, we have to use an emulsifying agent. An **emulsifying agent** is a molecule in which one end is water-loving and the other end is oil-loving. When oil, water, and an emulsifying agent are mixed, the water and oil molecules are kept together by the emulsifying agent (Figure 5).

Emulsions in which tiny oil droplets, surrounded by emulsifying agents, float in water are **oil in water** (O/W) emulsions. They wash off with water. Most hand creams are of this variety.

Fig. 5 *Oil spills are difficult to get rid of because oil and water do not mix.*

Emulsions in which tiny water droplets, surrounded by emulsifying agents, float in oil are **water in oil** (W/O) emulsions. They will not wash off with water. Most cleansing creams are of this variety.

7.4 Silk-Screening

Silk-screening is a process involving oil-loving and water-loving molecules. If the screening material is oil-loving, then the paint used must be water-loving in order to pass through the screen without damaging it. If the screening material is water-loving, then the paint used must be oil-loving.

In this experiment you will use a special silk-screening material called the ''RISO'' Screen. The design for your silk screen is first drawn on regular paper. The design and the screen are then passed through a Thermofax machine. During this process, the design is transferred to the screen material. Tiny holes develop in the screen material wherever your design is in contact with the screen. When paint is applied to the screen, the paint penetrates the design part of the screen.

Towards the end of the nineteenth century, artists began to number their prints. A ''6/25'' or ''VI/XXV'' notation on a print means that it is the sixth print out of a total of 25. Some people believe that the smaller the first number, the more valuable the print.

Fig. 6 *A print produced by silk-screening.*

Materials

RISO Screen
liquid Derivan Tempora Paint (or any water soluble paint)
paper for the design
absorbent paper for the print
a piece of board to act as a squeegee
cardboard overhead frame
tape

Method

1. Divide a piece of regular (21.6 × 28 cm) white paper into four quadrants (Figure 7a).
   Draw your design no bigger than one of these segments. You and three other students will then complete one full page. (The screening material is fairly expensive.)

2. Place the piece of paper (or a photocopy of it) under and in contact with the smooth side of the RISO Screen. Pass both through the Thermofax machine set to grey/black.

3. Mount the screen in the overhead frame. Use tape to ensure that no paint can leak through the edges (Figure 7b).

4. Place the screen on top of the absorbent paper. Squeeze some paint onto the screen and use the piece of stiff board as a squeegee to force the paint through the screen. Make several prints of your design (Figure 7c). If the screen is to be reused at a later time, wash out the paint with water before storing the screen.

5. When dry, your silk-screen print should be signed and numbered. It is now ready for display.

Fig. 7

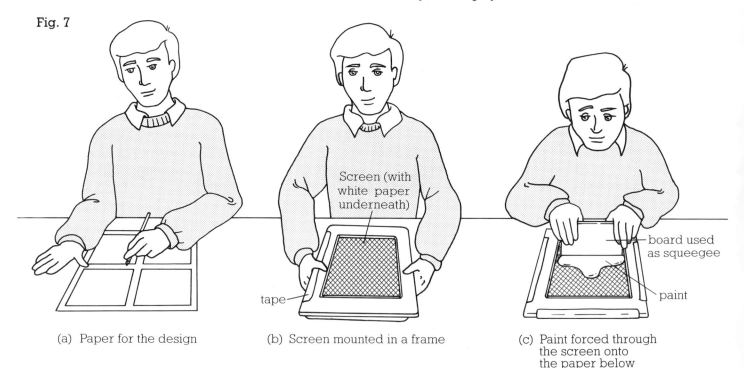

(a) Paper for the design

(b) Screen mounted in a frame

(c) Paint forced through the screen onto the paper below

7.5 Formula Writing for Covalent Compounds

The formulas of covalent compounds can be written in the same way as ionic compounds using valence values and the crossover rule.

sulfur(VI) oxide	SO_3	phosphorus(V) sulfide	P_2S_5
carbon(II) oxide	CO	hydrogen oxide	H_2O

There is another method for naming covalent compounds. A prefix is attached to the name of each element to indicate the number of atoms of that element. The most common prefixes used are:

mono- for 1   *tri-* for 3   *penta-* for 5
di- for 2   *tetra-* for 4   *hexa-* for 6

Using the prefix method, the above substances would be named:

monosulfur trioxide	SO_3	diphosphorus pentasulfide	P_2S_5
monocarbon monoxide	CO	dihydrogen monoxide	H_2O

The term monooxide is never used. It is shortened to monoxide.

If the first element has a prefix *mono-*, the prefix is not used. For example,

sulfur trioxide is used instead of monosulfur trioxide
carbon monoxide is used instead of monocarbon monoxide

Questions

1. Name the compounds below using the prefix system:

    CS_2 Cl_2 SO_3 As_2S_3

2. Write the correct formula for:

Find out why dinitrogen monoxide is called "laughing gas." Quartz and silica are two common names for silicon dioxide.

dinitrogen trioxide	carbon monoxide
diphosphorus pentasulfide	carbon tetrachloride
iodine monochloride	nitrogen dioxide
sulfur dioxide	sulfur trioxide
boron trifluoride	iodine trichloride
diphosphorus trioxide	dinitrogen monoxide
phosphorus pentabromide	sulfur hexachloride
carbon dioxide	silicon dioxide
oxygen difluoride	tricarbon tetraphosphide

7.6 Multiple Bonds

The element hydrogen has a formula H_2. This means that a hydrogen molecule is made up of two hydrogen atoms. A hydrogen atom needs to gain one more electron to resemble the electronic structure of the noble gas helium. This is achieved when two hydrogen atoms share one pair of electrons.

This sharing of a single pair of electrons between two atoms is called a **single covalent bond**. We can represent covalent bonding using Lewis diagrams or a simpler way called **stick diagrams**. In a stick diagram, each shared pair of electrons is represented by a single line (—). The unshared electrons are not shown.

H_2	H$\overset{x}{\cdot}$H	H—H
hydrogen molecule	Lewis diagram	stick diagram

Oxygen is known to have a formula O_2. Each oxygen atom has six valence electrons. Each oxygen atom therefore has to gain two more electrons to resemble neon in electronic structure. This is achieved when the two oxygen atoms share *two pairs* of electrons. This sharing of a double pair of electrons is called a **double covalent bond**.

Other elements that exist as diatomic molecules are chlorine (Cl_2), iodine (I_2), fluorine (F_2), and bromine (Br_2).

O_2	$\overset{x}{\underset{x}{\times}}O\overset{x}{\times}:\overset{\cdot}{\underset{\cdot}{O}}:$	O=O
oxygen molecule	Lewis diagram	stick diagram

A **triple covalent bond** occurs when *three pairs* of electrons are shared between two atoms. An example of this is nitrogen, N_2. Since each nitrogen atom has five valence electrons, each atom needs to gain three electrons.

N_2	$\overset{x}{\underset{x}{\times}}N\overset{x}{\times}:N:$	N≡N
nitrogen molecule	Lewis diagram	stick diagram

There is a limit to the number of "sticks" around an atom of an element. This limit is equal to the maximum valence value of the element.

	Valence value	Maximum number of sticks
hydrogen	1	1
oxygen	2	2
nitrogen	3	3
carbon	4	4

A molecule of carbon tetrachloride, CCl_4, is made up of one carbon atom and four chlorine atoms. Since carbon has a valence value of 4 and chlorine has a valence value of 1, the stick diagram should show four sticks around the carbon atom and one stick around each chlorine atom. The easiest way to draw this is to place the carbon atom in the middle of four chlorine atoms, and then join each chlorine to the carbon with one stick.

CCl_4

carbon
tetrachloride
molecule

Lewis diagram

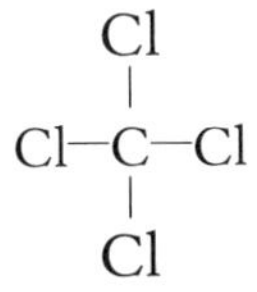

stick diagram

Questions

1. Draw a stick diagram to represent each of the following Lewis diagrams:
   (a) carbon dioxide, CO_2

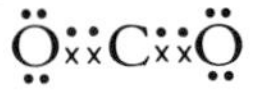

   (b) ethyne, C_2H_2

   (c) propanol, C_3H_8O

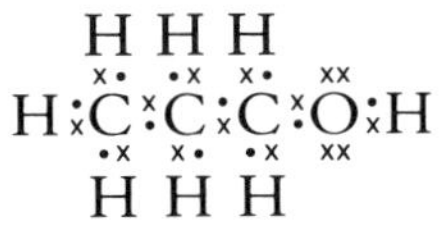

   (d) formaldehyde, CH_2O

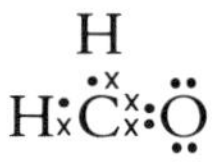

2. Draw a stick diagram to represent each of the following molecules:

   (a) hydrogen chloride, HCl
   (c) carbon disulphide, CS_2
   (b) methane, CH_4
   (d) hydrogen cyanide, HCN

Formalin, a solution of formaldehyde in water, can harden proteins and is therefore used as a preservative for biological specimens.

Hydrogen cyanide is a very poisonous chemical that paralyzes the central nervous system and stops respiration.

THE SHAPES OF MOLECULES

Stick diagrams have one disadvantage. They are two-dimensional drawings and do not really show how a molecule is put together in three-dimensional space. Since the electrons in the bonds have the same charge, these electron pairs will *repel* each other. This repulsion will affect the shape of the molecule.

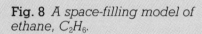

Fig. 8 *A space-filling model of ethane, C_2H_6.*

For example, the actual shape of the ammonia molecule, NH_3, is not as simple as its stick diagram, but is a pyramid with a triangular base.

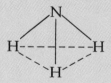

stick
diagram

3-dimensional shape

Chemists use model building kits to show the three-dimensional shape of molecules. Since there are many different types of kits, your teacher will explain how to use the kit available in your school. Use your kit to build models for the following molecules:

Name	Molecular formula	Stick diagram
water	H_2O	H—O—H
boron trihydride	BH_3	H—B—H with H below B
dinitrogen trioxide	N_2O_3	O=N—O—N=O
propane	C_3H_8	H_3C—CH_2—CH_3 stick diagram
ethanol	C_2H_6O	ethanol stick diagram
dimethyl ether	C_2H_6O	dimethyl ether stick diagram

Notice that ethanol (ethyl alcohol) and dimethyl ether have the same molecular formula, but are different in structure. Their physical and chemical properties are also different. Different substances with the same molecular formula are called **isomers**.

By drawing and using a model kit, find out how many isomers there are with the molecular formula C_4H_{10}. Also find out what each isomer is called.

P O I N T S · T O · R E C A L L

- Covalent compounds contain non-metallic elements only.
- Ionic compounds contain metallic and non-metallic elements.
- A covalent bond forms by the sharing of electrons.
- Covalent compounds are usually volatile and have relatively low melting points. Ionic compounds are non-volatile and have relatively high melting points.
- Covalent compounds are not good conductors of electricity. Ionic compounds conduct electricity when molten or when dissolved in water.
- Covalent compounds dissolve best in non-polar solvents. Ionic compounds dissolve best in polar solvents.
- Emulsifying agents are used to hold water-loving and oil-loving materials together.

- Silk-screening is a good example of utilizing oil-loving and water-loving properties.
- Two methods are used in naming covalent compounds: Roman numerals and the crossover rule, and also the prefix method.
- Two atoms may share one, two, or three pairs of electrons in order to form a single, double, or triple bond depending on how many electrons are needed to satisfy the octet rule.
- Stick diagrams are often used to represent covalent compounds. In a stick diagram, a single stick (—) represents a pair of shared electrons.
- Molecular models are used to represent the three-dimensional structure of covalent compounds.
- Most elements are written as single atoms. However, H_2, O_2, N_2, F_2, Cl_2, Br_2, and I_2 are always written as molecules with two atoms.

R E V I E W · Q U E S T I O N S

1. Indicate what type of bond will form between each of the following pairs of atoms:

S and Cl	Li and F	Si and C
I and Br	Zn and S	Cu and Cl
Mg and O	Fe and Br	C and H
N and O		

2. A white powder with a low melting point dissolves in water, but does not conduct electricity in solution. Is this an ionic or a covalent substance? Explain your answer.

3. A yellow powder dissolves readily in water. In solution it is a good conductor of electricity.
   Is this an ionic or a covalent substance? Explain your answer.

4. What type of substance dissolves best in polar solvents?

5. What type of substance dissolves best in non-polar solvents?

6. Give two examples of a mixture where an emulsifying agent has to be used to prevent the mixture from separating.

7. Which type of ink would you use with an oil-loving type of screen in print making?

8. Which type of ink would you use with a water-loving type of screen in print making?

9. Use stick diagrams to represent the following molecules:

   H_2O O_2 CF_4 PH_3 CS_2 C_7H_{14}

   $(CH_3)(CH_2OH)(CH_3)$

10. How many different isomers can you find for the molecule C_7H_{14}?

11. Write the correct formula for each of the following compounds:

carbon monoxide
iodine trichloride
iodine(VII) fluoride
dinitrogen trioxide
arsenic(III) oxide
phosphorus trihydride
phosphorus(V) sulfide
sulfur dioxide
xenon hexafluoride

boron trihydride
dichlorine monoxide
dinitrogen pentoxide
nitrogen monoxide
silicon dioxide
sulfur hexafluoride
water
krypton difluoride

12. Name the following compounds:

XeF_2 $\qquad$ $BrCl_3$
CS_2 $\qquad$ H_2S
BF_3 $\qquad$ AsF_3
P_2O_5 $\qquad$ SiH_4
SO_3 $\qquad$ NH_3

13. What is the common name for NH_3?

CHEMICAL EQUATIONS AND FORMULAS

In manufacturing chemicals, the correct amounts of substances must be used.

KET. 4300

CONTENTS

Investigation

8.1 Changes in Mass During Chemical Reactions

In Chapter 3, you learned that a chemical change produced a new substance with a different chemical composition from the reactant. You used some rules to complete the word equation for a chemical reaction.

Now that you also know how to write chemical formulas, you can convert word equations into equations that use chemical symbols. These are known as **chemical equations**. Before you learn how to do this, you should try the following experiment to discover the principle behind writing chemical equations.

Materials

safety goggles
balance
250-mL Erlenmeyer flask
small test tube
0.1 mol/L copper(II) sulfate solution
0.1 mol/L ammonium hydroxide solution
0.1 mol/L barium chloride solution
0.1 mol/L sodium sulfate solution
0.1 mol/L hydrochloric acid
0.1 mol/L sodium carbonate solution

Fig. 1

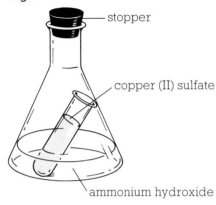

stopper

copper (II) sulfate

ammonium hydroxide

When hydrochloric acid reacts with sodium carbonate, a gas is produced. In this case, there is insufficient gas to pop the stopper, so all the products remain in the flask.

Method

1. Place approximately 20 mL of ammonium hydroxide solution in the Erlenmeyer flask.

2. Fill the small test tube with copper(II) sulfate solution.

3. Carefully wipe the outside of the test tube and place the test tube inside the Erlenmeyer flask.

4. Tightly stopper the Erlenmeyer flask (Figure 1).

5. Find the mass of the stoppered Erlenmeyer flask.

6. Carefully invert the Erlenmeyer flask and allow the chemicals to mix. Note down any evidence of a chemical change.

7. Find the mass of the stoppered Erlenmeyer flask after the reaction.

8. Rinse out the Erlenmeyer flask and test tube and repeat steps (1) to (7) using the following pairs of solutions:
   (a) barium chloride solution and sodium sulfate solution,
   (b) hydrochloric acid and sodium carbonate solution.

9. Record your results in a chart with the following headings:

Reactant in flask	Reactant in test tube	Evidence for chemical change	Total mass before mixing	Total mass after mixing

Follow-up

1. Write the word equation for each reaction.

2. Compare your results with those of other students. For each reaction, what is the difference between the total mass before mixing and the total mass after mixing?

8.2 Writing Balanced Chemical Equations

Fig. 2 *Antoine Lavoisier (1743–1794) made accurate measurements of mass. His work led to the law of conservation of mass.*

Your results in the previous experiment should show that mass is neither gained nor lost during a chemical reaction. This is known as the **law of conservation of mass**. For example, in the reaction

$$\text{hydrogen} + \text{oxygen} \rightarrow \text{water}$$

the mass of the hydrogen plus the oxygen must equal the mass of the water that is produced.

This law means that in any chemical reaction, we cannot lose or gain atoms. The total number of each type of atom must be the same on the reactant side as on the product side. To understand this further, let us write the formula of each chemical in the above word equation,

$$\text{hydrogen} + \text{oxygen} \rightarrow \text{water}$$
$$H_2 + O_2 \rightarrow H_2O$$

We can also show this in pictures:

On the reactant side, we have two hydrogen atoms and two oxygen atoms. On the product side we have two hydrogen atoms but only one oxygen atom. Because the number of atoms of each type is not balanced, the equation below is called a **skeleton equation**.

$$H_2 + O_2 \rightarrow H_2O$$

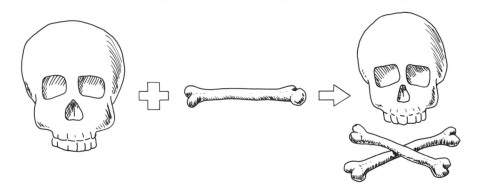

The only way we can get two oxygen atoms on the product side is to show another water molecule.

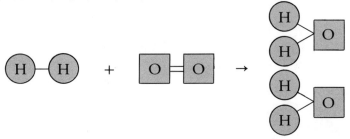

This causes another problem. The product side now contains four hydrogen atoms and the reactant side only two hydrogen atoms. We therefore have to include another hydrogen molecule on the reactant side.

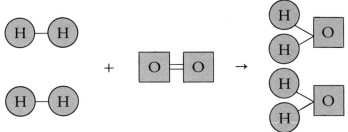

We have now balanced all the atoms that take part in this chemical reaction. All the atoms that we started with are still there, only rearranged into different molecules. The chemical equation should also show the correct balance of all the atoms. Of course we don't use pictures to write it. Instead we use symbols. In symbol form, the balanced chemical equation becomes:

$$2H_2 + O_2 \rightarrow 2H_2O$$

When balancing chemical equations, it is essential that you start with the correct formula of every reactant and product. Also you must be able to count the total number of each type of atom in a particular formula. For example, magnesium phosphate, $Mg_3(PO_4)_2$, contains three atoms of magnesium, two atoms of phosphorus, and eight atoms of oxygen.

Questions

Write the formula and indicate how many atoms of each type there are in each of the following:

aluminum carbonate	sodium hydroxide
calcium hydroxide	dinitrogen trioxide
nickel(III) sulfate	lithium carbonate
cobalt(III) hydrogen carbonate	nickel(II) phosphate
hydrogen sulfate	ammonium phosphate

8.3 How to Balance Chemical Equations

We balance chemical equations largely by trial and error. The usual steps are as follows:

1. Start with the word equation.

2. Convert the word equation into a skeleton equation by replacing each name with its correct formula.

3. If the equation contains a single element by itself, balance this type of atom at the end. The same rule applies when a particular element occurs in more than two substances in the equation.

4. In the skeleton equation, pick out the formula with the largest number of atoms in it, and start working from there.

5. Balance atoms only by placing whole numbers in front of formulas. You *cannot* alter a formula.

6. When finished, check to see that you have used the lowest possible whole numbers. If not, divide all the numbers by the highest common factor.

As an example, follow the above steps in writing a balanced equation for the burning of propane, C_3H_8 (Figure 3).

Difficulty in balancing an equation is often due to an incorrect formula.

Fig. 3 *Propane is the fuel used in gas barbeques and some vehicles.*

1. The word equation for the reaction is:

$$\text{propane} + \text{oxygen} \rightarrow \text{carbon dioxide} + \text{water}.$$

Remember oxygen gas has a formula O_2.

2. The word equation is converted into a skeleton equation:

$$C_3H_8 + O_2 \rightarrow CO_2 + H_2O$$

3. Here oxygen is a single element by itself, and it occurs in three of the substances in the equation. We will leave the balancing of oxygen until the end.

4. The formula C_3H_8 contains the most atoms. We will start our balancing from this formula.

5. The left-hand side of the equation contains three C atoms. To get three C atoms on the right-hand side, we place a ''3'' in front of the formula CO_2:

$$C_3H_8 + O_2 \rightarrow 3CO_2 + H_2O$$

The left-hand side of the equation contains eight H atoms. To get eight H atoms on the right-hand side, we place a ''4'' in front of the formula H_2O:

$$C_3H_8 + O_2 \rightarrow 3CO_2 + 4H_2O$$

Finally, we can balance oxygen atoms. The right-hand side of the equation contains a total of 10 oxygen atoms (6 from $3CO_2$ and 4 from $4H_2O$). To get 10 oxygen atoms on the left-hand side, we must place a ''5'' in front of the oxygen molecule. The equation now becomes:

$$C_3H_8 + 5O_2 \rightarrow 3CO_2 + 4H_2O$$

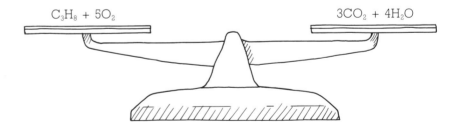

6. There is no common factor, other than 1, to the numbers 1, 5, 3, and 4, so our set of numbers represents the lowest possible whole numbers for the equation. The final equation represents the balanced chemical equation for the reaction.

Questions

1. Balance the following skeleton equations:
   (a) $Cu + O_2 \rightarrow CuO$
   (b) $Zn + HCl \rightarrow ZnCl_2 + H_2$
   (c) $P + H_2 \rightarrow PH_3$
   (d) $Al + CuSO_4 \rightarrow Al_2(SO_4)_3 + Cu$
   (e) $H_2SO_4 + Al \rightarrow Al_2(SO_4)_3 + H_2$
   (f) $Na + H_2O \rightarrow NaOH + H_2$
   (g) $NH_3 + O_2 \rightarrow NO_2 + H_2O$
   (h) $Na_2CO_3 + H_3PO_4 \rightarrow Na_3PO_4 + H_2O + CO_2$
   (i) $FeS + O_2 \rightarrow Fe_2O_3 + SO_2$
   (j) $Na_2CO_3 + FeCl_3 + H_2O \rightarrow Fe(OH)_3 + NaCl + CO_2$

2. Write a balanced chemical equation from each of the following word equations:
   (a) copper(II) oxide + water → copper(II) hydroxide
   (b) sodium hydroxide + sulfuric acid → sodium sulfate + water
   (c) sodium + oxygen → sodium oxide
   (d) copper(II) nitrate →
            copper(II) oxide + nitrogen dioxide + oxygen
   (e) nickel(II) sulfate → nickel(II) oxide + sulfur trioxide
   (f) iron + chromium(III) nitrate → iron(II) nitrate + chromium
   (g) sodium phosphate + ammonium nitrate →
            sodium nitrate + ammonium phosphate
   (h) potassium sulfate + ammonium nitrate →
            potassium nitrate + ammonium sulfate
   (i) silver nitrate + sulfuric acid → silver sulfate + nitric acid
   (j) lead(II) nitrate + sodium sulfide →
            lead (II) sulfide + sodium nitrate

3. Balance the following skeleton equations:
   (a) $C_{10}H_{22} + O_2 \rightarrow CO_2 + H_2O$
   (b) $K + H_2O \rightarrow KOH + H_2$
   (c) $Mg(OH)_2 + H_3PO_4 \rightarrow Mg_3(PO_4)_2 + H_2O$
   (d) $KClO_3 \rightarrow KCl + O_2$
   (e) $MnO_2 + HCl \rightarrow MnCl_2 + Cl_2 + H_2O$

4. Write a balanced chemical equation for each of the following word equations:
   (a) sodium hydroxide + iron(III) chloride →
            iron(III) hydroxide + sodium chloride
   (b) magnesium carbonate + nitric acid →
            magnesium nitrate + carbon dioxide + water
   (c) iron(II) sulfate + nitric acid + sulfuric acid →
            iron(III) sulfate + water + nitrogen dioxide

The formula of some common acids:
sulfuric acid H_2SO_4
nitric acid HNO_3
phosphoric acid H_3PO_4

Remember which elements are written as molecules with two atoms each: H_2, N_2, O_2, F_2, Cl_2, Br_2, I_2.

(d) copper + nitric acid →

copper(II) nitrate + water + nitrogen dioxide

5. Complete each of the following word equations and then write a balanced chemical equation for each one:
   (a) chromium(III) bromide + silver nitrate →
   (b) ammonium hydroxide + sulfuric acid→
   (c) calcium hydroxide + aluminum sulfate →

8.4 Atomic Mass and Formula Mass

In Chapter 4, you learned that the atomic mass of an element is found by averaging the relative masses of all the naturally-occurring isotopes making up that element. The atomic masses are given in the periodic table. You should use the values corrected to one decimal place for all calculations that follow.

When dealing with compounds and molecules of elements, we use the term **formula mass**. The formula mass is calculated by adding the atomic masses of all the atoms shown in the formula of the compound or molecule. For example,

- Formula mass of zinc, Zn
  = atomic mass of Zn
  = 65.4 u

- Formula mass of carbon dioxide, CO_2
  = 1 × atomic mass of C + 2 × atomic mass of O
  = 12.0 u + (2 × 16.0 u)
  = 44.0 u

- Formula mass of aluminum sulfate, $Al_2(SO_4)_3$
  = (2 × 27.0 u) + (3 × 32.1 u) + (12 × 16.0 u)
  = 342.3 u

Fig. 4

(a) atoms

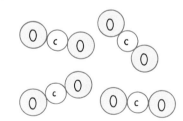

(b) molecules

(c) ions

Questions

Write the correct formula and calculate the formula mass for each of the following substances:
(a) aluminum sulfide
(b) water
(c) diphosphorus pentasulfide
(d) iron(III) hydrogen carbonate
(e) magnesium phosphate
(f) calcium hydroxide
(g) sodium phosphate
(h) sulfuric acid
(i) aluminum carbonate
(j) oxygen

8.5 Decomposition of Bluestone

Bluestone is used in copper plating, calico printing, and in batteries.

Bluestone is a crystalline form of copper(II) sulfate that contains water molecules. Crystalline materials that contain water molecules are often referred to as **hydrates**. Another example is washing soda or sodium carbonate decahydrate, $Na_2CO_3 \cdot 10H_2O$.

Fig. 5 *Drywall is made from calcium sulfate dihydrate, $CaSO_4 \cdot 2H_2O$, after all the water has been removed.*

The formula of a hydrate consists of the main formula, followed by a raised dot and the number of water molecules attached.

Many hydrates are highly coloured. The water molecules in a hydrate are relatively easy to remove, usually by gentle heating. When this is done, in most cases the colour is also lost.

In this experiment, you will remove the water molecules from the bluestone and use the results to calculate the number of water molecules in the formula of hydrated copper(II) sulfate.

$$\text{bluestone} \rightarrow \text{copper(II) sulfate} + \text{water}$$

Before you do the experiment, consider how you would do the following problem:

The total mass of all the boys in a room is 511 kg and the total mass of all the girls present is 270 kg. What information do you need to calculate the number of boys and the number of girls in the room?

You will realize that you need to know the average mass of the boys present and the average mass of the girls present.

$$\text{Number of boys} = \frac{\text{total mass of boys}}{\text{average mass of boys}}$$

$$\text{Number of girls} = \frac{\text{total mass of girls}}{\text{average mass of girls}}$$

The same approach is used to find the numbers of atoms of different elements in the formula of a substance. We must first find the mass of each element in the substance, and then divide it by the atomic mass of that element.

For example, in a compound made from zinc and chlorine, it is found that 0.654 g of zinc combines with 0.71 g of chlorine.

When finding the number of atoms of different elements in a compound, use atomic mass for the average mass of an element. Consider chlorine as a single atom, Cl, *not* Cl$_2$.

$$\text{ratio} \quad \frac{\text{mass of zinc}}{\text{atomic mass of zinc}} \quad : \quad \frac{\text{mass of chlorine}}{\text{atomic mass of chlorine}}$$

$$\text{equals} \quad \frac{0.654}{65.4} \quad : \quad \frac{0.710}{35.5}$$

$$\text{equals} \quad 0.0100 : 0.200$$

$$\text{equals} \quad 1 \ : \ 2$$

Therefore the formula of zinc chloride is ZnCl$_2$.

Materials

safety goggles
balance
test tube
bluestone crystals
Bunsen burner
clamp and retort rod
beaker

Fig. 6

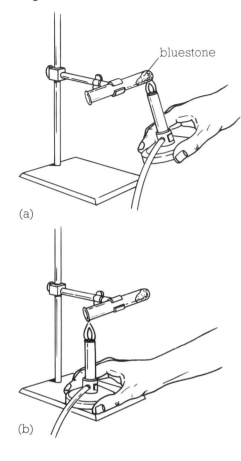

bluestone

(a)

(b)

Use the formula and the
periodic table.

Method

1. Find the mass of a clean, dry test tube.

2. Fill the test tube with bluestone crystals to about one-third full.

3. Find the mass of the test tube plus bluestone.

4. Place a clamp at the mouth of the test tube. Attach the clamp to a retort stand with the mouth of the test tube pointing slightly downwards.

5. Using a hand-held Bunsen, gently heat the bluestone to drive off the water. Continue heating until the remaining material is an off-white colour (Figure 6a).

6. To remove all the water from the test tube, allow it to cool. Move the clamp to the bottom end of the test tube. Heat the open end of the test tube (Figure 6b). Remember you do not want any of the water to run back into the remaining solid.

7. Allow the test tube to cool and find the mass of the test tube plus the remaining copper(II) sulfate.

Follow-up

1. Calculate the following quantities:
   (a) the mass of bluestone used (step 3 − step 1)
   (b) the mass of copper(II) sulfate left over after heating (step 7 − step 1)
   (c) the mass of water driven out of the crystal (step 3 − step 7)
   (d) the formula mass of copper(II) sulfate
   (e) the formula mass of water

   (f) $\dfrac{\text{mass of copper (II) sulfate}}{\text{formula mass of copper(II) sulfate}}$

   (g) $\dfrac{\text{mass of water}}{\text{formula mass of water}}$

   (h) the ratio of (f) to (g) to the nearest whole numbers

2. How many molecules of water are there in the formula of hydrated copper(II) sulfate?

3. What is the correct formula of bluestone?

8.6 The Mole

Chemists have shown that whenever atoms or molecules combine with each other, they do so in simple whole number ratios called **mole ratios**. A unit called the **mole** (symbol "mol") is used to measure the amount of a substance.

We use n to represent the number of moles of a substance. There are different ways of calculating n, but we will use only one method in this book:

$$n = \frac{\text{mass of substance}}{\text{average mass of 1 mol of the substance}}$$

The average mass of 1 mol of an *element* has the same numerical value as the *atomic mass* of the element. The average mass of 1 mol of a *compound* has the same numerical value as the *formula mass* of the compound. For example:

- The atomic mass of zinc is 65.4 u, so the average mass of 1 mol of zinc is 65.4 g/mol.
- The formula mass of sulfuric acid, H_2SO_4, is 98.1 u, so the average mass of 1 mol of sulfuric acid is 98.1 g/mol.

Fig. 7 *The mass of 1 mol of a substance has the same numerical value as the formula mass of the substance.*

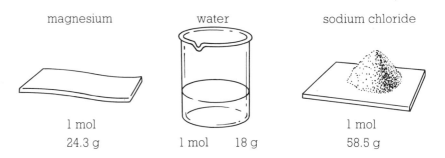

magnesium   water   sodium chloride

1 mol
24.3 g

1 mol   18 g

1 mol
58.5 g

To find the formula of a substance, we must analyze a sample of the material to find the mass of each element present. We then calculate the number of moles of each element according to the above formula, and look for the simplest whole number mole ratio.

For example, analysis of water shows that 0.35 g of hydrogen combines with 2.80 g of oxygen.

$$\text{Number of moles of H atoms} = \frac{0.35\,\text{g}}{1\,\text{g/mol}} = 0.35\,\text{mol}$$

$$\text{Number of moles of O atoms} = \frac{2.80\,g}{16\,g/mol} = 0.175\,mol$$

Mole ratio of hydrogen: oxygen $= 0.35 : 0.175$

Divide the two numbers in the mole ratio by the *smaller* number will give the lowest whole number ratio.

Therefore, there are 2 mol of hydrogen to 1 mol of oxygen. The formula of water from this analysis is H_2O.

Questions

1. Copy and complete the following chart in your notebook. (Please do not write in your textbook.)

Substance	Formula	Average mass of 1 mol of substance (g/mol)	Mass (g)	n (mol)
sodium			4.6	
hydrochloric acid				0.25
sulfuric acid			49.05	
sodium chloride				3.5
copper			1.27	
sodium hydroxide				2.0
magnesium phosphate			2.629	

In finding the formula of a compound, consider each element as a single atom, O or Cl, *not* O_2 or Cl_2.

2. Calculate the number of moles of each element. Then use the mole ratios to find the formula of the compound produced.
   (a) 5.87 g of nickel combines with 7.1 g of chlorine
   (b) 1.2 g of carbon combines with 1.6 g of oxygen
   (c) 1.116 g of iron combines with 0.48 g of oxygen
   (d) 2.4 g of carbon combines with 63.92 g of bromine
   (e) 9.3 g of phosphorus combines with 12 g of oxygen

8.7 Concentration of a Solution

When describing the concentration of a solution, chemists sometimes prefer to express the amount of substance in terms of moles rather than in grams or kilograms. It is useful, then, to express the concentration of a solution in terms of the amount of solute (in moles) dissolved in a certain volume of the solution (in litres). The unit of concentration is therefore mol/L.

$$\text{Concentration} = \frac{\text{amount of solute (mol)}}{\text{volume of solution (L)}}$$

If 8 g of sodium hydroxide is dissolved in 100 mL (0.10 L) of solution, the concentration of the solution is calculated as follows:

Formula of sodium hydroxide is NaOH.
Formula mass of NaOH = 23 u + 16 u + 1 u = 40 u
Average mass of 1 mol of NaOH = 40 g/mol

$$\text{No. of moles of NaOH} = \frac{\text{mass of NaOH}}{\text{average mass of 1 mol of NaOH}}$$

$$= \frac{8\,\text{g}}{40\,\text{g/mol}} = 0.2\,\text{mol}$$

$$\text{Concentration} = \frac{\text{amount (mol)}}{\text{volume (L)}}$$

$$= \frac{0.2\,\text{mol}}{0.10\,\text{L}} = 2\,\text{mol/L}$$

Questions

Remember 1000 mL = 1 L.

1. Calculate the concentration of each of the following solutions:
   (a) 5.85 g of sodium nitrate dissolved in 2.0 L of solution
   (b) 1.19 g of potassium nitrate dissolved in 10.0 mL of solution.
   (c) 0.74 g of calcium hydroxide dissolved in 100.0 mL of solution

2. What mass of sodium chloride must be used in order to make up 100 mL of a 0.20 mol/L solution? Copy and complete the calculations below in your notebook. (Please do not write in your textbook.)
   Formula of sodium chloride is NaCl.
   Formula mass of NaCl = ? u
   Average mass of 1 mol of NaCl = ? g/mol

From the formula: concentration $= \dfrac{\text{amount (mol)}}{\text{volume (L)}}$

we have: amount (mol) = concentration (mol/L) × volume (L)

Amount of NaCl = 0.20 mol/L × 0.10 L
= ? mol

From the formula: no. of moles $= \dfrac{\text{mass (g)}}{\text{average mass of 1 mol (g/mol)}}$

we have: mass (g) = no. of moles × average mass of 1 mol (g/mol)

Therefore, mass of sodium chloride = ? mol × ? g/mol
= ? g

3. Calculate the mass of solute in each solution:
   (a) 200.0 mL of a 0.40 mol/L solution of magnesium nitrate
   (b) 100.0 mL of a 0.25 mol/L solution of sulfuric acid
   (c) 20.0 L of a 0.50 mol/L solution of sodium hydroxide

Fig. 8 *What does windshield washer antifreeze contain?*

8.8 Concentration and Freezing Point

In Chapter 2, you learned that dissolving a solute in a solvent lowers the freezing point of the solvent. Common examples are the following substances dissolved in water:
(a) ethylene glycol, $C_2H_6O_2$—antifreeze in car radiators
(b) sodium chloride, NaCl—for salting roads in winter
(c) calcium chloride, $CaCl_2$—also for salting roads in winter

In Chapter 7, you showed that solutions of ionic substances in water are good conductors of electricity. The ionic substances split up into positive and negative ions when dissolved, and the free ions become the electrical carriers.

For example, when barium chloride, $BaCl_2$, dissolves in water, the solution contains positive barium ions and negative chloride ions in the ratio 1:2.

When a covalent substance, such as table sugar, $C_{12}H_{22}O_{11}$, dissolves in water, it does not split into ions. Solutions of covalent substances do not conduct electricity.

To compare the effect of different solutes on the freezing point of a solvent, we must work with equal concentrations (in mol/L) of the solutes.

The following data shows how many degrees Celsius the freezing point of water is lowered when different solutes are dissolved in the water:

Ethylene glycol		Sodium chloride		Calcium chloride	
Concentration (mol/L)	Temperature lowered (°C)	Concentration (mol/L)	Temperature lowered (°C)	Concentration (mol/L)	Temperature lowered (°C)
0.000	0.00	0.000	0.00	0.000	0.00
0.080	0.15	0.086	0.30	0.045	0.22
0.161	0.30	0.172	0.59	0.091	0.44
0.242	0.45	0.259	0.89	0.137	0.66
0.322	0.60	0.346	1.19	0.183	0.88
0.403	0.76	0.435	1.49	0.230	1.10
0.484	0.92	0.523	1.79	0.277	1.33
0.565	1.08	0.613	2.10	0.324	1.57
0.646	1.24	0.703	2.41	0.372	1.82
0.728	1.41	0.793	2.72	0.420	2.08
0.809	1.57	0.885	3.05	0.469	2.36
0.891	1.75	0.976	3.36	0.518	2.64
0.972	1.92	1.069	3.69	0.567	2.94
1.054	2.10	1.162	4.02	0.617	3.26
1.136	2.27	1.256	4.36	0.667	3.58
1.217	2.46	1.350	4.70	0.717	3.93
1.299	2.64	1.445	5.05	0.768	4.28
1.381	2.83	1.541	5.41	0.820	4.65
1.464	3.02	1.637	5.78	0.871	5.04
1.546	3.21			0.924	5.44
1.628	3.41			0.976	5.85
				1.083	6.73

1. On a sheet of graph paper, label concentration on the horizontal axis and temperature lowered on the vertical axis (Figure 9). Draw the graph of temperature lowered against concentration for each of the three solutes.

2. Identify the type of bonding (ionic or covalent) in each of the solutes.

3. When ethylene glycol dissolves in water, does it split into ions?

Fig. 9

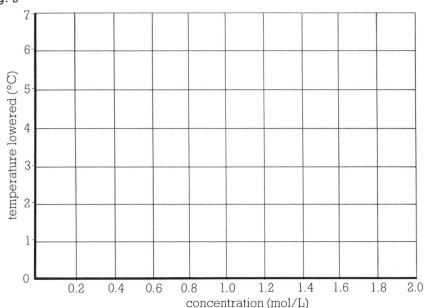

4. Sodium chloride and calcium chloride both split into ions in the solution. Which substance produces the greater number of ions?

5. If the three substances are of the same concentration, which substance lowers the freezing point the most? Explain using your answers to questions 3 and 4.

6. Which would have the lower freezing point, 1 mol/L calcium chloride solution or 1 mol/L iron(III) chloride solution? Explain your answer.

- In a chemical reaction, atoms are neither lost nor gained, only rearranged.
- The law of conservation of mass states that in a chemical reaction, the total mass of all the products equals the total mass of all the reactants.
- An unbalanced chemical equation is called a skeleton equation.
- Chemical equations are balanced by placing whole numbers in front of formulas in a chemical equation.
- The formula mass of a substance is found by adding up the atomic masses of all the atoms shown by the formula of the substance.
- A hydrate is a crystalline material which contains water molecules.
- A mole is a unit which represents the amount of material.

- The number of moles is calculated using:

$$n = \frac{\text{mass of substance}}{\text{average mass of 1 mol of the substance}}$$

- The average mass of 1 mol of a substance has the same numerical value as its formula mass but in units of g/mol.
- The concentration of a solution can be expressed in units of mol/L:

$$\text{concentration} = \frac{\text{amount of material (mol)}}{\text{volume of solution (L)}}$$

- The lowering of the freezing point of a solvent depends on the concentration (in mol/L) of the solute dissolved in the solvent.
- Ionic substances dissolved in water lower the freezing point more than covalent substances because ionic substances split up into ions in the solution.

1. Consider the reaction: $C + O_2 \rightarrow CO_2$
   What mass of carbon must be burned with 3.2 g of oxygen to produce 4.4 g of carbon dioxide?

2. Why must a chemical equation be balanced?

3. Balance the following skeleton equations:
   $N_2 + H_2 \rightarrow NH_3$
   $K + O_2 \rightarrow K_2O$
   $NaOH + H_3PO_4 \rightarrow Na_3PO_4 + H_2O$
   $Pb_3O_4 \rightarrow PbO + O_2$
   $(NH_4)_3PO_4 + ZnCl_2 \rightarrow NH_4Cl + Zn_3(PO_4)_2$

4. Write a balanced chemical equation for each of the following word equations:
   lead(II) nitrate + sodium iodide →
                  lead(II) iodide + sodium nitrate
   copper(I) nitrate + ammonium sulfide →
          copper(I) sulfide + ammonium nitrate
   octane (C_8H_{18}) + oxygen →
                carbon dioxide + water
   calcium hydroxide + hydrochloric acid →
              calcium chloride + water
   bromine + sodium hydroxide →
           oxygen + sodium bromide + water

5. Complete the following word equations and then write a balanced chemical equation for each:
   silver nitrate + calcium chloride →
   aluminum + lead(II) nitrate →
   ammonium phosphate + barium chloride →

6. Calculate the formula mass of each of the following:
   sodium phosphate
   aluminum sulfate
   diphosphorus pentasulfide
   nickel(II) nitrate
   oxygen gas (O_2)

7. Find the average mass of 1 mol (in g/mol) of each of the following:
   sodium carbonate
   magnesium fluoride
   carbon tetrachloride
   chromium(III) oxide
   copper(I) sulfate

8. Calculate the number of moles for each of the following:
   (a) 2.2 g of carbon dioxide
   (b) 1.86 g of sulfuric acid

9. Write the formula of the following:
   (a) barium chloride dihydrate
   (b) cobalt(II) chloride hexahydrate

10. Calculate the concentration (in mol/L) for each of the following:
    (a) 4.0 g of sodium hydroxide dissolved in 250 mL of solution
    (b) 13.64 g of zinc chloride dissolved in 200 mL of solution

11. What mass of copper(II) sulfate is needed to make up 250 mL of a 0.10 mol/L solution?

12. It is found in an experiment that 2.6 g of chromium reacts with 1.9 g of fluorine. What is the formula and the name of the chromium fluoride compound formed?

13. Which solution would have a lower freezing point, 0.1 mol/L potassium chloride or 0.5 mol/L potassium chloride? Explain your answer.

14. Which solution would have a lower freezing point, 0.5 mol/L lithium chloride or 0.5 mol/L barium chloride? Explain your answer.

Acids are used in making dynamite.

CONTENTS

9.1 Found in the Strangest Places

The word "acid" is derived from the Latin word "acidus," meaning sour. Think of the sour taste of lemons and vinegar, which contain acids. (But never taste any chemical unless your teacher asks you to do so!)

"Alkali" is another word for base. In ancient times, the kali plant was burned to produce a basic ash.

Acids and bases are part of our daily lives. The orange juice we drink contains citric acid. The vinegar on our French fries is acetic acid. Soap is made using sodium hydroxide, a base. This base is also used to manufacture the paper in this book.

Figures 1 to 10 are pictures relating to acids and bases in everyday life. Can you match them with the captions (a) and (j) on page 189? First, write the figure numbers in the margin of your notebook. Then beside each number, write the letter of the caption that fits best. The first one has been completed.

Fig. 1 −(j)

Fig. 2

Fig. 3

Fig. 5

Fig. 4

Fig. 6

Fig. 7

Fig. 8

Fig. 9

Fig. 10

Match Figures 1 to 10 with these captions:

(a) *Fertilizers often contain phosphoric acid.*

(b) *It is easier to beat egg whites until they are stiff if acid is added.*

(c) *The dark colour of chocolate cakes depends on how much base is added to the batter.*

(d) *Indigestion is caused by too much acid in the stomach. You can relieve the pain by taking an antacid; this is a base that destroys some of the acid.*

(e) *A car battery produces enough electrical energy to start the engine. One of the chemicals in a car battery is sulfuric acid.*

(f) *Acid rain causes millions of dollars worth of damage each year to the outsides of buildings, to marble statues, and to the environment.*

(g) *The enamel surface of appliances is stained by the lactic acid in milk.*

(h) *Pearls are damaged by perspiration, which is acidic, and by acidic foods or drinks.*

(i) *Solid drainpipe openers, which contain a base, clear blocked drains and sinks.*

(j) *Farmers add ammonia, a base, to soil so that crops will grow well.*

9.2 Common Sense With Acids and Bases

As you can see, acids and bases have many uses and are found in some unexpected places. Some acids, such as vinegar, and some bases, such as antacid tablets, are very safe to handle under normal circumstances. But others, such as the acid used in car batteries and the base used for cleaning drains, must be stored and handled very carefully. Here are some examples of what can happen when acids and bases are used or stored incorrectly.

A child was rushed to hospital after swallowing liquid drainpipe cleaner. An investigation showed that the liquid had been stored in a soft drink bottle under the kitchen sink. The child almost died, and doctors had to reconstruct his damaged esophagus. This took many months.

A mechanic dropped a car battery. It cracked and the sulfuric acid splashed into the mechanic's eyes. The mechanic suffered eye damage.

There is a story that the Emperor Nero played his fiddle while Rome burned. Some of the Roman nobility at that time showed signs of mental problems. Some scientists believe that the lead used in Roman times to make water pipes and wine goblets caused some of these mental problems. It is known that lead slowly reacts and dissolves in some water solutions, especially when the solutions are acidic. Today, we avoid storing acidic foods and drinks in lead containers, or in pottery with lead in the glaze.

If you spray an oven cleaning product into a hot oven without using rubber gloves or protecting your face, you may start to

Fig. 11 *Never add a hypochlorite bleach, such as Javex, to a toilet bowl that already contains a toilet bowl cleaner. Toilet bowl cleaners are acidic and react with hypochlorite bleach to produce the poisonous gas chlorine. For safety's sake, do not mix bleaches with other chemicals.*

cough, the skin on your hands and face may begin to sting and itch, and your eyes may hurt badly. These symptoms would be caused by the presence of powdered base in the cleaner.

A cook found that when canned pineapple was mixed with blueberries or strawberries, the berries turned an unpleasant blue colour. This did not happen with fresh pineapple. The acid from the pineapple had dissolved iron from the cans, and the iron had turned the red colour in berries blue!

Questions

1. Give three examples of foods or drinks you would avoid storing in lead containers or in pottery with a lead glaze. Explain why acidic foods or drinks should not be stored in these types of containers.

2. Why should you never store dangerous chemicals in soft drink bottles? Where and how should such chemicals be stored?

3. It is most important to read labels on product containers. Why?

4. How can you avoid being hurt when you handle a car battery or an oven cleaner?

5. List ten safety precautions and rules that all homes should have. Do not restrict your list to acids and bases.

| Investigation | 9.3 Household Products—Which Are Acidic, Which Are Basic? |

To make the best and safest use of acids and bases, we must be able to identify them. There is a simple way of doing this.

Certain chemicals, called *indicators*, change colour depending on whether they are in an acid or base. You will now use some indicators to test some household products to see if they are acids or bases.

Materials

safety goggles
5 test tubes
test tube rack
dilute hydrochloric acid—a typical acid
dilute sodium hydroxide solution—a typical base
litmus paper (blue and red)
phenolphthalein solution in dropper bottles
bromthymol blue solution in dropper bottles
household solids: aspirin (A.S.A.); baking soda (sodium bicarbonate);
    cream of tartar; drainpipe opener crystals; laundry detergent;
    toilet bowl cleaner crystals
household liquids or sprays: household ammonia; lemon juice; milk;
    oven cleaner; milk of magnesia; soft drink (pale coloured);
    shampoos; vinegar
household cream or gel: hair remover

*Bi*carbonate is the commonly used name for *hydrogen* carbonate.

Be careful when drainpipe opener crystals are added to water. The solution is corrosive and becomes very hot, and a flammable gas is produced.

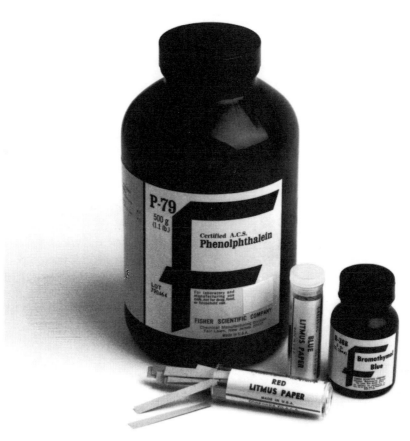

Fig. 12 *Some indicators: litmus, bromthymol blue (also known as bromothymol blue), and phenolphthalein.*

191

Method

1. In your notebook, prepare a chart like the one below to record your findings on all the materials you test:

| Substance tested | Colour of litmus paper | | Colour of phenol-phthalein | Colour of bromthymol blue | Conclusion |
	Red paper	Blue paper			Acidic/basic/unsure
hydrochloric acid					acidic
sodium hydroxide					basic

2. Rinse four clean test tubes thoroughly with tap water. Then rinse them with distilled water.

3. Pour about 1 mL dilute hydrochloric acid into each test tube.

4. Carry out the following tests and write your observations in your chart as you complete each step.
   (a) Add a piece of red litmus paper to test tube 1.
   (b) Add a piece of blue litmus paper to test tube 2.
   (c) Add a drop of phenolphthalein solution to test tube 3, and shake.
   (d) Add a drop of bromthymol blue solution to test tube 4 and shake.

First, find out how the indicators react in a *test for an acid*.

5. Wash, and rinse the four test tubes with distilled water.

6. Pour about 1 mL dilute sodium hydroxide solution in each of the four test tubes. Repeat steps 4 and 5.

Then, find out how the indicators react in a *test for a base*.

Now, test the household products with indicators.

7. Prepare each of the household products for testing. Write your observations for each product in the chart.

Solids:
(a) Use only enough solid to barely cover the bottom of a clean, rinsed test tube.
(b) Add about 4 mL distilled water to the test tube and shake to mix.
(c) Pour 1 mL of the sample into each of the four test tubes.
(d) Repeat steps 4 and 5.

Liquids and sprays:
(a) Barely cover the bottom of a clean, rinsed test tube by pouring or spraying the material into the tube.
(b) Add about 4 mL of distilled water and shake to mix.
(c) Pour 1 mL of the sample into each of the four test tubes.
(d) Repeat steps 4 and 5.

Creams and gels:
(a) Use a clean, dry glass rod to transfer enough material to just cover the bottom of a clean, rinsed test tube.
(b) Add about 4 mL of distilled water and shake to mix.
(c) Pour 1 mL of the sample into each of the four test tubes.
(d) Repeat steps 4 and 5.

Follow-up

1. You may have found that some materials did not change the colour of litmus paper. These materials are called *neutral*, because they are neither acidic nor basic. List all the neutral materials that you tested.

2. Aspirin is a well known pain killer. If you tested aspirin, did you find it acidic or basic?

3. Which material that you tested is used for relieving acid stomach? Why do you think it works?

4. What are the most common uses of the basic materials that you tested?

9.4 Acids and Bases in Action

Sulfuric acid is probably the world's most important industrial chemical. About 25 000 000 t are produced annually.

Study Figures 13 to 21. Consider the numerous uses of acids and bases in daily life and in the manufacture of industrial and consumer products. The world would not be the same without acids and bases.

Fig. 13 *Hydrochloric acid, HCl, is used in the manufacture of many drugs and for cleaning mortar from bricks. Here it is used to control the amount of acid in swimming pools.*

Fig. 14 *Nitric acid, HNO_3, is used in the manufacture of explosives such as TNT. It is also the active ingredient for etching plates.*

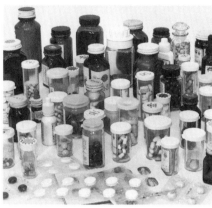

Fig. 15 *Sulfuric acid, H_2SO_4, is a most important chemical—being used to make dyes, drugs, detergents and explosives. It is an ingredient in car batteries.*

Fig. 16 *Phosphoric acid, H_3PO_4, is an ingredient in cola drinks and rust removers, and is used in the manufacture of fertilizers.*

Fig. 17 *Ammonium hydroxide, NH₄OH, is the household ammonia used for various cleaning purposes.*

Fig. 18 *Sodium hydroxide, NaOH, commonly known as caustic soda, is used in the manufacture of soap, rayon, and paper.*

Fig. 19 *Calcium hydroxide, Ca(OH)₂, is the slaked lime used to make mortar and plaster for buildings.*

Fig. 20 *Potassium hydroxide, KOH, commonly known as caustic potash, is used to make soft soap. It is also the active ingredient in oven cleaners.*

Fig. 21 *Aluminum hydroxide, Al(OH)₃, is used in the manufacture of glass*

9.5 Getting Your Greens Really Green!

Acids and bases change the appearance and texture of certain foods. Have you ever wondered why green vegetables sometimes look or feel awful when they are cooked? Let us investigate this by cooking some leafy green vegetables in a household base and some in a household acid.

Materials

safety goggles
three 250-mL beakers
teaspoon
tongs or fork
distilled water
1 teaspoon sodium bicarbonate (baking soda)
50 mL vinegar
spinach, cabbage, broccoli, or other leafy green vegetable

Method

1. Copy the chart below into your notebook.

	With water	With base	With acid
Colour			
Texture (feel)			

2. Prepare three 250-mL beakers as follows:
   (a) Add 100 mL of distilled water to beaker 1.
   (b) Add 1 teaspoon of sodium bicarbonate to 100 mL of distilled water in beaker 2.
   (c) Add 50 mL of vinegar to 50 mL of distilled water in beaker 3.

3. Bring the liquid in each beaker to the boil, and add a leaf of spinach or of another green vegetable to each beaker. Cook for three minutes.

4. Remove the vegetables with tongs or a fork. Cool on a paper towel. Then observe the colour, and test the texture by rubbing each sample between two fingers.

The results with the base probably reminded you of the joke line: "First the good news and then the bad news!" Although the colour is greener than that of the vegetable cooked in vinegar or water, the base destroys the cell walls of the vegetable, making it too mushy to hold on a fork.

Follow-up

1. Tap water in some homes may be basic because of a high mineral content in the water. How can a cook overcome this problem when cooking green vegetables?

2. Would you add lemon juice when cooking green vegetables? Explain your answer.

Here's the Secret!

The cells of green vegetables contain green chlorophyll and yellow carotene. The colour of the chlorophyll dominates, so the vegetables appear green. The cells also contain acids. During cooking (in water or acid), the acids are set free and destroy some of the green chlorophyll but not the yellow carotene. The combination of yellow carotene and the remaining green chlorophyll gives an unappetizing olive green colour.

The best way to keep green vegetables green and appetizing when cooking them is to steam them. Place them in a container such as a sieve, colander, or steamer *above* boiling water. Do not cover them for the first part of the cooking. Any acids from the plant cells either escape in the steam, or drip into the water below.

9.6 General Properties of Acids and Bases

"How do drainpipe openers work?"
"Why do cakes rise?"
"Why should you be careful how you store foods?"
"Why is acid rain destroying statues?"

You will find the answers to these questions in the next series of investigations.

Be careful! The acids and bases used here are fairly concentrated. Wear your goggles.

Materials

safety goggles
3 test tubes
test tube rack
baking soda (sodium bicarbonate)
mossy zinc
3 mol/L sodium hydroxide solution
filtered limewater
marble chips (calcium carbonate)
ammonium chloride solution
long glass dropper
aluminum pieces
3 mol/L hydrochloric acid (hydrogen chloride in water)
sodium hydroxide pellets
red and blue litmus paper
wooden splints
spatula

Method

Draw up a data chart ahead of time. Record all the observations in your chart.

Chemicals used	Observations

I. *The Reaction of an Acid With a Metal*

1. Pour about 3 mL of hydrochloric acid into a test tube. Add a piece of zinc.

2. Bring a lighted splint up to the mouth of the test tube.

Fig. 22 The lighted splint test.

The lighted splint test is used to identify hydrogen. Hydrogen is flammable.

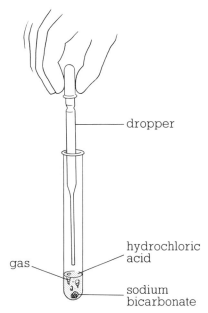

gas

dropper

hydrochloric acid

sodium bicarbonate

Fig. 23 *Capturing the gas produced.*

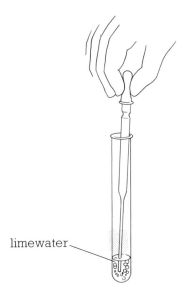

limewater

Fig. 24 *The limewater test is used to identify carbon dioxide gas.*

(a) What do you observe during the lighted splint test?

(b) The reaction of zinc metal with an acid is a displacement reaction. The gas produced is hydrogen. Complete the word equation for the reaction:

zinc + hydrochloric acid → _____ + _____

(c) Complete and balance the chemical equation for the above reaction:

Zn + HCl →

(d) What might happen if you spilled soft drink on the metal surface of your car and left it there?

(e) Why do soft drink manufacturers line their aluminum cans with plastic coating?

II. *The Reaction of an Acid With a Bicarbonate and a Carbonate*

1. Pour about 1 mL of hydrochloric acid into a test tube.

2. Place a pea-sized quantity of solid sodium bicarbonate (baking soda) in a dry test tube.

3. Add ten drops of filtered limewater to a clean test tube.

4. Add the acid to the sodium bicarbonate. Capture the resulting gas by drawing it into the long glass dropper, which is placed just above the reaction mixture (Figure 23).

5. Remove the dropper from the test tube. Place the open end of the dropper below the surface of the limewater in the second test tube. Squeeze the bulb of the dropper to bubble the gas through the limewater (Figure 24). Carefully observe what happens to the limewater.

6. Repeat steps 1 to 5 but use two marble chips (calcium carbonate) instead of sodium bicarbonate.

The reaction of a carbonate or bicarbonate with an acid produces carbon dioxide gas.

The word equations for the experiments that you did are:

sodium bicarbonate + hydrochloric acid →
                 sodium chloride + water + carbon dioxide

calcium carbonate + hydrochloric acid →
                 calcium chloride + water + carbon dioxide

(a) Use these word equations to write a balanced chemical equation for each of these reactions.

(b) Describe the chemical test for carbon dioxide gas.

(c) Why do bakers mix milk with sodium bicarbonate in many recipes?

(d) Why does acid rain damage marble statues?

III. *The Reaction of a Base With Aluminum*

1. Pour about 2 mL sodium hydroxide solution into a test tube. Add a few pieces of aluminum to the test tube and shake. Feel the test tube and observe its contents.

2. If a gas is produced, test the gas with a lighted splint. The reaction of aluminum with a base solution is the same as the reaction that takes place when powdered drainpipe opener is added to water. This is because a powdered drainpipe opener is a mixture of aluminum and a base.

   (a) Balance the chemical equation for the reaction:

   $$Al + NaOH \rightarrow Na_3AlO_3 + H_2$$

   (b) (i) Besides the production of a gas, what else did you observe in this reaction?

   (ii) Does this observation help explain why the reaction can clear a drain clogged with fat? Explain your answer.

   (c) Oven cleaners are basic. Why should you *not* use these cleaners on aluminum pots and pans?

IV. *The Reaction of a Base With Ammonium Salts*

1. Pour 1 mL of ammonium chloride solution into a test tube. Using the spatula, carefully add 1 pellet of sodium hydroxide to the solution.

2. Wet a piece of red litmus paper with distilled water. Hold the paper *over* the test tube mouth while gently warming the mixture over a *very low* flame (Figure 25). Observe any changes in the litmus paper.

3. Remove the test tube from the flame. Using the method shown in Figure 26, carefully smell the gas coming from the test tube. The odour is that of ammonia gas.

Do not touch the pellet with your hands! It is corrosive.

Ammonia gas is often formed when a base, such as sodium hydroxide, is added to an ammonium salt. The reaction is a test for ammonium salts.

Fig. 25

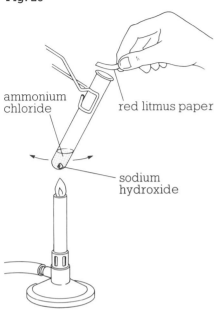

ammonium
chloride

red litmus paper

sodium
hydroxide

(a) Write a balanced chemical equation for the reaction. The word equation is:

ammonium chloride + sodium hydroxide →
sodium chloride + water + ammonia

(b) Copy the following chart into your notebook. Then complete the chart and keep it for future reference.

Substance used	Reaction in	
	Acid	Base
zinc		N.A.
a bicarbonate (sodium bicarbonate)		N.A.
a carbonate (calcium carbonate)		N.A.
aluminum	N.A.	
an ammonium salt (ammonium chloride)	N.A.	
red litmus *	stays red	turns blue
blue litmus *		
phenolphthalein *		
bromthymol blue *		

* Look back at earlier investigations to fill these out.

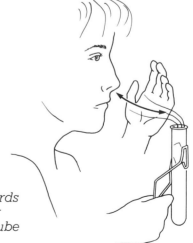

Fig. 26 *To detect the odour of a chemical, wave the fumes towards you. Do this only if your teacher asks you to. Never put the test tube under your nose.*

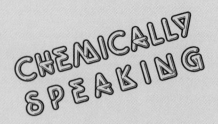

ACIDS AND BASES

For many acids, there is at least one hydrogen atom in the formula. A molecule of such an acid splits up in water and sets free a positive hydrogen ion (H^+).

Hydrochloric acid: $HCl(aq) \rightarrow H^{1+}(aq) + Cl^{1-}(aq)$

Nitric acid: $HNO_3(aq) \rightarrow H^{1+}(aq) + NO_3^{1-}(aq)$

Many reactions of acids are actually reactions of hydrogen ions. Because all acids give hydrogen ions, we can expect all acids in water to be chemically similar in some ways. For example, all acids turn blue litmus red.

Solutions of bases in water contain hydroxide ions (OH^{1-}).

Sodium hydroxide: $NaOH(aq) \rightarrow Na^{1+}(aq) + OH^{1-}(aq)$

Calcium hydroxide: $Ca(OH)_2(aq) \rightarrow Ca^{2+}(aq) + 2OH^{1-}(aq)$

Hydroxide ions are responsible for many of the properties of bases. Since hydroxide ions are present in all bases in water, we expect all bases to be chemically similar in some ways. For example, all bases turn red litmus blue.

Investigation

In 1909, Soren Sorenson, a Danish biochemist, was trying to control the amount of acid in beer. He developed the pH scale to describe the degree of acidity.

9.7 The pH Scale

Almost daily, you hear terms such as pH balanced shampoo, the pH of swimming pool water, and the pH of soil. What does pH mean?

In many situations, it is important to know how acidic or basic something is. Farmers, for example, may need to know how acidic or basic their soil is so that they can treat the soil for the crops they grow.

The pH scale has been developed to describe how acidic or basic a solution is. The following experiment will help you understand this: you will dilute acid and base solutions and measure the pH of each solution using a wide range pH paper.

Materials

safety goggles
8 small test tubes
100-mL volumetric flask
10-mL pipette

250-mL beaker
distilled water
wide range pH paper plus colour chart
0.1 mol/L hydrochloric acid
0.1 mol/L sodium hydroxide solution

Fig. 27 *In swimming pools, eye irritation is mainly caused by incorrectly balanced pH rather than by too much chlorine in the water.*

Method

1. Copy the chart below into your note book:

	ACID Concentration decreasing →				BASE ← Concentration decreasing			
Solution number	1	2	3	4	8	7	6	5
Concentration (mol/L)	0.1	0.01	0.001	0.0001	0.0001	0.001	0.01	0.1
pH								

Fig. 28

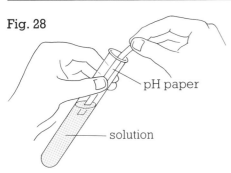

pH paper

solution

Starting with solution 1 (0.1 mol/L HCl), you will be making solutions 2, 3, and 4. Starting with solution 5 (0.1 mol/L NaOH), you will be making solutions 6, 7, and 8.

2. Half-fill a dry test tube with 0.1 mol/L hydrochloric acid. Dip a piece of wide range pH paper into the solution (Figure 28). Shake off any extra liquid on the paper, and compare the colour of the paper with the colours on the pH chart provided. Estimate the pH of acid solution 1, and record this finding in your chart.

If you are diluting a concentrated acid, the volumetric flask (Figure 30b) should be partly filled with distilled water *before* the acid is added.

3. Make up a 0.01 mol/L hydrochloric acid solution using the methods shown in Figures 29 and 30. Use a 10–mL pipette to transfer 10 mL of 0.1 mol/L hydrochloric acid to a 100–mL volumetric flask previously rinsed with distilled water. Test the pH of this more dilute solution (2), and record the result in your chart.

Fig. 29 *The correct use of a pipette to transfer an exact volume of liquid to another container.*

(a) Partly fill the pipette with distilled water.

(b) Turn the pipette to rinse the inside thoroughly with the distilled water.

(c) Discard the distilled water.

(d) Partly fill the pipette with the solution to be used.

(e) Turn the pipette to rinse it with the solution.

(f) Discard the rinse solution.

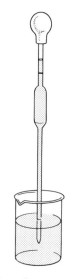

(g) Fill the pipette above the line with the solution.

(h) Remove the bulb and quickly replace it with a moist forefinger.

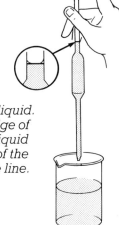

(i) Lift the pipette out of the liquid. Slowly raise the inside edge of the finger and allow the liquid to drain until the bottom of the meniscus just touches the line.

(j) Transfer the pipette to an empty vessel. Place the tip of the pipette along the inside of the vessel. Remove your forefinger from the top of the pipette and allow the liquid to drain out. Wait about 10 s before removing the pipette and always leave the last drop in the pipette.

Fig. 30 *Diluting a solution:*

(a) Fill a pipette with the concentrated solution given.

(b) Use the pipette to transfer a known volume of the solution into a volumetric flask.

(c) Swirl the contents as distilled water is added to the flask until near the mark.

(d) Mix well by capping the flask and shaking.

(e) Then add distilled water to the mark.

(f) Again mix well.

205

4. Pour the 0.01 mol/L hydrochloric acid (2) into a dry beaker. Rinse the pipette with distilled water and then with the 0.01 mol/L hydrochloric acid. Rinse the volumetric flask with distilled water. Make up a 0.001 mol/L hydrochloric acid solution using the methods in Figures 29 and 30. Test the pH of this even more dilute solution (3) and record the result in your chart.

5. Now pour the 0.001 mol/L hydrochloric acid (3) into a dry beaker. Rinse the pipette with distilled water and then with the 0.001 mol/L hydrochloric acid. Rinse the volumetric flask with distilled water. Make up a 0.0001 mol/L hydrochloric acid solution using the methods in Figures 29 and 30. Test the pH of this very dilute solution (4) and record the result in your chart.

6. Repeat steps 2 through 5, but this time start with the 0.1 mol/L sodium hydroxide solution. When you have finished, you will have tested solutions 5, 6, 7, and 8.

Follow-up

1. Why must the pipette be rinsed with the solution that is to be diluted?

2. Suppose you spill some acid or base solution out of the pipette while transferring it to the volumetric flask. How would this spill change the concentration of the solution you prepare in the flask?

3. (a) What is the pH of the 0.1 mol/L hydrochloric acid that you started with?
   (b) Generally speaking, what happens to the pH as an *acid* solution is made more dilute?

4. (a) What is the pH of the 0.1 mol/L sodium hydroxide solution that you started with?
   (b) Generally speaking, what happens to the pH as a *base* solution is made more dilute?

What Is the Effect of Dilution on pH?

If you continue with the above experiment by further diluting the acid solution and base solution one step at a time, you will find that both solutions will eventually have a pH value close to 7. A solution with a pH value of 7 is neither acidic nor basic. It is neutral. A sample of freshly boiled distilled water at 25°C should have a pH of exactly 7. A very dilute acid or base solution has a pH close to 7.

As a solution becomes more acidic or more basic, its pH is further from 7 most pH values lie in the range 0 to 14.

Would you expect the pH value of each of the following to be above 7 or below 7?
vinegar
household ammonia
milk
lemon juice
laundry detergent
soft drink
shampoo
aspirin
drain cleaner
baking soda

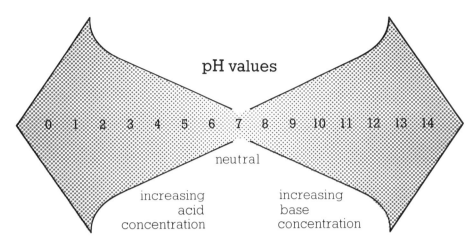

In your experiment, a ten-fold change in concentration of each solution gave a change of 1 pH unit. This means an acid with pH 2 is 10 times more acidic than one with pH 3. A base with pH 10 is 100 times more basic than one with pH 8.

Investigation

9.8 Natural Indicators

In the first activity of this chapter, you used indicators to find out whether a material was acidic or basic. Chemists use many indicators that occur naturally in plants. Like the wide range pH paper that you used, natural indicators change colour at different pH values.

Natural indicator	pH						
	2	4	6	8	10	12	14
geranium petals	Pink	Pink	Pink	Pink	Violet	Green	Yellow
plum skin	Red	Red	Pink	Green	Green	Green	Green

Materials

safety goggles
distilled water
plastic spot plate
coloured crayons
solutions of pH 2, pH 4, pH 6, pH 8, pH 10, and pH 12 in dropper bottles
natural indicators such as carrots, tea, red cabbage, grape juice, blueberry juice, beet juice, and cranberry juice

If you have time, try other
natural indicators from the
following list:
red apple skin
cherry juice
red onion skin
yellow onion skin
peach skin
pear skin
radish skin
rhubarb skin
tomato
turnip (rutabaga) skin

Method

1. Copy the following chart into your notebook.

Natural indicator	pH					
	2	4	6	8	10	12

2. If the indicators are already prepared, start at step 3. Otherwise:
   (a) Put raw grated carrots in enough distilled water to just cover the carrots. Boil the carrots until the water takes on some of the colour of carrot. Allow the mixture to cool, and pour off the liquid into a clean, labelled container. Prepare solutions from tea and red cabbage in a similar way.
   (b) For grape juice, blueberry juice, and beet juice, add 5 mL of juice to 20 mL of distilled water in separate, clean, labelled containers.
   (c) Add 10 mL of cranberry juice to 10 mL of distilled water in a clean, labelled container.

3. Drop about 1 mL of the solution with pH 2 into one section of the spot plate (Figure 31). Then drop 1 mL of the solution with pH 4 into a second section. Continue until each of the six sections of the spot plate contains 1 mL of solution.
   Choose an indicator, and add 1 or 2 drops of it to each solution. Mix carefully by gently agitating the spot plate. Record the colour of the indicator at different pH values using coloured crayons.

4. Rinse the spot plate and repeat the process for each of the other indicator solutions.

Fig. 31

208

We should never use more than a few drops of a chemical indicator to test an acid or base. As an indicator is itself an acid or base, too much of it will affect the pH of the solution.

Follow-up

Indicators change colour over a fairly narrow range of pH values, and not always around pH 7. The indicator phenolphthalein, for example, changes from colourless to red over the pH range 7 to 9. It cannot be used to tell the difference between an acid solution of pH 2 and an acid solution of pH 5. To do this, you choose an indicator that changes colour over the range of pH 2 to pH 5.

1. If you had only the natural indicators used in this activity, which one would you use to tell the difference between
   (a) a solution of pH 4 and a solution of pH 7,
   (b) a solution of pH 6 and a solution of pH 8,
   (c) a solution of pH 7 and a solution of pH 9?

2. Give reasons for each of your choices in question 1.

3. If you could use only one natural indicator to help you decide the pH of different solutions, which one would you choose?

4. Explain your choice in question 3.

Investigation

9.9 Is There Anything to Advertising Hype?

The term pH is often mentioned in advertisements for hair products. Is this just an advertising gimmick, or is the pH of hair products really important?
The following activity shows what happens when hair and some other natural fibres are placed in a basic solution.

Materials

safety goggles
8 test tubes
250-mL beaker or test tube rack that can be heated in an oven
glass rod
1.0 mol/L sodium hydroxide solution
distilled water
oven set at 40°C to 50°C
samples of pure wool, silk, cotton, and hair

Sodium hydroxide solution is corrosive.

Method

1. Set up eight test tubes as shown in Figure 32. Cover each test tube with plastic wrap. The four test tubes with distilled water added to the fibres will act as a control.

Fig. 32

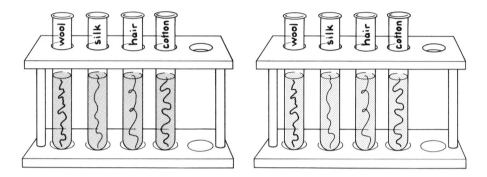

each sample in
distilled water

each sample in 1 mol/L
sodium hydroxide solution

2. Stand the test tubes and their contents overnight in an oven at about 40–50°C or in a warm place.

3. Remove the test tubes from the oven and stir the contents. Test the texture of the fibres by prodding with a glass rod. Return the test tubes to the oven or warm place. Repeat the test with the glass rod each day over the next few days.

4. Write down your observations in a chart.

	Substance soaked in							
	Base (sodium hydroxide solution)				Distilled water (control)			
	Wool	Silk	Hair	Cotton	Wool	Silk	Hair	Cotton
Daily test on texture								
Strength of fibre after drying								

5. If any solid materials remain, pour off the liquid. Rinse the fibres in the tube with cold water. Remove them with the rod and then dry them.

6. Test the dry remaining material for strength by pulling it lengthwise until it breaks. Compare its strength to that of the same material extracted and dried from the control group.

Follow-up

1. For the material that remained, was any fibre strengthened or weakened by the base?

2. Did the base destroy any of the materials? If so, which ones? Which materials appeared to be least changed by the base?

3. Were any of the materials changed by standing in water?

4. Explain why water was used in the second group of test tubes.

5. Would you use a very basic detergent on silk or wool? Give a reason for your answer.

6. Would you use a very basic detergent on cotton? Give a reason for your answer.

7. Would you use a very basic shampoo on your hair? Give a reason for your answer.

8. The pH of most shampoos is ideal for hair. Should you only buy shampoos advertised as pH balanced? Give reasons for your answer.

9. Silk and wool, like hair, are animal fibres. What kind of fibre is cotton?

10. Oven cleaners are basic. Why should you protect your hair when you use a spray–type oven cleaner?

11. We can clear blocked drains by using products that give very concentrated base solutions when mixed with water. Explain how drainpipe openers work when hair is the reason for the blockage.

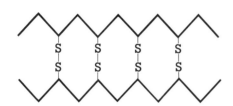

Fig. 33 *A hair fibre is made up of a number of very long molecules of the protein keratin (represented by the zigzag lines), linked together by pairs of sulfur atoms (-S-S-). Some bases can break the S-S link between protein molecules, causing the hair to fall apart.*

9.10 How pH is Used in Industry

Fig. 34 *"Tears free" baby shampoos have the same pH as a baby's tears, and so these shampoos do not sting if they get into eyes.*

Have you ever bought a milk product that tasted awful? Or ruined clothes by washing them? Or used a product that irritated your skin? Or made a chocolate cake too pale? Each of these problems might be traced to a wrong pH level.

The checking of pH levels is important in many industries. For example, the pH of shampoos has to be carefully controlled (Figure 34). In the manufacture of chocolate cake mixes, baking soda (sodium bicarbonate) is added to increase the pH if a dark brown cake is desired. The rate of growth of bacteria in cosmetics and food depends on the pH. The pH of some products is tested during manufacturing and before shipping. Some companies buy samples of their products from stores and then test their pH.

In the next activity you will measure the pH values of several consumer products. If a pH meter (Figure 35) is available, you can test all the materials listed. If a meter is not available, test only *pale-coloured* products with universal indicator solution or wide range pH paper.

Fig. 35 *A pH meter is an expensive instrument used to measure pH in industry. If you use one, follow the correct procedure shown by your teacher.*

Materials

safety goggles
a calibrated pH meter, universal indicator solution, or wide range
   pH paper
one 100-mL and one 250-mL beaker
stirring rod or magnetic stirrer
balance
distilled water
consumer products: milk powders and milk products;
         candies that dissolve (try fruit drops);
         soft drinks;
         flour (bleached and unbleached all-purpose, cake
         and pastry, whole wheat);
         cocoa powders;
         juice crystals;
         baked goods such as cookies, cakes, bread,
         muffins;
         mixes such as cake, muffin, bread, and pancake;
         personal care products such as shampoos, hair
         conditioners, and hair removers;
         detergents.

Method

1. Weigh a 10 g sample of the consumer product. Crush with a fork or crumble any chunky materials to obtain small pieces. Place the material in a clean and dry 250-mL beaker.

2. Add 100 mL of distilled water and stir for two or three minutes until an even mixture is obtained. If solids are present, allow the mixture to stand for 15 minutes so that the solids can settle. Pour off about half the liquid, which should be almost clear, into a dry 100-mL beaker.

3. *If a pH meter is used,* make sure the meter has been standardized. Place the electrode of the meter into the solution. Read the meter to obtain the pH. Do not stir the solution during the reading. Rinse the electrode with distilled water, and leave the electrode in a beaker of distilled water.

   If universal indicator or pH paper is used, add 3 or 4 drops of universal indicator to the solution. Use the pH scale for the universal indicator to decide on the pH of the solution. Alternatively, dip a piece of wide range pH paper into the solution and compare the paper's colour to a pH chart.

To standardize a pH meter, we use a solution of known pH. The meter is adjusted so that the pH reading equals the pH of the solution.

4. Record your observations in a chart, giving the type (and brand) of product, the pH, and whether the material is acidic, basic, or neutral.

Type of product	Brand name	pH	Acidic/basic/neutral

Follow-up

1. Why is a pH meter required to measure pH if the product is highly coloured?

2. Why are many industries concerned about the pH of their products?

Investigation

9.11 Acid Rain and the Two Faces of Oxygen

Rain is naturally acidic, with a pH of about 5.6. Acid rain is more acidic and can have a pH as low as 2.0. In the worst cases, acid rain is about as acidic as vinegar.

You can slow the "browning" of some sliced fruits and vegetables by dipping the slices in an acidic solution, such as lemon juice. Try this when you next cut avocados, apples, bananas, pears, artichokes, and potatoes.

Almost daily, we hear that acid rain is destroying our buildings, lakes, crops and forests. Even snow samples taken in the Far North are becoming more acidic. Where do acids in precipitation come from? To understand this, we have to investigate the chemical reactions of oxygen. This element reacts with many substances to form products called oxides.

Without oxygen, plant and animal life could not survive. But there are other, less beneficial effects of oxygen. Have you noticed that an apple or potato, once cut and exposed to air, goes brown? This is because of the reaction of oxygen with the foods. Some foods rot because of this reaction. Another negative effect of oxygen is its reaction with iron to form rust, sometimes called iron(III) oxide.

Fig. 36 *Millions of dollars are spent each year to prevent cars from rusting and to remove rust from cars.*

Many oxides are formed in combustion reactions, in which substances burn in oxygen. Combustion reactions are of great benefit to humans. For example, we use the burning of fuels to produce heat and other forms of energy. However, combustion also results in acid rain.

In the experiment that follows, pure samples of some of the metals and non-metals that occur in fuels will be burned in pure oxygen. The oxide products will be tested to see if they are acidic or basic in water.

Materials

safety goggles
4 gas jars
4 gas jar cover slips
1 deflagrating spoon (lined with aluminum foil)
universal indicator solution plus colour chart
cold, freshly boiled distilled water
crucible tongs
oxygen gas
powdered sulfur
carbon chips
steel wool
magnesium ribbon
Bunsen burner

Method

1. Copy the chart into your notebook.

Element burned			Observations of burning		Oxide in water tested with universal indicator		
Name and symbol	Metal or non-metal	Name of oxide	Air	Pure oxygen	Colour	pH	Acidic/basic/neutral

2. For each test, use one jar of oxygen gas. Add the oxygen to each gas jar from the gas cylinder or generator as directed by your teacher. Cover each gas jar immediately with a cover slip. Remove the cover slip and quickly add distilled water to a depth of about half a centimetre to each gas jar. Quickly cover the jar again (Figure 37).

3. Clean the deflagrating spoon and line its cup with a double thickness of aluminum foil. Place sulfur—about half a pea in size—in the spoon (Figure 38).

4. Heat the contents of the spoon over a Bunsen flame until the sulfur starts to burn, giving off smoke. Place the spoon's cup into the first jar of oxygen (Figure 39).

You must not inhale the fumes. Work in a fume hood or in a well ventilated room.

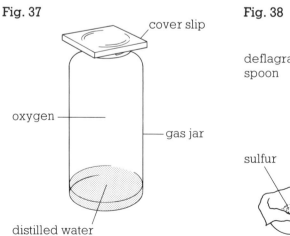

Fig. 37

cover slip

oxygen

gas jar

distilled water

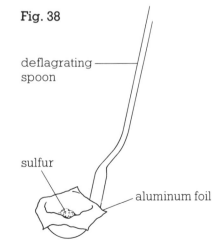

Fig. 38

deflagrating spoon

sulfur

aluminum foil

Fig. 39

Fig. 40

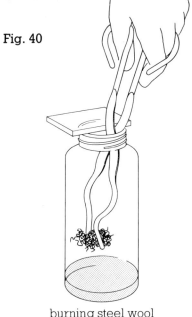

burning sulfur

burning steel wool

5. When the reaction is over, remove the spoon, and cover the jar completely. Shake the contents of the jar with the cover slip still on until no further change occurs.

6. Test the resulting solution in the jar by adding a drop of universal indicator. Write the colour of the indicator and the pH in the chart.

7. Repeat steps 3 to 6. This time put burning carbon chips (instead of sulfur) into the second jar of oxygen.

8. Repeat steps 4 to 6. This time use crucible tongs to put burning steel wool into the third jar of oxygen (Figure 40).

9. Repeat steps 4 to 6. This time use crucible tongs to put glowing magnesium ribbon into the fourth jar of oxygen.

10. If there is time, your teacher may demonstrate the burning of red phosphorus and sodium.

Follow-up

1. How did the burning of the elements in oxygen compare with the burning in air?

2. What general name is given to the type of compound formed when an element reacts with oxygen?

3. When metal oxides react with water, what is formed? Copy the equation and enter the word *acid* or *base*.
   metal oxide + water →

Do not allow the hot steel to touch the glass of the jar.

Do not stare directly at the flame of burning magnesium. Permanent eye damage could result.

4. When non–metal oxides react with water, what type of substance is formed? Complete the general equation for this type of reaction.
non-metal oxide + water →

5. The iron in the steel wool burns in oxygen to produce an insoluble oxide. When this insoluble oxide is added to water, does the pH of the water change?

6. Fuels such as wood and gasoline contain compounds of carbon and hydrogen. When the fuels are burned, the carbon and hydrogen are changed into their oxides. Name the two oxides formed.

7. Copy and complete the word equations for the burning of each of the elements used in this experiment.
(a) _____ + oxygen → sulfur dioxide
(b) carbon + oxygen → _____
(c) iron + _____ → iron(III) oxide
(d) magnesium + _____ → _____
(e) _____ + _____ → phosphorus(V) oxide
(f) sodium + _____ → _____

8. Which type of chemical reaction occurred in all the reactions in question 7?

9. Using your answers to question 7, write the balanced chemical equation for each reaction.

10. Briefly explain how acid rain is formed in the atmosphere.

11. Acid rain is often mentioned in the news. Why is acid rain considered so important?

12. The exhaust gases of cars contain oxides of nitrogen, as well as other oxides. Are oxides of nitrogen acidic or basic?

13. Many major industries burn huge amounts of coal, which contains sulfur impurities. What can these industries do to reduce their emissions of oxides that cause acid rain?

14. Buildings and marble and metal statues suffer the effects of air pollution in cities. Explain these effects.

15. There is water on the surface of your skin. What type of substance can form on your skin if you live in or visit a city in which there are many cars? What effect can this type of substance have on metal jewellery or pearls worn next to the skin?

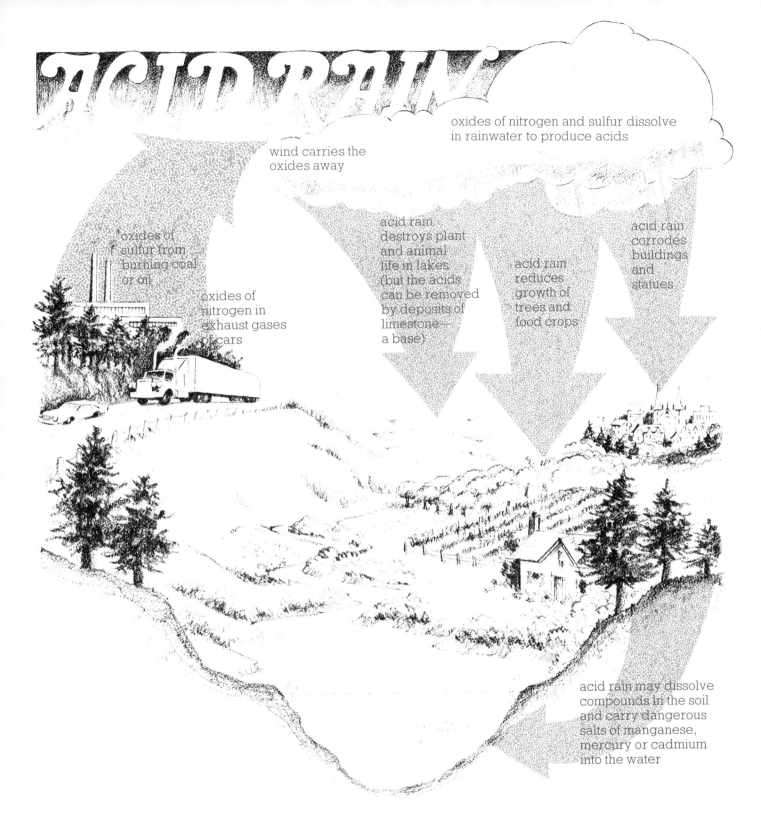

ACID RAIN

oxides of nitrogen and sulfur dissolve in rainwater to produce acids

wind carries the oxides away

oxides of sulfur from burning coal or oil

oxides of nitrogen in exhaust gases of cars

acid rain destroys plant and animal life in lakes (but the acids can be removed by deposits of limestone—a base)

acid rain reduces growth of trees and food crops

acid rain corrodes buildings and statues

acid rain may dissolve compounds in the soil and carry dangerous salts of manganese, mercury or cadmium into the water

219

Below is a partially completed "web" or "mind map" summarizing this chapter. Copy it on a fresh page of your notebook. For the top half of the web, add any extra information you have learned about acids. Then complete the lower half of the web for bases.

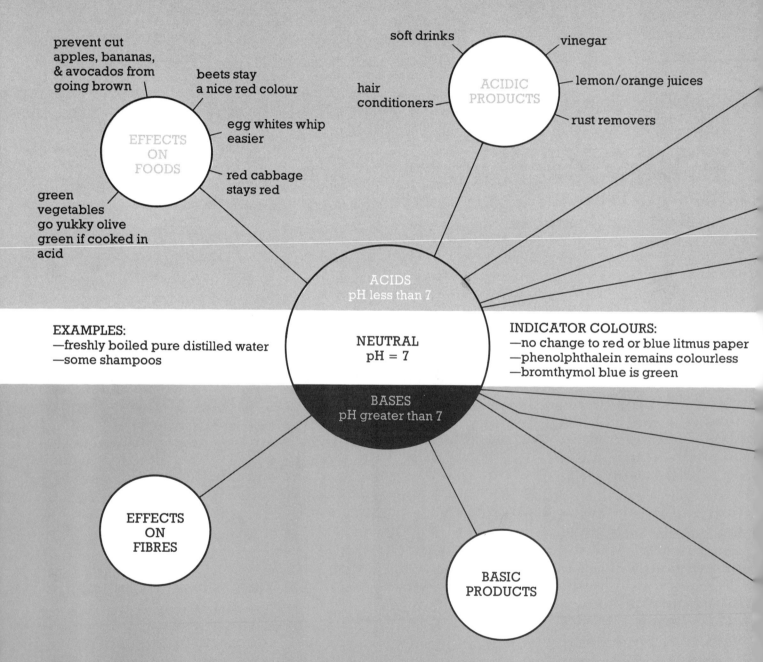

prevent cut apples, bananas, & avocados from going brown

beets stay a nice red colour

egg whites whip easier

red cabbage stays red

green vegetables go yukky olive green if cooked in acid

EFFECTS ON FOODS

soft drinks

vinegar

hair conditioners

ACIDIC PRODUCTS

lemon/orange juices

rust removers

ACIDS
pH less than 7

NEUTRAL
pH = 7

BASES
pH greater than 7

EXAMPLES:
—freshly boiled pure distilled water
—some shampoos

INDICATOR COLOURS:
—no change to red or blue litmus paper
—phenolphthalein remains colourless
—bromthymol blue is green

EFFECTS ON FIBRES

BASIC PRODUCTS

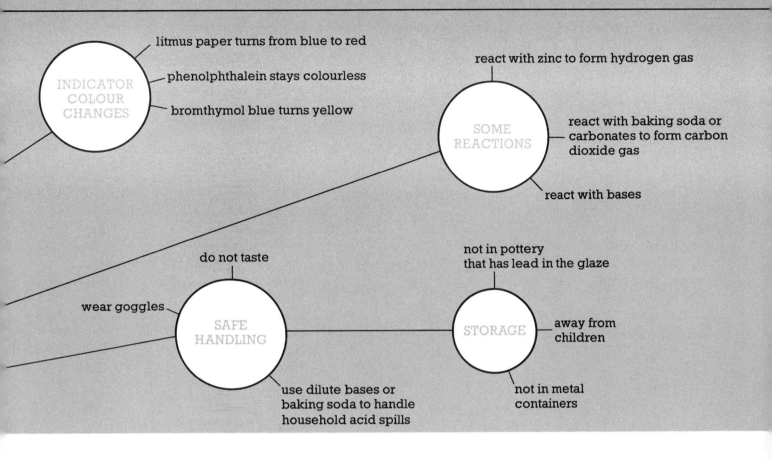

litmus paper turns from blue to red

phenolphthalein stays colourless

bromthymol blue turns yellow

INDICATOR COLOUR CHANGES

react with zinc to form hydrogen gas

react with baking soda or carbonates to form carbon dioxide gas

react with bases

SOME REACTIONS

do not taste

wear goggles

SAFE HANDLING

use dilute bases or baking soda to handle household acid spills

not in pottery that has lead in the glaze

STORAGE

away from children

not in metal containers

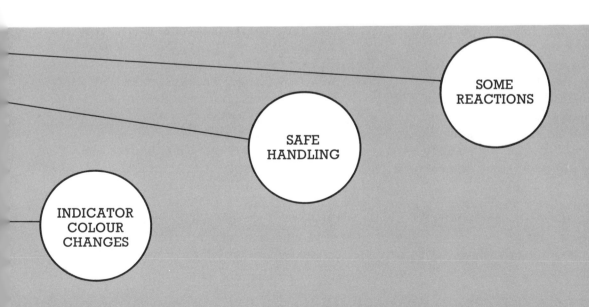

SOME REACTIONS

SAFE HANDLING

INDICATOR COLOUR CHANGES

- Many acids and bases are poisonous and corrosive. They must be stored and handled carefully.
- Some chemical indicators change colour when they are in contact with an acid or a base. For example, acids turn blue litmus paper red, and bases turn red litmus paper blue.
- Acids and bases may change the appearance and texture of certain foods. Be careful when cooking food or choosing a food container.
- Acids react with metals to produce hydrogen; acids also react with carbonates or bicarbonates to produce carbon dioxide.
- Bases react with certain metals (e.g. aluminum) to produce hydrogen; bases also react with ammonium salts to produce ammonia.
- The properties of acids are due to the presence of hydrogen ions in water.
- The properties of bases are due to the presence of hydroxide ions in water.
- Most solutions have pH values in the range 0 to 14. A neutral solution has a pH of 7. The more acidic a solution is, the further its pH is below 7. The more basic a solution is, the further its pH is above 7.
- The pH value of a solution can be measured with a pH meter, universal indicator solution, pH paper, or some natural indicators.
- The pH value of a product may affect the properties of the product. Therefore the checking of pH levels is important in many industries.
- Some bases can destroy animal fibres, such as hair. Therefore, shampoos should not be basic.
- Acid rain is caused by acidic oxides of sulfur and nitrogen. Large quantities of these oxides result from combustion reactions in some industries and in car engines.

1. Why is it necessary to protect your hair and skin when using an oven cleaner spray?
2. Why should a container of hydrochloric acid never be stored on a high shelf?
3. When a concentrated acid solution is diluted with water, a considerable amount of heat is given off. Which would be safer, diluting the acid by adding a small amount of the acid to a lot of water, or by adding the water to the acid? Explain.
4. Containers of many household cleaning products have hazard warning labels. Why do you think they are necessary?
5. Why should you never mix toilet bowl cleaner with a hypochlorite bleach?
6. Historians and scientists believe that many of the nobility in the ancient Roman Empire suffered from lead poisoning. (a) How did most of these people get the lead into their bodies? (b) Why did the poorer people not suffer in the same way? (c) Are there any ways we can get lead poisoning today?
7. List at least five household products that are (a) acidic, (b) basic.
8. What is an acid–base indicator?
9. List at least three substances in the home that can be used as acid–base indicators.
10. Why, when measuring the pH of some products, is it necessary to use a pH meter?

11. Ceramic tiled floors are often found in bathrooms and in kitchens. Why should the grout used between the tiles be acid resistant?

12. Why do cooks usually add vinegar to beet salads?

13. Describe the effects of cooking green vegetables in acidic and in basic water. Why do cooks steam the vegetables for the best results?

14. Describe a chemical test for (a) carbon dioxide gas, (b) hydrogen gas, and (c) ammonia gas.

15. Kettles, coffee makers, dishwashers, and steam irons, which all use tap water, eventually build up scale on their inside surfaces. This scale is made up of materials such as calcium carbonate and magnesium carbonate. (a) How would you remove this scale safely? (b) Institutions such as hotels can run into expensive repairs if their water pipes become heavily scaled. What can they do to prevent scale from forming?

16. Concrete is a very common building material. Find out the main components in concrete. Hydrochloric acid is often used to control the pH of swimming pool water. Why should you not mix the hydrochloric acid with water over a concrete deck?

17. Marble table tops, kitchen pastry boards, and bathroom vanities have been popular for many years. What precautions would you take when using them in your home?

18. Oxalic acid is sometimes used to remove rust stains. Why should oxalic acid never be used when removing such stains from marble tops?

19. Pearls consist mostly of calcium carbonate crystals. Why should you not splash vinegar, orange juice, or wine on pearls?

20. Sort the following chemical formulas into two lists under the headings "Acids" and "Bases": HCl, $LiOH$, $Mg(OH)_2$, H_2SO_3, NH_4OH, $HC_2H_3O_2$.

21. In point form, indicate how you would use a 25-mL pipette and a 250-mL volumetric flask to make up a 0.001 mol/L hydrochloric acid solution from a 0.1 mol/L hydrochloric acid solution.

22. The pH of a 0.0032 mol/L solution of hydrochloric acid is 2.49. If this acid solution was diluted one hundred fold, what would be the pH of the more dilute solution?

23. A 0.000 56 mol/L solution of sodium hydroxide has a pH of 10.75. What would be the pH of a sodium hydroxide solution that was ten times more concentrated?

24. When using an indicator to determine whether a solution is acidic or basic, why should you never use more than a few drops of the indicator?

25. Universal pH paper or universal indicator solution can be used to determine the pH of an acid or base solution across the entire pH range. How do you think these indicator solutions are made?

26. Why would it be bad to wash your hair with regular soap each day?

27. Linen is made from the flax plant. Why is it safe to wash linen in basic detergents while it is not safe to wash silk or wool in such a detergent?

28. One of the most common pieces of equipment found in a quality control laboratory in industry is a pH meter. Why do you think this is so?

29. Why is the term "pH" so often used in the advertising of personal care products, such as hair shampoos, hair conditioners, and cosmetics.

30. How is acid rain created?

31. Why are lakes with limestone (calcium carbonate) basins or bottoms considered to be safe from the effects of acid rain?

32. Create a poster showing the "good" and the "bad" sides of oxygen.

10 NEUTRALIZING ACIDS AND BASES

Lime is added to a lake to neutralize the effect of acid rain.

CONTENTS

Fig. 1 *Finger bowls of warm water and lemon slices are used to remove the odour of shellfish. Why do restaurants not provide finger bowls of vinegar?*

10.1 Acid Versus Base

As you learned in the previous chapter, a neutral solution is neither acidic nor basic. In fact, an acid solution can be used to destroy a base solution, and a base solution can be used to destroy an acid solution. This process is called **neutralization** and is often used in our everyday life.

Some restaurants provide finger bowls with lemon juice squeezed into the water (Figure 1). This is used to rinse hands after a shellfish meal. The chemicals that leave a fish-like odour on your hands are bases. The acids in the lemon juice neutralize the bases and this removes the odour.

In the last chapter you discovered that bases damage animal fibres. However, years ago, many shampoos contained soaps, which were basic. These shampoos cleaned hair well but did harm if left on the hair for too long. To neutralize any base left on the hair, people often used an acid rinse, such as lemon juice or an acid hair conditioner, after shampooing. In the same way, if a little vinegar or lemon juice is added to the rinse water when washing wool and silk, the rinse removes any base which may damage the fabric.

SMOKING AND NEUTRALIZATION

A smoker craves a cigarette most after a meal, when drinking alcohol, or when under stress. Smokers obtain poisonous nicotine from the cigarettes they inhale. The inhaled nicotine is first absorbed into the lungs. It is then transported throughout the body in the bloodstream, reaching the brain in about 7 s. Some of the nicotine is stored in the brain.

The acidity of the blood increases after a person eats a meal, drinks alcohol, or is under stress. Nicotine is a base. The more acidic the blood, the more soluble the nicotine is in the blood. If the nicotine that is stored in the brain becomes dissolved in the blood, then the person starts to crave more nicotine.

Investigation

10.2 A Simple Neutralization

Fig. 2

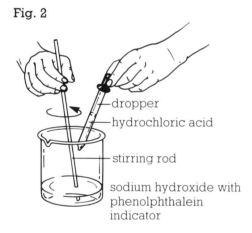

dropper
hydrochloric acid
stirring rod
sodium hydroxide with phenolphthalein indicator

Materials

safety goggles
evaporating dish or 100-mL beaker
10-mL graduated cylinder
0.5 mol/L sodium hydroxide solution
0.5 mol/L hydrochloric acid
phenolphthalein indicator solution
eye dropper
stirring rod
pH paper or universal indicator solution

Method

1. Place 10 mL of the 0.5 mol/L sodium hydroxide in an evaporating dish or in a beaker. Add one drop of phenolphthalein indicator solution.

2. Use the eye dropper to add the 0.5 mol/L hydrochloric acid to the sodium hydroxide solution drop by drop (Figure 2). After each drop, stir well. Continue until the red phenolphthalein colour *just* becomes colourless.

3. Use universal indicator or pH paper to find the pH of the solution.

NEUTRALIZATION

The product of the neutralization reaction between sodium hydroxide and hydrochloric acid is sodium chloride, or table salt. The term "salt" is now commonly used by chemists to describe any product that can be formed from a neutralization reaction. In general, a neutralization reaction always produces a "salt" and water.

$$acid + base \rightarrow \text{``salt''} + water$$

Water forms when a positive hydrogen ion from the acid combines with a negative hydroxide ion from the base.

$$H^{1+} + OH^{1-} \rightarrow H_2O$$

At the same time, the negative ion from the acid combines with the positive ion from the base to form the "salt."

$$Cl^{1-} + Na^{1+} \rightarrow NaCl$$

The word equation for the reaction is:

hydrochloric acid + sodium hydroxide →
sodium chloride + water

The overall chemical equation is:

$$HCl + NaOH \rightarrow NaCl + H_2O$$

Note that the positive ion of the salt (the part that is written first) always comes from the base, and the negative ion always comes from the acid. For example:

sulfuric acid + potassium hydroxide → potassium sulfate + water

$$H_2SO_4 + 2KOH \rightarrow K_2SO_4 + 2H_2O$$

Follow-up

1. Is the final solution acidic, basic, or neutral?

   The reaction between sodium hydroxide and hydrochloric acid is a neutralization represented by the equation:

$$NaOH + HCl \rightarrow NaCl + H_2O$$

   Refer to the reaction types you studied in Chapter 3. To which type do neutralization reactions belong?

3. A neutralization reaction always produces water and another compound. (In the experiment you just did, the compound produced was sodium chloride.) Write a balanced chemical equation for each of the following neutralization reactions:
   (a) potassium hydroxide + nitric acid
                   (hydrogen nitrate in water)
   (b) calcium hydroxide + hydrochloric acid
                   (hydrogen chloride in water)
   (c) sodium hydroxide + sulfuric acid
                   (hydrogen sulfate in water)
   (d) magnesium hydroxide + sulfuric acid
                   (hydrogen sulfate in water)
   (e) calcium hydroxide + phosphoric acid
                   (hydrogen phosphate in water)

4. Why are many commercial hair conditioners mildly acidic?

Investigation	*10.3 Concentration of an Acid*

Quantitative analysis is the determination of the amounts of substances in a given material. Titration is a method of quantitative analysis by which the volumes of two reacting solutions are compared.

In an earlier experiment, you neutralized sodium hydroxide solution by slowly adding hydrochloric acid solution to it from an eye dropper. A **titration** is essentially the same procedure, but carried out using a burette and a pipette. As with the technique using the eye dropper, the **end point** of the titration is reached when the colour of an indicator *just* changes.

In this experiment you will be given acid solutions of unknown concentrations. You will titrate each acid solution against 0.10 mol/L sodium hydroxide solution, and use the results to find the concentration of the acid solution.

Fig. 3 *The correct use of a burette.*

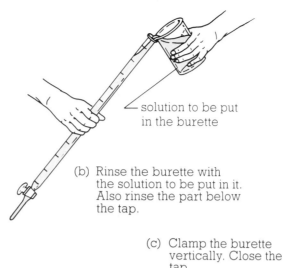

distilled water

50 mL burette

tap

(a) Rinse the burette with distilled water. Open the tap to let the water run out. This rinses the part below the tap.

solution to be put in the burette

(b) Rinse the burette with the solution to be put in it. Also rinse the part below the tap.

(c) Clamp the burette vertically. Close the tap.

funnel

(d) Use a funnel to fill the burette to above the zero mark. Open the tap to allow some solution to run out. Close the tap again.

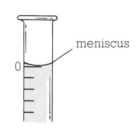

meniscus

(e) Add or run out more solution until the bottom of the meniscus is at the zero mark (or any other mark).

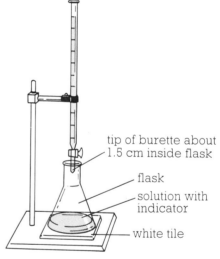

tip of burette about 1.5 cm inside flask

flask

solution with indicator

white tile

(f) Pipette the required volume of another solution into a clean flask. Place the flask on a white tile under the tip of the burette. Add indicator into the flask.

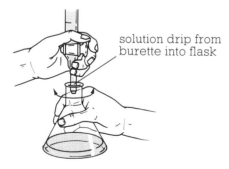

solution drip from burette into flask

(g) Control the tap by placing one hand around it from the rear. Use the other hand to swirl the flask as the solution in the burette runs down.

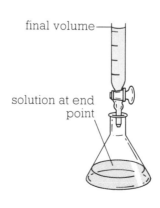

final volume

solution at end point

(h) When the end point is reached, close the tap immediately. Record the final volume of the solution in the burette.

Materials

safety goggles
50-mL burette
25-mL pipette
pipette bulb
Erlenmeyer flask
white tile or piece of white paper
funnel
burette clamp
retort stand
distilled water
0.1 mol/L sodium hydroxide solution
phenolphthalein indicator solution
hydrochloric acid (of unknown concentration)
nitric acid (of unknown concentration)
sulfuric acid (of unknown concentration)

Method

1. Follow the procedure described in Figure 3. Rinse the burette with distilled water and then with a little of the 0.10 mol/L sodium hydroxide solution. Fill the burette with the 0.10 mol/L sodium hydroxide solution. Clamp the burette in position and record the starting volume.

2. Rinse the Erlenmeyer flask with distilled water.

3. Rinse the pipette with the acid solution of unknown concentration. Then use it to add 25.00 mL of the acid solution to the Erlenmeyer flask.

4. Add two to three drops of phenolphthalein indicator solution to the Erlenmeyer flask. Place the flask on a white tile and under the burette.

5. Slowly run the sodium hydroxide solution from the burette into the Erlenmeyer flask. Keep swirling the flask. As the end point is approached, add the solution from the burette one drop at a time. Close the tap immediately when a pale pink end point is obtained. The pink colour should remain for at least 20 to 30 s before it begins to fade. Record the final volume.

6. Calculate the actual volume of solution run out of the burette as follows:

volume of solution
= final burette reading − starting burette reading

7. Refill the burette and repeat the titration until you obtain at least three volumes of sodium hydroxide that are within 0.10 mL of one another.

8. Summarize all your results in a chart.

Name of acid:				
	Trial 1	Trial 2	Trial 3	Trial 4
Concentration of sodium hydroxide solution (mol/L)	0.10	0.10	0.10	0.10
Initial burette reading (mL)				
Final burette reading (mL)				
Volume of sodium hydroxide solution (mL)				
Volume of acid solution (mL)	25.0	25.0	25.0	25.0

9. Repeat steps 1 to 8 for each of the other acid solutions of unknown concentrations.

Follow-up

1. Find the average volume of 0.1 mol/L sodium hydroxide needed to neutralize each acid solution.

2. Write a balanced chemical equation for each neutralization reaction.

3. Calculate the unknown concentration of each acid solution as follows. Show the concentration (in mol/L) to two decimal places.

For hydrochloric acid and nitric acid:

$$\frac{\text{concentration of}}{\text{acid (mol/L)}} = \frac{\text{concentration of base (mol/L)} \times \text{volume of base (mL)}}{\text{volume of acid (mL)}}$$

The calculation for sulfuric acid is different from that for hydrochloric acid (and nitric acid) because the ratios in the equation are different.

For sulfuric acid:

$$\frac{\text{concentration of}}{\text{acid (mol/L)}} = \frac{\text{concentration of base (mol/L)} \times \text{volume of base (mL)}}{2 \times \text{volume of acid (mL)}}$$

231

10.4 Concentration of Ammonia in Household Cleaner

Many household cleaners contain ammonia. Ammonia gas dissolves in water to form ammonium hydroxide solution, which helps in the removal of greases and oils.

The ammonium hydroxide solution can be neutralized with hydrochloric acid according to the following equation:

ammonium hydroxide + hydroxide acid →

ammonium chloride + water

$$NH_4OH + HCl \rightarrow NH_4Cl + H_2O$$

You will use a 0.5 mol/L solution of hydrochloric acid. The indicator used is bromcresol green, which changes from blue to yellow-green at the end point.

Ammonium hydroxide is more correctly known as "aqueous ammonia." The term ammonium hydroxide is used here to emphasize that ammonia forms a base in water.

Materials

safety goggles
funnel
white tile or a piece of white paper
50-mL burette
10-mL pipette
pipette bulb
Erlenmeyer flask
0.5 mol/L hydrochloric acid
bromcresol green indicator solution
colourless liquid household cleaner containing ammonia
distilled water

Fig. 4 *Ammonia is the active ingredient in many household cleaners.*

Method

1. Rinse and fill the burette with the 0.5 mol/L hydrochloric acid. Record the starting volume.

2. Pipette 10 mL of the household cleaner into the Erlenmeyer flask and add about 20 mL of distilled water.

3. Add two or three drops of bromcresol green indicator solution.

4. Titrate until the indicator changes from a blue to a yellow-green colour. Record the final volume.

5. Repeat the titration until you obtain at least three volumes of hydrochloric acid that are within 0.10 mL of one another.

6. Summarize all your results in a chart.

Choose three volumes of hydrochloric acid that are within 0.10 mL of one another to find the average volume.

1. Find the average volume of 0.5 mol/L hydrochloric acid needed to neutralize the ammonia in the household cleaner.

2. Calculate the percentage of ammonia (in grams per 100 mL of solution) in the household cleaner to one decimal place as follows:

   percentage of ammonia
   = volume of HCl (mL) × concentration of HCl (mol/L) × 0.17

Investigation	# 10.5 Concentration of Acetic Acid in Vinegar

Vinegar is a solution of acetic acid. To find the concentration of acetic acid in a sample of vinegar, you titrate it with 0.1 mol/L sodium hydroxide. The indicator used will be phenolphthalein.

acetic acid + sodium hydroxide → sodium acetate + water

$$HC_2H_3O_2 + NaOH \rightarrow NaC_2H_3O_2 + H_2O$$

Vinegar is too concentrated to be titrated directly. Therefore you will dilute the vinegar before titrating it.

Fig. 5 *Vinegar is a solution of acetic acid.*

Materials

safety goggles
white tile or a piece of white paper
funnel
commercial white vinegar — any brand
0.1 mol/L sodium hydroxide solution
phenolphthalein indicator solution
distilled water

100-mL volumetric flask
10-mL pipette
25-mL pipette
pipette bulb
50-mL burette
Erlenmeyer flask

Method

1. Rinse and fill the burette with the 0.1 mol/L sodium hydroxide solution. Record the starting volume.

2. To dilute the vinegar solution, pipette 10.0 mL of vinegar into a clean 100-mL volumetric flask. Add distilled water to bring the final volume up to the 100 mL mark. Cap the flask and mix the contents.

3. Pipette 25.0 mL of the dilute vinegar solution into the Erlenmeyer flask.

4. Add two or three drops of phenolphthalein indicator solution into the Enlenmeyer flask.

5. Titrate to a pale pink end point. Record the final volume.

6. Repeat at least twice more. If you run out of dilute vinegar solution, repeat step 2.

Choose three volumes of sodium hydroxide that are within 0.10 mL of one another.

7. Summarize all your results in a chart.

Follow-up

1. Find the average volume of 0.1 mol/L sodium hydroxide needed to neutralize the dilute vinegar solution.

2. The concentration of commercial vinegar is usually expressed as a volume percentage, that is, millilitres of acetic acid per 100 mL of solution. This can be calculated using the following expression:

$$\text{volume percentage} = \frac{\text{volume NaOH (mL)} \times \text{concentration NaOH (mol/L)} \times 57.2}{\text{volume of dilute vinegar (mL)}}$$

4. Check the manufacturer's label to see how close your answer is to the stated volume percentage.

10.6 Acidity of Milk and Milk Products

Fresh cow's milk has a pH between 6.5 and 6.7. Bacteria in the milk change milk sugar (lactose) into lactic acid. Therefore the acidity increases with time.

In the dairy industry, where cream and milk are used to make butter, cheese, and ice cream, it is most important that the milk and cream be of the right acidity. Also, we drink an enormous amount of milk, and we expect the milk to have a good appearance and taste. If the acidity is too high, milk does not taste good and cannot be used in many processes. Below is a chart showing what happens to the condition of the milk as the acidity increases.

% acidity (% lactic acid)	Condition of the Milk
0.14–0.18	normal fresh milk
0.16–0.18	limit for acceptable milk
0.25–0.27	unacceptable—acid odour
0.26–0.30	unacceptable—acid taste
0.50–0.60	unacceptable—milk curdles

Fig. 6 *The condition of milk is affected by the amount of lactic acid in it.*

In dairies and companies that use milk, quality control technicians carry out chemical tests on the milk. One of the most important tests is to find out the percent acidity in the milk or milk product. You will now perform this test. It depends on the neutralization reaction between lactic acid (the acid found in milk) and sodium hydroxide.

lactic acid + sodium hydroxide → sodium lactate + water

$$CH_3CH(OH)COOH + NaOH \rightarrow CH_3CH(OH)COONa + H_2O$$

Materials

safety goggles	balance
milk	100-mL Erlenmeyer flask
sweet cream	white tile or a piece of white paper
skim milk	funnel
sour cream	
whey	
white ice cream (melted)	
reconstituted condensed milk (unsweetened)	
reconstituted skim milk powder	
0.1 mol/L sodium hydroxide solution	
phenolphthalein indicator solution	
10-mL burette (a larger one will also do)	

Method

1. Weigh exactly 9.0 g of the milk or milk product into the Erlenmeyer flask.

2. Add two or three drops of phenolphthalein indicator solution.

3. Rinse and fill the burette with the 0.1 mol/L sodium hydroxide solution. Record the starting volume.

4. Place the flask on a white tile under the burette.

5. Titrate to the first definite and relatively permament shade of pale pink. Record the final volume.

6. Repeat the procedure with at least two more samples of the same material.

7. Record all you data in a chart. Be sure to show the type of material, the brand name, the "best before" date, and the volume of sodium hydroxide needed to neutralize the sample.

Fig. 7 *Which is more acidic, milk or yoghurt?*

Follow-up

1. For each material you tested, calculate the percentage by mass of lactic acid as follows:

$$\text{percentage of acidity (\%)} = \text{volume of NaOH (ml)} \times \text{concentration of NaOH (mol/L)}$$

2. Compare your results with those of others in the class using the same material. If your results differ from theirs, suggest a reasons for the difference.

3. Which would you expect to have a higher percent acidity, yoghurt or milk? Explain your answer.

4. What do you think you would like about being a quality control technician? What do you think you would *not* like about the job of a quality control technician?

Investigation

10.7 Buffers

For many chemical processes — in a factory, a laboratory, or the human body — it is important to keep a constant pH. This is done with special chemicals called buffers. **Buffers** are chemical mixtures that protect a solution from large changes in pH even when acids or bases are added.

In this experiment you will observe what happens to the pH of pure water when a small quantity of acid or base is added. You will then observe the effect of an acid or a base on the pH of a buffer solution.

Fig. 8 *Fruit drink crystals usually contain buffers.*

Materials

safety goggles	universal indicator solution or pH paper
balance	boiled distilled water
100-mL graduated cyclinder	0.1 mol/L hydrochloric acid solution
two 250-mL beakers	0.1 mol/L sodium hydroxide solution
stirring rod	0.1 mol/L acetic acid solution
small test tubes	solid sodium acetate

Method

1. Half-fill a small test tube with cold boiled-out distilled water. Add one drop of universal indicator solution. Mix well and determine the approximate pH of the boiled water by referring to the indicator chart.

2. Mix 90 mL of cold boiled-out distilled water with 10 mL of 0.1 mol/L hydrochloric acid in a beaker. Half-fill a test tube with this mixture. Find the approximate pH of the mixture as in step 1.

3. Mix 90 mL of cold boiled-out distilled water with 10 mL of 0.1 mol/L sodium hydroxide in a beaker. Find the pH of the mixture as in step 1.

4. Prepare a buffer solution by dissolving 1.6 g of sodium acetate in 200 mL of 0.1 mol/L acetic acid in a beaker. Find the pH of this buffer solution as in step 1.

5. Mix 90 mL of the buffer solution with 10 mL of 0.1 mol/L hydrochloric acid in a beaker. Find the pH of the mixture as in step 1.

6. Mix 90 mL of the buffer solution with 10 mL of 0.1 mol/L sodium hydroxide in a beaker. Find the pH of the mixture as in step 1.

7. Record your results in a chart similar to the following:

Sample	pH
Distilled water	
Distilled water + hydrochloric acid	
Distilled water + sodium hydroxide solution	
Buffer solution	
Buffer solution + hydrochloric acid	
Buffer solution + sodium hydroxide solution	

Follow-up

1. Which had the greater effect on pH,
   (a) adding acid to water or adding acid to the buffer solution,
   (b) adding base to water or adding base to the buffer solution?

2. Keeping the pH of swimming pool water in the range 7.2 to 7.6 is most important. It is in this range that the chlorine is most effective in killing bacteria in the water. How can a buffer be used to maintain the correct pH?

3. What connection do you notice between the two chemicals used to make the buffer solution?

BUFFERS PLAY AN IMPORTANT ROLE IN BLOOD

The normal pH of blood is in the range 7.35 to 7.45. If the pH of blood drops below 7.35, then a condition known as "acidosis" exists. If the pH of blood increases above 7.45, then "alkalosis" exists. If acidosis or alkalosis is not quickly remedied, death soon occurs.

Normally, blood stays within the safe pH range because of the presence of buffers. There are bicarbonate buffers, phosphate buffers, and hemoglobin buffers. These buffers react with excess acid and protect the body from acidosis, or they can react with excess base and protect the body from alkalosis. In either case the pH of the blood will remain within the safe limit.

Acidosis is commonly caused by starvation, diabetes, kidney failure, and shock. In the event of shock, the normal oxygen supply to body cells is highly reduced. As a result, the body cells produce lactic acid and the blood rapidly becomes acidic.

Alkalosis occurs less frequently. It may be caused by breathing too rapidly, using great amounts of laxatives, and as a side effect of pneumonia.

Fig. 9 *The pH of blood is kept within a narrow range by buffers.*

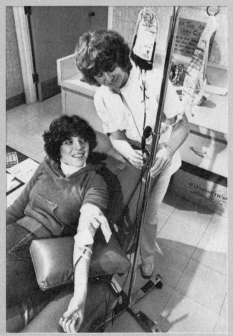

10.8 Analysis of Antacids

Antacids are among the most widely used, self-prescribed medications. They are used almost daily to relieve heartburn and upset stomach (hyperacidity). In some cases, people use antacids on a regular basis as part of ulcer therapy.

Most commercially available antacids contain one or more of the following chemicals: sodium hydrogen carbonate, calcium carbonate, magnesium hydroxide, and aluminum hydroxide. Each of these chemicals neutralizes acids. The effectiveness of the antacid depends on the speed of the neutralization and also on how much of the stomach acid (hydrochloric acid) is neutralized.

Antacid treatment neutralizes excess stomach acid and raises the pH. However, if the pH rises to about 5, the stomach responds by producing more acid. Therefore, an effective antacid should be able to maintain a final pH of about 3 in the stomach. To do so, most antacids contain buffers to keep the pH at about this value.

Fig. 10 *Antacids contain bases to neutralize stomach acid.*

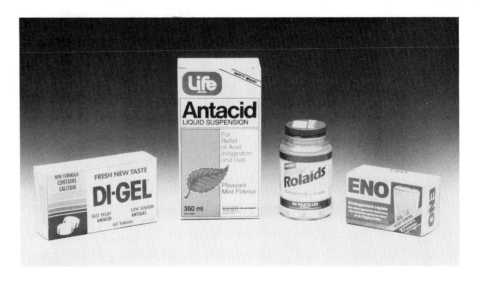

Materials

safety goggles
50-mL burette
25-mL pipette
pipette bulb
funnel
balance
white tile or a piece of white paper
250-mL Erlenmeyer flask

mortar and pestle
bromphenol blue indicator solution
0.1 mol/L hydrochloric acid solution
0.1 mol/L sodium hydroxide solution
antacid tablets — a variety of brands

Method

1. Rinse and fill the burette with the 0.1 mol/L sodium hydroxide solution. Record the starting volume.

2. Pipette 25 mL of 0.1 mol/L hydrochloric acid into the Erlenmeyer flask. Add two or three drops of bromphenol blue indicator solution. Titrate against the 0.1 mol/L sodium hydroxide to a blue end point. Record the final volume. Calculate the volume of sodium hydroxide used to neutralize the 25 mL of acid.

3. To calculate the volume of sodium hydroxide needed to neutralize 100 mL of the 0.1 mol/L hydrohloric acid, multiply the volume used in step 2 by 4.

4. Find the mass of one antacid tablet. Carefully use the pestle to crush the tablet in the clean, dry mortar. Add all the crushed material to 100 mL of 0.1 mol/L hydrochloric acid in an Erlenmeyer flask. Gently swirl the mixture to dissolve as much of the solid as possible. There may be some undissolved "filler."

5. Add three to five drops of bromphenol blue indicator solution to the flask. Refill the burette with 0.1 mol/L sodium hydroxide and titrate the contents of the flask to a blue end point.

6. Repeat steps 4 and 5 for other brands of antacid tablets.

7. Record your results in a chart similar to the following:

	Step 4	Step 3	Step 5	Step 3 – Step 5
Name of antacid tablet	Mass of antacid tablet (g)	Volume of NaOH needed to neutralize 100 mL HCl (mL)	Volume of NaOH needed to neutralize HCl + antacid (mL)	Volume of 0.1 mol/L HCl neutralized by antacid (mL)

1. For each of the antacids used, calculate the following ratio:

$$\frac{\text{volume of HCl neutralized by the antacid}}{\text{mass of the antacid tablet}}$$

Summarize your results in a suitable chart.

2. Which antacid is the most effective in neutralizing hydrochloric acid?

3. If you have the prices of the antacid tablets, compare effectiveness in neutralizing hydrochloric acid versus price paid per tablet.

P O I N T S · T O · R E C A L L

- Neutralization is the reaction between an acid and a base to form a salt and water.
- In a titration, the unknown concentration of a chemical can be found using volume measurements and a solution of known concentration.
- A colour indicator is often used to signal the end point of a titration.
- Burettes and pipettes are instruments used for measuring volumes in titrations.

- The concentrations of chemicals in commercial products are expressed in different ways, for example, percentage by volume, percentage by mass, or mass per 100 mL of solution.
- Buffers are chemical mixtures that protect solutions from large changes in pH.
- Buffers are very important in living organisms and are present in consumer products such as antacids.

1. Soap is slightly basic. If you use soap to wash hair or wool, why should you use vinegar in the final rinse water? Why are many commercial hair conditioners mildly acidic?

2. If you had an acid spill in the kitchen, how could you safely neutralize it?

3. Balance the following equations that represent neutralization reactions:
   (a) $Ca(OH)_2 + H_3PO_4 \rightarrow Ca_3(PO_4)_2 + H_2O$
   (b) $LiOH + H_2SO_4 \rightarrow Li_2SO_4 + H_2O$
   (c) $Al(OH)_3 + HCl \rightarrow AlCl_3 + H_2O$

4. Certain antacids contain aluminum hydroxide or magnesium hydroxide which reacts with stomach acid. Write a balanced chemical equation for the reaction of magnesium hydroxide with the hydrochloric acid in the stomach.

5. Before an actual titration, why must a burette be rinsed with the solution you are going to use in it?

6. Why must you fill the section of the burette below the tap with solution before you start a titration? Why must you remove all air bubbles below the burette tap?

7. Why must you use a white tile, or a piece of white paper, underneath the flask in a titration? Why must you prevent the meniscus from falling below the 50-mL mark in the burette?

8. Why must you use a pipette bulb when filling a pipette?

9. In each diagram in Figure 11, what is the volume reading on the burette?

10. How can you tell if the end point of the titration has been reached?

11. Pasteurization is a process used to kill the bacteria in milk. How does this prevent the milk from becoming sour?

12. The key chemical in tooth enamel is hydroxyapatite, $Ca_{10}(PO_4)_6(OH)_2$. Why does lactic acid in milk damage a child's teeth if the child has milk just before going to sleep?

13. A farmer may add lime (calcium oxide) or slaked lime (calcium hydroxide) to soil that is too acidic. Explain why.

14. (a) What does a buffer do?
    (b) Describe a test you could do to see if a solution contained a buffer.

15. Buffers are sometimes added to headache tablets containing acetylsalicyclic acid (ASA). Explain why.

16. List the ingredients shown on the labels of at least three different brands of antacids.

17. List the ingredients on a bottle of Bufferin. Which chemicals act as buffers in this non-prescription medication?

18. A tanker truck has overturned and spilled concentrated sulfuric acid into a lake.
    (a) What could happen to the environment?
    (b) Would you neutralize the spill? Explain.
    (c) If you did decide to neutralize the spill, how could you minimize the damage to the environment?
    (d) What safeguards should governments take to prevent environmental damage from spills of dangerous chemicals?

Fig. 11

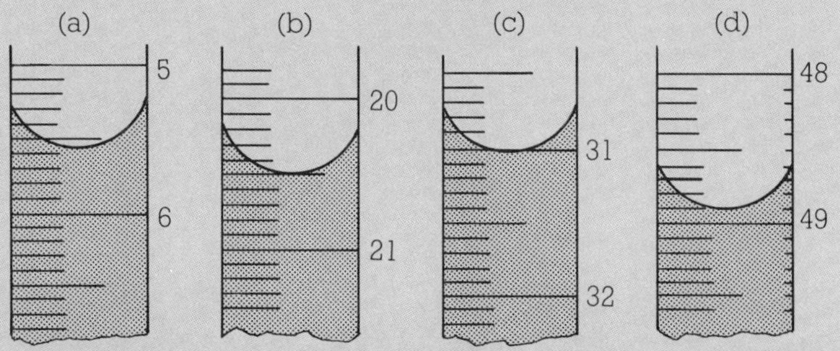

(a) (b) (c) (d)

11 QUALITATIVE ANALYSIS

Qualitative analysis is sued to identify the chemicals present in a substance.

CONTENTS

11.1 The Need to Analyze

Imagine visiting a supermarket and writing down all the ingredients listed on all the product labels. Even if you avoid duplication, your list will still be very long. Your list deals only with substances used in consumer products. Each year many other substances are produced or found, and the total list of known compounds grows longer and longer.

If you list an unfamiliar substance or find a product which does not have the ingredients listed, how do you find out what chemicals are present? Sometimes such information is important. A person who is allergic to bisulfites needs to know that bisulfites are not being used to keep salad greens looking fresh in a restaurant. A child is rushed to hospital after swallowing some chemical. What treatment should the doctors use? A geologist finds a strange looking mineral. What is it?

To find out what chemicals are present in a sample, the chemist carries out a process called **qualitative analysis**. If it is necessary to find out *how much* of a particular chemical is present in a sample, the chemist will carry out another process called **quantitative analysis**.

Chemists do not have time to start testing the chemicals that start with the letter ''a'' and then work their way through the alphabet. A knowledge of the type of sample, where it was found, and what chemicals are usually found in that location all help in the decision of what to look for. In the case of the child rushed to hospital, the symptoms would suggest a list of possible poisons that the chemist should look for. Even then, the search can be a hit-or-miss affair.

Fortunately, qualitative analysis is not always carried out in a life-threatening situation. In many cases, the chemist is simply told to test the product for the possible presence of, say, five or six chemicals. This type of analysis is much easier. The analyst has to carry out only five or six specific tests.

Because so many new chemicals are being introduced into the marketplace each year, there must be new tests to detect them (Figure 1). Also, many older tests must be made more accurate. For example, dioxin is the name given to a group of related compounds that are highly toxic. It is absolutely essential that we know how much dioxin is present in our drinking water, air, and food. We can now detect the presence of dioxin in quantities as low as 1 part in 100 000 000 000 000.

Fig. 1 *This "super sniffer", developed at the University of Toronto, can detect incredibly small amounts of chemicals. It was used in 1979 to sniff out toxic chlorine gas from a train derailment in Mississauga, Ontario.*

Questions

1. List 10 occupations in which it is important that the workers should know what chemicals are present in the materials with which they are working.

2. What materials are checked for in drinking water samples?

3. How are athletes tested for illegal drugs?

4. Some athletes take steroid drugs. These drugs are supposed to build up muscle tissue and give extra strength. Find out what effect this type of drug has on the body and then make a case for or against the use of such drugs by athletes.

11.2 A Chemical Detective Story

In this investigation you will play the role of a detective. You are asked to investigate some ionic compounds. The name of each compound is made up of a letter (which represents the positive ion) and a numeral (which represents the negative ion). A particular letter or numeral always represents the same ion. The chemicals $A1$ and $A3$ both contain the same positive ion, A.

Only double displacement reactions are used in this investigation: For example,

$$X9 + Y8 \rightarrow X8 + Y9$$

All the chemicals are dissolved in water. When two chemicals react, one product may be a precipitate. If a precipitate is observed in the above reaction, then either $X8$ or $Y9$ is the precipitate. To check whether it is $X8$ or $Y9$, you must carry out a second experiment:

$$X7 + Z8 \rightarrow X8 + Z7$$

If a precipitate does not form in this case, you know that $X8$ and $Z7$ are soluble in water. You can now conclude that the precipitate in the first reaction is $Y9$.

Materials

safety goggles
a spot plate or small test tubes
glass rod
solutions of chemicals in dropper bottles marked:
     A1
     B2
     C1
     D3
     E4
     D4
     D5
     F6
     G7

Method

1. You have seven different chemicals: *A1, B2, C1, D3, E4, D4,* and *D5*. Each chemical must be reacted with each of the other chemicals. This means that there are 21 possible reactions. Carry out each reaction by placing a few drops of the first chemical into a spot plate well or a small test tube. Add a few drops of the second chemical. Mix well and check whether any solid material has precipitated (Figure 2).

Fig. 2 *Remember, solutions are always clear. If a precipitate forms, then the mixture becomes cloudy.*

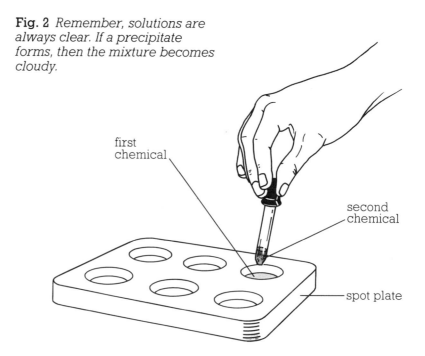

first chemical

second chemical

spot plate

2. Record your results in a copy of the chart below. Use "YES" to indicate if a precipitate formed and "NO" if a precipitate did not form. At the same time, indicate in the space provided the two possible products of the reaction. Remember these are all double displacement reactions.

	D5	D4	E4	D3	C1	B2	A1
A1	YES — A5 / B1						
B2							
C1							
D3							
E4							
D4							
D5							

For example, mixing *A1* with *B2* gives a precipitate. You should record the results as follows:

	B2
A1	YES — A2 / B1

This means that in the reaction:

$$A1 + B2 \rightarrow A2 + B1,$$

one of the products, *A2* or *B1*, must be the precipitate.

3. You will be given two more solutions, *F6* and *G7*. They were chosen so that:
   F could be *A* or *B* or *C* or *D* or *E*
   G could be *A* or *B* or *C* or *D* or *E*
   6 could be *1* or *2* or *3* or *4* or *5*
   7 could be *1* or *2* or *3* or *4* or *5*

Your job is to identify *F*, *G*, *6*, and *7*.
React *F6* and *G7* with each of the other seven chemicals.
Record your results as before.

	A1	B2	C1	D3	E4	D4	D5
F6							
G7							

Follow-up

1. Look at the chart for the first seven chemicals. Determine which chemicals do and which do not form a precipitate.

Precipitate	No precipitate
A5	D1

2. Answer the following questions:
   (a) *A* forms a precipitate when joined to which numerals?
   (b) *B* forms a precipitate when joined to which numerals?
   (c) *C* forms a precipitate when joined to which numerals?
   (d) *D* forms a precipitate when joined to which numerals?
   (e) *E* forms a precipitate when joined to which numerals?
   (f) *1* forms a precipitate when joined to which letters?
   (g) *2* forms a precipitate when joined to which letters?
   (h) *3* forms a precipitate when joined to which letters?

(i) *4* forms a precipitate when joined to which letters?

(j) *5* forms a precipitate when joined to which letters?

3. Look at the chart for *F6* and *G7*. Determine which chemicals do and which do not form a precipitate.

Precipitate	No precipitate

4. Answer the following questions:
   (a) *F* forms a precipitate when joined to which numerals?
   (b) *G* forms a precipitate when joined to which numerals?
   (c) *6* forms a precipitate when joined to which numerals?
   (d) *7* forms a precipitate when joined to which numerals?

5. Identify *F, G, 6,* and *7* in terms of the other chemicals. You may have to look at the first seven chemicals once again.

11.3 Solubility Tests

In the previous experiment, you investigated what negative ions form insoluble compounds with a particular positive ion. Chemists have built up charts of just such data. They use the charts in analyzing an ionic substance to see which ions are present. For example, silver chloride is insoluble in water, whereas potassium chloride and sodium nitrate are soluble. If you suspect that a solution contains either silver nitrate or potassium nitrate, then you add some sodium chloride solution to the solution.

silver nitrate + sodium chloride → silver chloride + sodium nitrate

potassium nitrate + sodium chloride →
potassium chloride + sodium nitrate

If a precipitate forms, the precipitate must be silver chloride, and the unknown substance must be silver nitrate. If a precipitate does not form, then the unknown substance is potassium nitrate.

Here are some solubility rules:
- All nitrates are soluble.
- All compounds of sodium, potassium, and ammonium are soluble.
- All chlorides are soluble except those of silver, mercury(I), and lead(II).
- All sulfates are soluble except those of silver, mercury(I), lead(II), calcium, and barium.
- All hydroxides are insoluble except those of sodium, potassium, and ammonium.

What is the precipitate when a solution of lead(II) nitrate is mixed with a solution of sodium chloride?

lead(II) nitrate + sodium chloride →
lead(II) chloride + sodium nitrate

According to the above rules, sodium nitrate is soluble, and lead(II) chloride is insoluble. The precipitate must therefore be lead(II) chloride.

Questions

1. Apply the above rules to the following double displacement reactions. Does a precipitate form in each of the following reactions? If so, what is the precipitate?
   (a) sodium chloride and mercury(I) nitrate
   (b) barium chloride and sodium sulfate
   (c) copper(II) nitrate and sodium hydroxide
   (d) calcium nitrate and ammonium hydroxide
   (e) sodium phosphate and barium nitrate

2. What further information would you need in order to answer question 1(e)?

11.4 Identifying an Unknown Ionic Substance

In this experiment, you are asked to compare the chemical behaviour of an unknown material with that of known materials. This is very similar to what you did in the previous investigation in your role as a chemical detective.

All the unknown materials in this investigation are water soluble ionic substances. When ionic substances dissolve in water, the positive and negative ions separate.

$$NaCl_{(aq)} \rightarrow Na^{1+}_{(aq)} + Cl^{1-}_{(aq)}$$

$$(NH_4)_2SO_{4(aq)} \rightarrow 2NH_4^{1+}_{(aq)} + SO_4^{2-}_{(aq)}$$

Analyzing for ionic substances is relatively easy. We test to see which positive ion and which negative ion are present in solution. We do not have to test for every single ionic substance known.

Materials

safety goggles
unknown sample
clean spatula
a set of small test tubes
distilled water in a squirt bottle
red litmus paper
lead acetate paper
cobalt blue glass
fine copper or nichrome wire
chlorine water (to be kept in the fume hood)
solid iron(II) sulfate
1, 1, 2-trichloro-1, 2, 2-trifluoroethane, TCTFE
concentrated sulfuric acid (to be handled by the teacher only)

dropper bottles containing
5 mol/L hydrochloric acid
5 mol/L nitric acid
5 mol/L ammonium hydroxide solution
5 mol/L ammonium chloride solution
5 mol/L sodium hydroxide solution
2 mol/L ammonium carbonate solution
0.5 mol/L barium chloride solution
3 mol/L ammonium sulfide solution (to be kept in the fume hood)
0.5 mol/L potassium chromate solution
0.05 mol/L silver nitrate solution

The symbol (aq) after a formula means that the substance is dissolved in water.

The first part of an ionic compound is always the positive ion. The second part is always the negative ion. The size of the charge on an ion is simply the valence value of that ion.

Use distilled water throughout this experiment. Before using a test tube, rinse it with distilled water. Dissolve all samples in distilled water. Regular tap water contains dissolved substances that can interfere with the analysis.

Method

The procedure is in two parts. The first part (the P tests) is to identify the positive ion present in the unknown. The second part (the N tests) is to identify the negative ion.

Your unknown contains one of the following positive ions:

Ag^{1+}, Pb^{2+}, Cu^{2+}, Sn^{2+}, Cd^{2+}, Sn^{4+}, Fe^{3+}, Al^{3+}, Zn^{2+}, Ni^{2+}, Mn^{2+}, Ca^{2+}, Ba^{2+}, Mg^{2+}, NH_4^{1+}, Na^{1+}, K^{1+}

and one of the following negative ions:

Cl^{1-}, Br^{1-}, I^{1-}, S^{2-}, CO_3^{2-}, SO_4^{2-}, PO_4^{3-}, NO_3^{1-}

Theoretically, 136 unknown substances are possible but you will not have to carry out more than 15 simple tests to determine the ions present in your sample.

I. *Tests for Positive Ions* (P Tests)
Carry out the following tests in the sequence given until you identify the positive ion. Stop at that stage and proceed immediately to the first negative ion test.

P1 Test for Ag^{1+} and Pb^{2+}

Place a *small quantity* of the unknown sample in a clean, dry test tube (Figure 3). Dissolve the sample in 1 mL of distilled water (Figure 4). Add 1 mL of hydrochloric acid. A white precipitate indicates that the positive ion could be Ag^{1+} or Pb^{2+}. To tell which of these two positive ions it is, go to P2. If a precipitate does not form, Ag^{1+} and Pb^{2+} are not present. Keep the solution and proceed to P3.

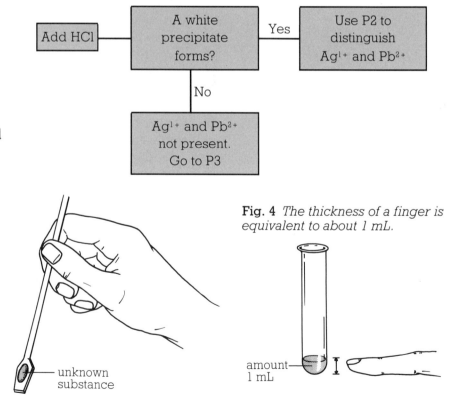

Fig. 4 *The thickness of a finger is equivalent to about 1 mL.*

amount 1 mL

Fig. 3 *Never use large quantities of the unknown, otherwise it will be difficult to tell the difference between a precipitate and undissolved unknown material.*

unknown substance

P2 Distinguishing Ag^{1+} and Pb^{2+}

To the precipitate from P1, add 5 mL of ammonium hydroxide, a few drops at a time, and mix well after each addition.

   If the precipitate begins to dissolve, the positive ion is Ag^{1+}. Now go to N1.

   If the precipitate does not dissolve, the positive ion is Pb^{2+}. Now go to N1.

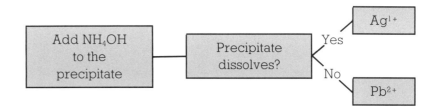

P3 Test for Cu^{2+}, Sn^{2+}, Cd^{2+}, and Sn^{4+}

To the solution from P1, add 5 to 10 drops of ammonium sulfide *in the fume hood* and mix well. If a thick brown/black or yellow precipitate does not form, Cu^{2+}, Sn^{2+}, Cd^{2+}, and Sn^{4+} are not present. Proceed to P6.

   A thick dark brown or black precipitate indicates Cu^{2+} or Sn^{2+}. Use P4 to tell these two ions apart.

   A yellow precipitate indicates Cd^{2+} or Sn^{4+}. Use P5 to tell these two ions apart.

   Discard the contents of the test tube in the fume hood whatever the outcome of P3.

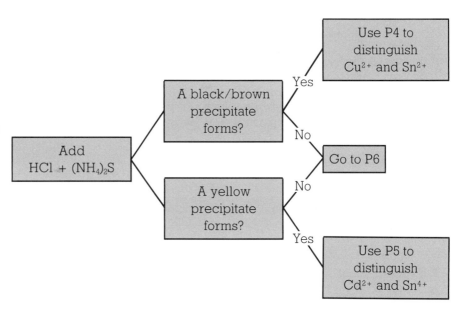

P4 Distinguishing Cu^{2+} and Sn^{2+}

Dissolve a small quantity of the unknown sample in 1 mL of distilled water. Add 3 mL of sodium hydroxide, a few drops at a time, mixing well after each addition. A permanent precipitate indicates Cu^{2+}. Now go to N1.

   If a precipitate forms and then begins to redissolve, the positive ion is Sn^{2+}. Now go to N1.

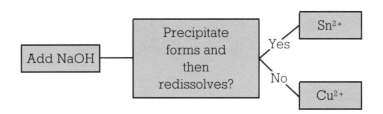

P5 Distinguishing Cd²⁺ and Sn⁴⁺

Dissolve a small quantity of the unknown sample in 1 mL of distilled water. Add 3 mL of sodium hydroxide, a few drops at a time, mixing well after each addition. A permanent precipitate indicates Cd^{2+}. Now go to N1.

    If a precipitate forms and then begins to redissolve, the positive ion is Sn^{4+}. Now go to N1.

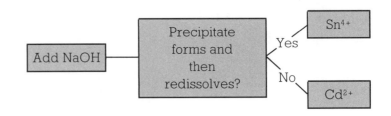

P6 Test for Fe³⁺ and Al³⁺

Dissolve a small quantity of the unknown sample in 1 mL of distilled water. Add 1 mL of ammonium chloride and 5 to 10 drops of ammonium hydroxide. Mix well. If a precipitate does not form, Fe^{3+} and Al^{3+} are not present. Keep the solution for P7.

    A rust-brown precipitate indicates Fe^{3+}. Now go to N1.

    A very fine white precipitate indicates Al^{3+}. Now go to N1.

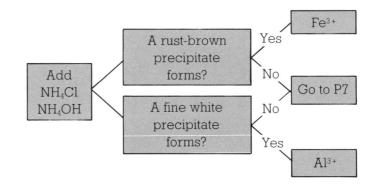

P7 Test for Zn²⁺, Ni²⁺, and Mn²⁺

To the solution from P6, add 5 to 10 drops of ammonium sulfide *in the fume hood* and mix well. If no precipitate forms, Zn^{2+}, Ni^{2+}, and Mn^{2+} are not present. Proceed to P8.

    A white precipitate indicates Zn^{2+}. Now go to N1.

    A black precipitate indicates Ni^{2+}. Now go to N1.

    A beige precipitate indicates Mn^{2+}. Now go to N1.

    Discard the contents of the test tube in the fume hood whatever the outcome of P7.

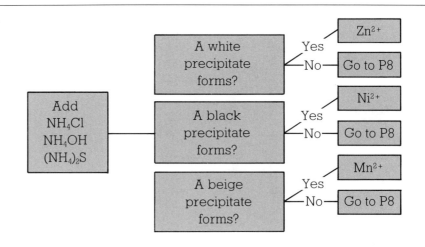

256

P8 Test for Ca²⁺ and Ba²⁺

Dissolve a small quantity of the unknown sample in 1 mL of distilled water. Add 1 mL of ammonium chloride, 1 mL of ammonium hydroxide, and 5 to 10 drops of ammonium carbonate. Mix well. If no precipitate forms, Ca^{2+} and Ba^{2+} are not present. Discard the contents of the test tube and proceed to P10.

A white precipitate indicates Ca^{2+} or Ba^{2+}. Use P9 to tell these two ions apart.

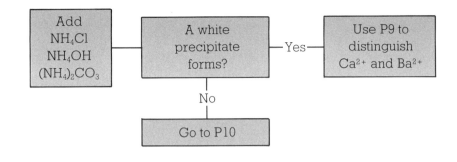

P9 Distinguishing Ca²⁺ and Ba²⁺

Dissolve a small quantity of the unknown sample in 1 mL of distilled water. Add 10 drops of potassium chromate. Mix well.

A yellow solution indicates Ca^{2+}. Now go to N1.

A yellow precipitate indicates Ba^{2+}. Now go to N1.

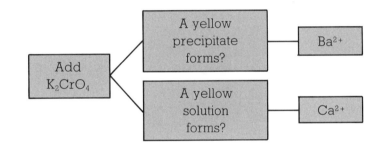

P10 Test for Mg²⁺

Dissolve a small quantity of the unknown sample in 1 mL of distilled water. Add 10 drops of sodium hydroxide. If no precipitate forms, Mg^{2+} is not present. Discard the contents of the test tube and proceed to P11.

A white precipitate indicates Mg^{2+}. Now go to N1.

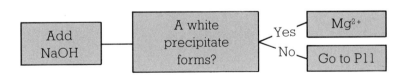

257

P11 Test for NH_4^{1+}

Place sufficient solid unknown sample in a clean, dry test tube to just cover the bottom of the test tube. Add 1 mL of sodium hydroxide and mix well. *Warm gently* over a low Bunsen flame. Carefully check whether a gas that smells like ammonia is given off and place a piece of moist red litmus paper about 0.5 cm above the mouth of the test tube (Figure 5). If there is no odour of ammonia and the moist litmus is not changed, NH_4^{1+} is not present. Go to P12.

If you detect the odour of ammonia and the moist litmus turns blue, then NH_4^{1+} is present. Now go to N1.

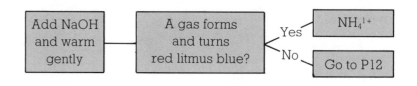

Fig. 5

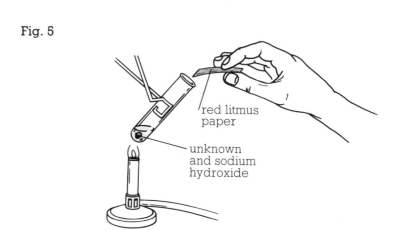

red litmus
paper

unknown
and sodium
hydroxide

P12 Distinguishing Na^{1+} and K^{1+}

Make a small loop at one end of a piece of thin copper or nichrome wire. Heat the wire strongly in a Bunsen flame until only a faint red-yellow flame is observed. Wet the loop with some distilled water and pick up some of the solid unknown sample with the loop. Reheat the loop with the sample in the Bunsen flame (Figure 6). Note the colour of the flame when observed directly and also through cobalt blue glass.

A bright yellow flame which is invisible through the cobalt blue glass indicates Na^{1+}.

A pale purple flame which is still visible through the cobalt blue glass indicates K^{1+}.

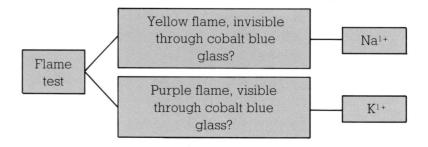

Fig. 6 *The flame test to distinguish N^{1+} and K^{1+}.*

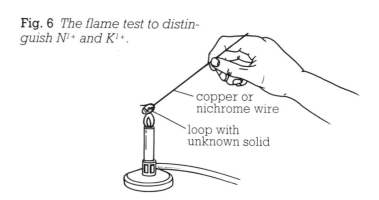

copper or
nichrome wire

loop with
unknown solid

N1 Test for Cl^{1-}, Br^{1-}, and I^{1-}

Dissolve a small quantity of the unknown sample in 1 mL of distilled water. Add 1 mL of nitric acid and 5 to 10 drops of silver nitrate. Mix well. If no precipitate forms, Cl^{1-}, Br^{1-}, and I^{1-} are not present. Discard the contents of the test tube and proceed to N3.

A thick, white or yellow precipitate indicates the presence of Cl^{1-}, Br^{1-}, or I^{1-}.

Use N2 to distinguish between these three ions.

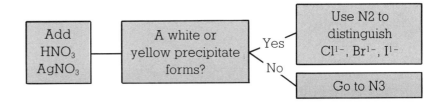

N2 Distinguishing Cl^{1-}, Br^{1-}, and I^{1-}

Dissolve a small quantity of the unknown sample in 1 mL of distilled water. *In the fume hood*, carefully add about 1 mL of TCTFE and 1 mL of chlorine water. Mix well and note the colour of the bottom layer in the test tube.

A colourless bottom layer indicates Cl^{1-}. Now write up your report.

A brown or yellow bottom layer indicates Br^{1-}. Now write up your report.

A pink or purple bottom layer indicates I^{1-}. Now write up your report.

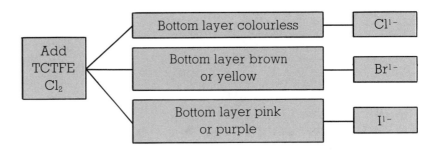

N3 Test for S^{2-}

This test should be carried out *in the fume hood.* Dissolve some of the unknown sample in 1 mL of hydrochloric acid. Warm gently with a Bunsen burner. Place a piece of moist lead acetate paper over the mouth of the test tube. If there is no change in the lead acetate paper, S^{2-} is not present. Proceed to N4.

If the lead acetate paper turns black, the negative ion is S^{2-}. Now write up your report.

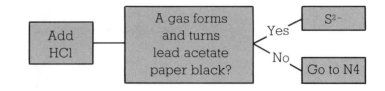

A highly toxic gas, hydrogen sulfide, is given off. It has the smell of rotten egg.

N4 Test for CO_3^{2-}

Place a small quantity of the solid unknown sample in a dry test tube. Slowly add about 1 mL of hydrochloric acid. If no fizzing occurs, CO_3^{2-} is not present. Go to N5.

If fizzing occurs and the solid dissolves, then CO_3^{2-} is present. Now write up your report.

N5 If your *positive* ion is Ag^{1+} or Pb^{2+}, go straight to N8. If it is any other positive ion, go to N6.

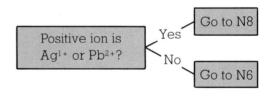

N6 Test for SO_4^{2-}

Dissolve a small quantity of the unknown sample in 1 mL of distilled water. Add 1 mL of hydrochloric acid and 5 to 10 drops of barium chloride. Mix well. If there is no precipitate, SO_4^{2-} is not present. Proceed to N7.

A white precipitate indicates SO_4^{2-}. Now write up your report.

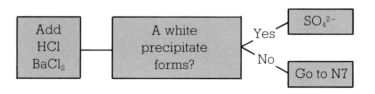

N7 Test for PO₄³⁻

Dissolve a small quantity of the unknown sample in 1 mL of distilled water. Add 1 mL of barium chloride and mix well. If no precipitate forms, PO_4^{3-} is not present. Proceed to N8. A white precipitate indicates PO_4^{3-}. Now write up your report.

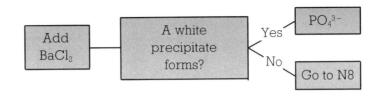

N8 Test for NO₃¹⁻

Place a small amount of the solid unknown sample in a test tube and add an equal amount of solid iron (II) sulfate. Dissolve both solids in about 3 mL of distilled water. Take the test tube to the teacher who will add 1 mL of concentrated sulfuric acid.

The concentrated sulfuric acid is added slowly from an eye dropper so that it forms a layer beneath the water layer. If a brown ring forms at the acid/water junction, then NO_3^{1-} is present (Figure 7). Now write up your report.

Both solids must be completely dissolved before adding concentrated sulfuric acid.

The contents of the test tube should be discarded in the sink with lots of running water. Do not shake before discarding. It is preferable if the teacher discards the contents.

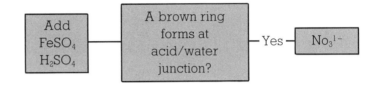

Fig. 7 *The brown-ring test to show the presence of NO_3^{1-}.*

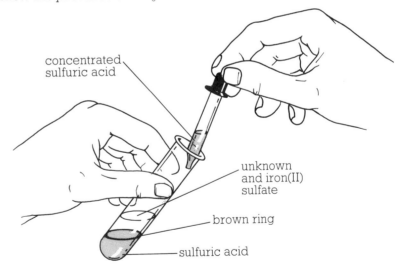

concentrated sulfuric acid

unknown and iron(II) sulfate

brown ring

sulfuric acid

Follow-up

Hand in a report of your findings. On the following page is an example of a report.

STUDENT NAME _____

1. Physical description of the unknown material

The unknown material was a white crystalline solid.
It had no appreciable odour.
It dissolved readily in water to form a colourless solution.

2. Test results to find the positive ion

Reagent(s) used	Result	Conclusion
HCl	No precipitate formed	Not Ag^{1+}, Pb^{2+}
HCl + $(NH_4)_2S$	No precipitate formed	Not Cu^{2+}, Cd^{2+}, Sn^{2+}, Sn^{4+}
NH_4Cl + NH_3	No precipitate formed	Not Fe^{3+}, Al^{3+}
NH_4Cl + NH_3 + $(NH_4)_2S$	No precipitate formed	Not Zn^{2+}, Ni^{2+}, Mn^{2+}
NH_4Cl + NH_3 + $(NH_4)_2CO_3$	No precipitate formed	Not Ca^{2+}, Ba^{2+}
NaOH	No precipitate formed	Not Mg^{2+}
NaOH + heat	No odour and litmus not changed	Not NH_4^{1+}
Flame test	Yellow flame present but not visible through cobalt blue glass	Na^{1+} present

3. Test results to find the negative ion

Reagent(s) used	Result	Conclusion
NHO_3 + $AgNO_3$	Yellow or white precipitate formed	Cl^{1-}, Br^{1-}, or I^{1-} present
TCTFE + Cl_2	Bottom layer is pink	I^{1-} present

4. Overall conclusion

Positive Ion is Na^{1+}. Negative Ion is I^{1-}.
The unknown substance is **sodium iodide** and its formula is **NaI**.

11.5 Additives in Wheat Flour

Manufacturers add chemicals to their products for a variety of reasons. In most cases, it is to improve the performance of the product, prolong its shelf life, improve its appearance, or restore nutrients lost in the manufacturing process. You will analyze some products for some common additives. All the investigations use specific tests developed for particular additives.

Cereals such as wheat are an important food source. This is partly due to the fact that, at the proper temperature and humidity, these grains can be stored for long periods without any significant loss of quality.

Wheat contains two special proteins, **gliadin** and **glutenin**. Stirring these proteins with water gives a tough, elastic, and complex mixture called **gluten**. During baking, the gluten traps the carbon dioxide given off by the fermentation of yeast or the decomposition of sodium hydrogen carbonate. This allows the dough to rise.

Fig. 8 *Additives in flour help to make these delicious products.*

To tell the two types of flour apart, squeeze and then release a fistful of the flour. Soft flour will hold it shape, but hard flour will not.

There is no reliable scientific way to test the quality of flour. A standard bread baking procedure is still commonly used. The volume, colour, appearance, and texture of the final loaf of bread is usually the only indication of the quality of the flour.

The amounts of vitamins and minerals (for example, iron) added to flour are controlled by government.

There are two types of wheat flour: hard and soft. Hard wheat flour gives a high strength gluten and is used in baking bread. Soft wheat flour gives a low strength gluten and is usually used in cake and pastry making. All purpose flour is a mixture of the two types of flour.

Chemicals are added to hard wheat flour to help the formation of gluten and speed up the bread baking process. The following is a list of additives found in flour:

- alpha-amylase: to convert damaged starch granules in the wheat into simpler sugars (which will be used in the fermentation process)
- potassium bromate: to help in the formation of gluten
- cysteine: to help in the formation of gluten
- ascorbic acid (vitamin C): to help in the formation of gluten, and as a nutrient
- minerals and vitamins: to replace the minerals and vitamins lost during the milling process; iron is a common additive in flour
- chlorine: to bleach soft flour and to improve baking quality

You will now test different kinds of flour for the presence of some of the above additives.

Materials

safety goggles
different brands and types of flour
smooth piece of plastic with a straight edge
plastic teaspoon
fine mesh sieve (number 48 or 50)
0.05 g/L 2, 6-dichlorophenolindophenol dye solution
1 mol/L potassium thiocyanate solution
2 mol/L hydrochloric acid
3% (volume/volume) hydrogen peroxide solution
1 mol/L potassium iodide solution
2 mol/L lactic acid solution
0.08 mol/L sodium thiosulfate solution

Method

1. Prepare the flour samples for each test as follows:
   (a) If whole-wheat flour is used, first pass it through a fine mesh sieve to remove the bran.
   (b) Place a double layer of paper towel on the desk, large enough to hold all the flour samples.

(c) Pour about three tablespoons of each flour sample on the paper towel in the form of a small mound. The mounds should be about 10 cm apart.

(d) Label each brand of flour used.

(e) Use the piece of plastic and plastic spoon to form a rectangular cube of each mound of flour. The cube should be large enough for you to make three small indents on the top with the plastic spoon (Figure 9).

Fig. 9

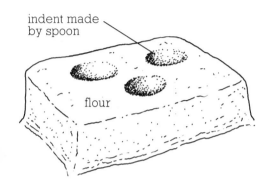

indent made by spoon

flour

2. *Test for iron*

To the first indent, add 3 or 4 drops of hydrogen peroxide solution (a foam will form) followed by 3 or 4 drops of hydrochloric acid, and finally 3 or 4 drops of potassium thiocyanate solution. Let the mixture stand for about 20 min. The formation of deep red coloured spots indicates that iron compounds have been added to the flour.

3. *Test for ascorbic acid*

To the second indent, add 3 or 4 drops of the 2, 6-dichloro-phenolindophenol dye solution and let stand for 8 to 10 min. The development of white spots in a dark blue background indicates the presence of ascorbic acid.

4. *Test for bromate*

To the third indent, add, in turn, 5 drops of sodium thiosulfate solution, 5 drops of lactic acid solution, and 5 drops of potassium iodide solution. Let the mixture stand for about 2 min. If black spots form, then bromate has been added to the flour.

Follow-up

1. Summarize your results for all the brands of flour tested in a suitable chart.

2. Which brands and types of flour contain
   (a) iron, (b) bromate, (c) ascorbic acid?

3. Why is each of the additives in question 2 present in flour?

4. Which brands and types of flour are used to make
   (a) bread, (b) cakes and pastries?

5. Explain your answers to question 4.

11.6 Nitrilotriacetic Acid in Detergents

Personal cleanliness is very important in our society. That is probably why we have so many different types of detergents and soaps. Each product contains additives to:

- improve the whiteness of the clothing
- maintain the correct acidity level of the detergent
- react with and prevent the minerals in the water from interfering in the cleaning process
- prevent corrosion of aluminum and porcelain surfaces
- act as perfumes and colouring agents to attract the consumer and mask any unpleasant odour

Phosphates were previously added to detergents to prevent scum formation. However, when the waste water carries phosphates into rivers and lakes, the population of algae increases rapidly. This may result in the depletion of dissolved oxygen, and the death of all life in the water. To control this water pollution, governments have restricted the amount of phosphates in detergents.

When soap or additive-free detergent is used in regular tap water, a scum forms. This scum results from reactions between the soap or detergent and the minerals dissolved in the water. If nothing is done to remove the scum, it can settle on clothing and cause a dull grey colour. Nitrilotriacetic acid, NTA, is added to detergents to prevent scum formation. The NTA is usually added as the sodium salt of the acid.

Fig. 10 *Detergents contain additives that prevent scum formation.*

Materials

safety goggles
50-mL beaker
a white spot plate or a glass or plastic spot plate on a white
    background
funnel and filter paper
laundry detergent samples
alcohol (95% ethanol)
8 mol/L ammonium hydroxide solution
30% hydrogen peroxide solution
0.02 mol/L cobalt(II) sulfate solution
2.5 mol/L sodium hydroxide solution
pH paper
spatula

Method

1. In a 50-mL beaker, mix a small amount of the detergent with a
   little distilled water to make a slurry. Test the pH of the slurry
   using pH paper. If the pH of the slurry is about 12, proceed to
   step 2.
   If the pH of the slurry is 10 or less, add two scoops of the
   detergent to the beaker with sufficient distilled water to form a
   slurry. Add sodium hydroxide solution, drop by drop with
   stirring, until the pH of the mixture is about 12.

2. Evaporate the mixture in the beaker to dryness (Figure 11a).
   Add alcohol to just cover the dry detergent in the beaker (Figure
   11b). Stir well and pass the mixture through a piece of filter
   paper in a funnel (Figure 11c). Keep the material *in the filter
   paper* for the next step.

Oxydol should not be used as
it contains perborate as the
scum preventing agent. The
perborate interferes with the
test for NTA.

Fig. 11

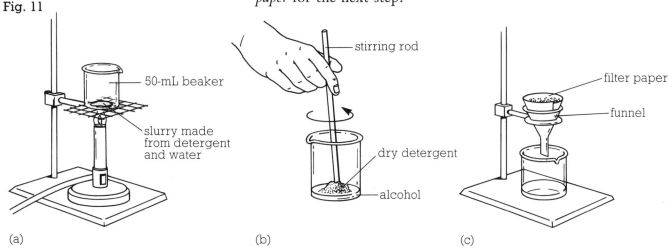

(a)   (b)   (c)

Handle ammonium hydroxide and hydrogen peroxide solutions with great care. Do not get the chemicals on your skin or clothing.

3. Mix the sample from the filter paper with 15 to 20 mL of distilled water and filter through a fresh piece of filter paper.

4. Place 6 to 8 drops of the *filtrate* from step 3 into a well of the spot plate. Add 3 drops of ammonium hydroxide solution followed by 3 drops of cobalt(II) sulfate solution.

5. Mix the solution in the well with a glass rod. Add one drop of hydrogen peroxide solution and mix again.

6. The formation of a purple colour indicates the presence of nitrilotriacetic acid in the detergent.

Investigation

11.7 Vitamin C and Reducing Sugars in Consumer Products

Many of the foods we consume today are processed. During processing, many of the nutrients in the foods are destroyed. Some manufacturers then add natural or artificial nutrients. In most cases these benefit the consumer. Other additives, however, may not be beneficial.

Many of us have grown to like our foods sweetened (Figure 12). There are many different types of sugars in the foods we eat. Sucrose from sugar cane or sugar beet is the most common sweetener in pop, artificial fruit drinks, and many processed foods.

It is wise to limit your intake of sugar because it causes tooth decay, and may be related to other diseases, such as diabetes, indigestion, and heart disease.

Fig. 12 *Sugarbeets harvested in Canada.*

Other sugars such as glucose, fructose, maltose, and lactose are found naturally in fruits, vegetables, and milk. Most sugars are referred to as reducing sugars because of the type of reactions they undergo. Sucrose is not a reducing sugar but can be broken down into reducing sugars by reacting it with a dilute acid.

Vitamin C or ascorbic acid is not produced in the human body. Our daily requirements must be obtained from the food we eat. Fresh fruit and vegetables are good sources of vitamin C (Figure 13). At one time, ships carried lemons or limes to prevent the sailors from coming down with scurvy, a disease caused by a lack of vitamin C. Very few people in developed countries now suffer from scurvy as we know that vitamin C intake prevents this disease. Some people today also believe that vitamin C helps fend off the common cold.

Materials

saftey goggles
potassium iodide/iodine solution (0.6 g iodine and 0.6 g potassium iodide in a 10% ethano/water mixture)
soluble starch solution (1 g in 100 mL of water)
canned fruit juices (pale-coloured)
Benedict's solution
2 mol/L sulfuric acid
2 mol/L sodium hydroxide solution
funnel and filter paper
pH paper
Bunsen burner
test tubes

Method

1. Filter the fruit juice to obtain a solution reasonably free of any pulp.

2. *Test for vitamin C*
   (a) Pour about 10 mL of the fruit juice solution into a test tube.
   (b) Add about 5 drops of the soluble starch solution to about 5 mL of potassium iodide/iodine solution. This should produce a deep blue-black colour.
   (c) Add a few drops of the blue-black liquid to the fruit juice solution. The presence of vitamin C in the fruit juice will cause the blue-black colour to disappear.

269

3. *Test for reducing sugars*
   (a) Add about 2 mL of the sulfuric acid to about 10 mL of the fruit juice solution. Boil for about 5 min. Allow the mixture to cool. Check the pH of the solution using pH paper. If the pH is below 5, add sodium hydroxide solution drop by drop with thorough mixing until the pH is approximately 7.
   (b) Add about 5 mL of the fruit juice to 5 mL of Benedict's solution in a test tube.
   (c) Put the test tube in a beaker of water heated by a Bunsen burner.
   (d) Boil the mixture for about 2 min in the water bath.
   (e) Allow the mixture to cool slowly. If an orange-red colour begins to form, the test solution contains reducing sugars.

ARTIFICIAL SWEETENERS

Today scientists have a good idea how molecules cause sweetness. The surface of the tongue consists of taste buds. These taste buds contain proteins that can bond with molecules placed in the mouth. Different tastes arise when the molecules in the mouth activate a different grouping of proteins.

Although sugar cane was known in India over 5000 years ago, sugar or sucrose (which is refined from sugar cane or sugar beet) only became popular in Europe in about 1800. The ancient Greeks and Romans were the first people to produce an artificial sweetener. They found that when grape juice was heated in a lead pot, a very sweet tasting syrup was produced. Today we know that this syrup consisted mostly of a toxic substance named lead(II) acetate or "sugar of lead."

There are now about 50 artificial sweeteners. The common ones are listed below:

Taste is still the only way to estimate the degree of sweetness of a sweetener. If 0.5 g of a sweetener produces the same sweetness as 1 g of sucrose, then the sweetener is considered to be twice as sweet as sucrose.

Artificial sweetener	Relative sweetness
cyclamate	25
saccharine	300
aspartame	200
acesulfame	200
thaumatin	3000

1. Did all the juices tested contain vitamin C?

2. Did all the juices tested contain reducing sugars?

3. Artificial fruit drinks are often sweetened. Would such a drink test positive for reducing sugars? Explain your answer.

4. Based on the colour, what ion do you think is present in Benedict's solution? What causes the orange-red colour when Benedict's solution reacts with a reducing sugar?

Saccharin was first prepared in 1879 and was immediately used as a substitute sweetener for diabetics. It was never widely used until the 1950s when diet soft drink became popular.

Cyclamate and acesulfame were both discovered accidentally by people who had forgotten about safety rules in the laboratory! A researcher placed a cigarette on the laboratory counter and the cigarette picked up a cyclamate crystal. The researcher later noticed that the cigarette tasted sweet. With acesulfame, a researcher licked his fingers to pick up a piece of filter paper.

Aspartame, discovered in 1965, is the most widely used artificial sweetener today. It cannot be used for baking as the aspartame molecule decomposes on heating and loses its sweetness.

Thaumatin is too sweet tasting for use in foods or beverages, but has been used in chewing gums, unpleasant tasting medicines, and some pet foods.

How safe are these artificial sweeteners? In 1957 a British research group implanted cyclamate pellets directly into the bladders of some mice. The mice later developed cancer. Tests in the U.S.A. in 1970 showed that high doses of cyclamate were likely to cause bladder cancer in rats. Similar tests with saccharine in Canada in 1977 produced similar results. Because of this, cyclamate and saccharine were banned in Canada. Not everyone, however, was convinced by the results of these tests. The dose of saccharin given to rats would be equivalent to a human drinking 800 cans of artificially sweetened soft drink each day. A study of the eating habits of a group of people with bladder cancer showed no link to the use of saccharine or cyclamate. Saccharine is available in most countries today, but cyclamate remains banned in Britain and the U.S.A.

11.8 Sulfur Compounds in Foods

To prevent discolouration and bacterial attack, manufacturers use certain sulfur compounds in foods such as sauerkraut, frozen apples, jams, bottled olives, pop, cider, honey, wine, molasses, and dried fruits.

Fig. 13 *Sulfur compounds are added to foods in different ways. Drying fruits are exposed to fumes of burning sulfur or vapours of liquid sulfur dioxide. Vegetables are sprayed with solutions of the sulfur compounds.*

Compound or ion	Formula
sulfur dioxide	SO_2
sodium metabisulfite	$Na_2S_2O_5$
sodium bisulfite	$NaHSO_3$
sulfites	SO_3^{2-}

In the human body, these sulfur compounds and ions are changed to harmless sulfates and excreted in urine. Some people, however, suffer from an allergic reaction to these sulfur compounds. Symptoms vary, but headaches and breathing difficulties are common. It is important that these people know which foods contain sulfur compounds. The presence of these sulfur compounds is listed on food labels but not always on menus or wine labels.

The following experiment is a simple test for sulfur compounds.

Materials

safety goggles
petri dishes (one for each sample, plus one for the water-dye colour control)
glass rod
balance (rough)
sauerkraut with bisulfite
sauerkraut without bisulfite
dried fruits
Realemon® or any other product containing bisulfite
malachite green solution in dropper bottles (1% mass/mass)
distilled water
knife for chopping some of the solid samples

Method

1. Spread each sample in a labelled petri dish. If the sample is a solid, it should be finely chopped.

2. Add 20 mL of distilled water and stir with a glass rod.

3. Add one drop of malachite green solution to each petri dish. Stir to mix uniformly. Be sure to clean the rod between stirring each sample. If the green dye becomes colourless, then sulfites are present. You should be able to observe changes after about 15 min in some products, but Realemon® will take longer.

Follow-up

1. List the brand names of at least three store products that contain a bisulfite or a metabisulfite.

2. Give two reasons why sulfur dioxide, sulfites, and metabisulfites are used in foods.

3. What protection should the law give to a consumer who is allergic to sulfites?

4. Discuss the advantages and disadvantages of using sulfur dioxide, sulfites, and metabisulfites in foods. Should they be used or not?

- Qualitative analysis is used to find what chemicals are present in a sample.
- Quantitative analysis is used to find how much of a chemical is present in a sample.
- In many cases, specific tests are developed to detect the presence of a specific chemical in a sample.
- Many qualitative tests used today can detect a substance even if present in extremely small quantities.

- Solubility rules of ionic materials can be used to identify the presence of a particular ion in solution
- Chemical additives are used to improve the performance or appearance of a product, prolong its shelf life, or restore nutrients lost during manufacture.
- Large quantities of phosphates are no longer used in detergents.
- Some people are allergic to sulfur compounds added to foods.

1. What precipitate forms when a solution of lead(II) nitrate is mixed with a solution of potassium carbonate?
2. What precipitate forms when a solution of calcium chloride is mixed with a solution of sodium sulfate?
3. What precipitate forms when a solution of ammonium nitrate is mixed with a solution of sodium chloride?
4. A solution of an ionic substance does not produce a precipitate when hydrochloric acid is added to the solution. When ammonium sulfide is added to the solution, a brown precipitate forms. Which two positive ions are possibly present in the original substance? How would you distinguish between these two ions?
5. Why is cobalt blue glass used in the flame test for sodium and potassium?
6. If tests for an unknown substance show the presence of Mg^{2+} and NO_3^{1-}, name and write the formula of the unknown substance.
7. What is the role of gluten in flour?
8. What chemicals are added to flour to assist in the formation of gluten?
9. Why is soft flour treated with chlorine?
10. What is the difference between soft flour and hard flour?
11. Why is calcium added to some foods as a nutrient?
12. Why is iodine added to table salt?
13. What are the vitamins and nutrients commonly added to milk and breakfast cereals?
14. What artificial sweeteners are commonly used in pop and other foods?
15. Fluoride is added to our drinking water to reduce tooth decay. Should governments decide when such additives should be used or should the public always be given the choice?
16. Vitamin and mineral supplements are available in drug stores and many health-food stores. Why are so many consumers purchasing these products? How can people ensure that they get these vitamins and minerals from the foods they eat?
17. Find a method to test for phosphates present in a detergent. Your teacher might allow you to check for phosphates in detergent samples.
18. Why have phosphates been restricted as an additive for detergents?
19. The element phosphorus is an important nutrient for plant growth. Find out how plants use phosphorus.
20. Should food additives be automatically banned simply because tests show that large doses cause cancer in test animals? Explain.
21. Why do researchers use very large doses when testing the effect of additives on test animals such as mice?
22. Should manufacturers be forced to indicate all possible side effects of the additives used in their products?
23. If you could synthesize an ''ideal'' artificial sweetener, what properties should it have?
24. Should restaurants be forced to show on their menus whether sulfites are used in various dishes?

12 CRAFTS AND CHEMISTRY

The simple joys of living are all related to chemistry.

CONTENTS

12.1 Welcome to the Home of a Fibre Artist!

You have come to interview Susan, the fibre artist, and have been invited to stay to lunch with her. Lunch is on the table in a beautiful room filled with items that please the eye. Take in the surroundings and discuss with your friends all you see! The artist, Susan, enters the room and greets you warmly.

You: What type of art are you involved in?

Susan: I am a weaver and I now use fibres to make felted works of art.

You: Do you spend a lot of time designing your work?

Susan: Yes. I spend a lot of time at the drawing board. The initial planning is very necessary, and then I have to do trials to see if my plans will actually work.

You: How long does it take you to complete a piece of work, and what things frustrate you?

Susan: It can often take several months between the start and finish of a piece, and this can be both satisfying and frustrating!

You: How do you get all the beautiful colours that go into your work?

Susan: Sometimes I can't buy the dyed fibres I want, and I have to do my own dyeing of yarns or other materials. Since my art pieces are for the wall, I have to be careful about the dyes I use. Natural dyes are wonderful and soft coloured, but often fade in sunlight.

You: Do you have to be knowledgeable about the chemistry behind the dyeing process?

Susan: It would be most helpful, but more important is the ability to work safely with chemicals. Many artists work with chemicals, and if they are not careful, their health could suffer.

You: Do you enjoy your work and do you make a lot of money?

Susan: There is a sense of excitement when I am working on a piece but it takes a lot of time and I don't make a lot of money.

You: What are your greatest satisfactions about your work?

Susan: I gain satisfaction from doing work that I feel is truly worth doing. I am not doing work which has been assigned by others because they think it's important. This means that I have to be a self-starter and have a lot of self-discipline. Deadlines must be met for commissioned work and shows.

You: Is is hard to put your work on view where others can criticize it?

Susan: The viewers are not always supportive! You have to accept that not everyone will like your work. Artists do not make it big overnight! It takes several years of submitting work to galleries and entry into art shows and sales to become known. I constantly have to ask myself the question whether I have what it takes to stay in this field.

You: What are some of the chores you have to worry about?

Susan: I have to deal with galleries and agents in a professional way, and make presentations for major commissions. I also have to deal with the public and suppliers, do costings, and keep accounts in order to make a living. In a nutshell, I have to be organized, economical, and dedicated to doing quality work.

You: What is good training to be an artist?

Susan: An art college diploma or a fine arts degree would be a good beginning. It also helps if you are qualified to teach. I have to teach to make enough money to support myself.

Design courses are a must! At high-school, courses in art, drafting, business, mathematics, chemistry, English, machine shop, wood shop, and even computer science would be helpful, depending on what type of craft/art interests you. The use of computers in planning, designing, and record keeping, is becoming more and more common.

You: I see that there are hand-made things on the table and all over the room. Did you make all the fibre work?

Susan: Most of the pieces. Some pieces use natural dyes and some use synthetic dyes. The pottery was made by a local potter who mixes his own glazes, the copper napkin ring was made by a student, and I have made the salad and the fluffy souffle dessert. Since you are interested in chemistry, I will give you details of some of the chemistry that's useful in my art and in my life.

You: Thank you. I know I'll enjoy trying out all the things you give me!

What follows are some of the interesting things about Susan's art and the chemistry of the art pieces in her home.

Questions

1. Write a report on how a knowledge of chemistry is useful in the art world.

2. Interview an artist or craftsperson and report your findings in the form of a newspaper article.

12.2 Natural Dyeing

Natural dyes from plants are as varied as the plants themselves (Figure 1). When these dyes are used on fibres, the colours are soft and appealing. A dye can be extracted by simmering a plant, or parts of a plant, in water. The dye dissolves in the water, and the coloured water is then drained from the solid parts of the plant. The coloured water is used as liquid dye to give beautiful colours to wool and silk.

The dye must be "fixed" to the fibre. This is done by the use of chemicals called mordants. Examples of common mordants are:

alum: aluminum potassium sulfate
tin: tin(II) chloride
chrome: potassium dichromate
iron: iron(II) sulfate
copper: copper(II) sulfate pentahydrate

Materials

safety goggles
rubber gloves
Ivory liquid detergent
brown onion skins or carrot tops (about 20 g)
ten 5-g skeins of white wool
mordants (see step 1 below for chemicals and quantities)
cream of tartar (about 1 mL)
hotplate
label tags
glass rods
test tubes
balance
five 600-mL beakers
3-L or 4-L beaker, or a 4-L enameled pot
1 mL plastic measuring spoons
optional: vinegar, ammonia solution

Method

1. Prepare each of the four mordants by mixing in a test tube *approximate* amounts of the chemicals listed below. The amount shown is for a 400-mL dye bath and 5 g of wool.

    alum: 1.25 mL aluminum potassium sulfate
            + 0.6 mL cream of tartar
    tin: 0.3 mL tin(II) chloride + 0.3 mL cream of tartar

Fig. 1 *Sources of natural dyes.*

Cream of tartar is potassium bitartrate, $KHC_4H_4O_6$. It is used in baking powder, for medicine, and as an acid and buffer in foods.

The enameled pot and plastic measuring spoons must never be used again for foods!

Wear rubber gloves throughout this activity. Do not get any mordants or dyes on your skin.

chrome: 0.3 mL potassium dichromate
+ 0.3 mL cream of tartar

iron: 0.3 mL iron(II) sulfate

copper: 0.6 mL copper(II) sulfate pentahydrate

The quantity of onion skins is not critical. The more skins, the darker the dye.

2. Prepare dye materials using onion skins and carrot tops.
   (a) *For onion skins:* Use only the outer brownish dry skins of onion. Soak about 25 g of skins overnight in about 2 L of distilled water. Bring to a simmer on a hotplate and keep simmering for 1 h.
   Pour off 400 mL of dye solution into each of five clean 600-mL beakers. To each beaker add one of the above mordants. Label each beaker with the name of the mordant used.
   (b) *For carrot tops:* Use only the green tops of carrots. Pour 400 mL of water into each of five clean 600-mL beakers. To each beaker add each of the above mordants. Then add four carrot tops to each beaker.

3. Measure ten 5-g skeins of wool. Wash them in warm water with Ivory liquid detergent. Rinse the wool in warm water. Allow the wool to soak in warm water until needed.

4. Add one wet wool sample to each beaker of dye bath. Heat to simmering on a hotplate and keep simmering for 30 min to 1 h. Remove the wool with a glass rod, rinse in warm water, and allow to dry. Using tags, label each skein showing the dye and mordant used.

5. Make a visual display showing the different colours obtained with the different mordants.

6. If you have time, check whether the colour of your dyed wools can be altered by dipping the dyed yarn in (a) dilute vinegar solution, (b) dilute ammonia solution. Try various dilutions of vinegar or ammonia. Also test how well these dyed yarns stand up to the effect of sunlight.

Follow-up

1. Why was the wool washed with detergent before dyeing?

2. Did you notice any colour effects caused by the different mordants?

3. Did you notice any differences in the feel of the dyed yarns with the different mordants? How would these differences influence the choice of mordants when dyeing wool to be used for making clothing?

BLUE JEANS AND NATURAL DYEING

Indigo is a blue dye that has been used with cotton for a long time. A colourless form of the dye is soluble in water. The cotton cloth is dipped into the colourless solution and then exposed to the oxygen of the air. The cloth turns blue! Repeated dippings and exposure to air cause the colour to darken. This reaction is still used today, particularly for dyeing blue jeans (Figure 2).

Indigo is available in the natural form (that is, extracted from the indigo plant), or the synthetic form as a paste or powder. The synthetic form is much cheaper.

Natural indigo is still used in dyeing the wonderful traditional cotton cloths in Nigeria, on many Pacific islands, and in Japan.

Fig. 2 *Since indigo dyes only the surface of fibres, it rubs off with wear. This accounts for the typical loss of colour on the seats, knees, and thighs of most jeans.*

12.3 Synthetic Dyeing

If you wash a bunch of clothes together, some of them may change colour. This is because some clothes contain dyes that are quick to dissolve or run; the dyes then get into the wash water and attach themselves to any fabric that reacts with them.

Natural dyes gives beautiful results, but they may fade when exposed to sunlight. Their colours are not always predictable because the strength of the dye depends on the natural source, which can vary with soil and weather conditions. Also, natural sources are not always available. Synthetic dyes were a great breakthrough and changed the economies of many parts of the world. Synthetic dyes, like synthetic drugs, depend on the oil industry to provide starting materials.

There are many different types of synthetic dyes. Each dye has to react with fibre molecules. Thus certain dye types react better with certain fibres. What works really well with wool and silk (protein fibres) may not work as well with cotton or linen (non-protein fibres).

Fig. 3 *Fabrics being dyed.*

You can make your own rainbow of dyed wool or silk yarns. Since silk is very expensive, you will use wool in this experiment. Working with just three primary dye colours, red, blue, and yellow, you can make hundreds of different colours (Figure 3).

Materials

safety goggles
rubber gloves
5-g skeins of white wool
dye powders in the three primary colours, red, blue, and yellow
dark storage bottles for stock dye solutions
syringes (one 5-mL syringe for measuring each stock dye solution, 10-mL and 20-mL syringes or graduated cylinders for other solutions)
0.7 mol/L sodium sulfate solution
5% (volume/volume) acetic acid
Ivory liquid detergent
100-mL beaker
four 250-mL beakers
hotplate
thermometer
2 glass rods
label tags
balance

Method

1. First make the stock dye solutions. Weigh 4 g of dye powder of one of the three colours. Put the powder in a 100-mL beaker. Add enough drops of distilled water to the dye and stir until you make a smooth dye paste. Add the paste to about 150 mL of distilled water in a 250-ml beaker. Heat the solution to about 95°C with stirring. Add distilled water to bring the total volume of the solution to 200 mL. Repeat for the dye powders of the other two colours. Cool the three stock dye solutions and store them in dark, labelled bottles.

2. Use syringes to mix different volumes of the stock dye solutions to produce any colour you like. The total volume must be 5 mL, which is the amount for 5 g of wool fibre. Do not use the "blue" syringe in the other dye solutions! A suggested combination is 2 mL of yellow, 2 mL of blue, and 1 mL of red dye.

3. Pour 150 mL of distilled water into a 250-mL beaker and heat to 50°C. This water will be used to keep the wool wet and at the same temperature as the dye baths.

Do not breathe in the dye powders as some of them are toxic. Avoid getting the powders on your skin or clothes as they do stain. Wear rubber gloves.

4. Weigh out 5-g skeins of white wool yarn. Use as many skeins as you wish to make colours. Wash the wool skeins in warm water with Ivory liquid detergent and rinse in warm water. Then place them in the beaker described in step 3.

5. For each colour, place 150 mL of distilled water, 5 mL of your chosen dye mixture, and 20 mL of sodium sulfate solution in a clean 250-mL beaker. Heat this dye bath on a hotplate to 50°C. Add a sample of wool from the beaker in step 4 to each dye bath. Stir and raise the temperature to 85°C.

6. After 15 min at 85°C, remove the wool briefly with a glass rod. Add 5 mL of acetic acid to the dye bath with stirring. Put the wool back into the dye bath. Wait 5 min and add a further 5 mL of acetic acid in the same way. Note what happens.

7. After a total time of about 30 min at 85°C, or when all the colour appears to have left the dye bath and has been taken up by the wool, remove the wool with a glass rod. Rinse the wool in warm water and squeeze the water out of the wool. Allow the skeins to air dry. Label each skein with a tag showing the dye mixtures used. Allow the dye baths to cool. Then pour them down the sink.

8. Mount the dyed skeins and give details of how you achieved the colours.

Follow-up

1. What two roles did the acetic acid play? (Hint: Check to see what effect pH has on wool in Chapter 9.)

2. What colours did you and your classmates obtain? Describe how they were made.

3. You may want to make up a wheel of primary and complementary colours using dye mixtures. Describe how you would go about doing this and carry out your ideas.

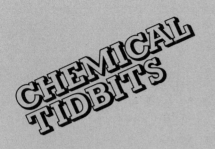

CHEMICAL TIDBITS

THE COLOUR OF BUTTER

It is stated on a butter wrapper that colour "may be added" or colour is one of the ingredients. Colour has been added to butter since the Middle Ages, especially in winter! The colour of butter is related to the grass the cow eats. If the cow is given fresh green grass (as in summer), the colour of butter is a darker yellow. If the cow is given grain or hay (as in winter), the colour of butter is pale yellow. The source of the colour added to butter has been carrot juice, marigold, and saffron. In recent times, oil-soluble synthetic dyes and annato, a natural dye extracted from a South American tree, have been used.

Investigation

12.4 Burn Tests for Types of Fibres

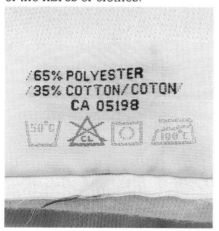

Fig. 4 *Label showing the content of the fibres of clothes.*

Most countries require that manufacturers show the content of the fibres used to make clothes. People who work with fibres need a way to find out what fibres they are working with. Burning the fibre is the traditional way of finding its content.

Materials

safety goggles
candle or Bunsen burner
tweezers
magnifying glass
microscope
different types of fibres: cotton, linen, silk, wool, polyester, nylon
unknown fibre samples

Method

1. Read through the entire method and draw up an observation chart.

2. Observe a known fibre sample under the microscope and draw what it looks like under high power.

3. Use the tweezers to pick up about 2 to 3 cm of the fibre. Move it slowly toward the flame of a candle or Bunsen burner (Figure 5). Note how the fibre reacts to the approaching flame.

Fig. 5 *The burn test to identify types of fibres.*

Avoid inhaling the fumes when fibres are burned. Some fibres, such as Teflon, produce poisonous fumes.

4. Place the fibre sample into the flame. Note the colour of the flame as the fibre burns.

5. Remove the fibre sample from the flame. Note whether it continues to burn or not. If the fibre continus to burn, put out the flame. The fibre may continue to smoulder after the flame is out. The colour of the smoke may also be used to indicate the type of fibre.

6. When the ash is cool, carefully examine it. A magnifying glass may be necessary. Rub the ash between your fingers. A hard ball or cinder may indicate a synthetic fibre, while a soft, slippery ash indicates a cellulose (plant) fibre.

7. Repeat steps 2 to 6 for all of the known fibre samples.

8. Use the above observations to decide on the types of fibres of the unknown samples.

Follow-up

1. Which group of fibres burns most easily?

2. Which group of fibres burns with the smokiest flame?

3. Which group of fibres is the hardest to extinguish?

4. Which type of fibre extinguishes itself?

5. Why is it important to know the content of the materials in your clothes? Give at least two reasons.

6. Why is it important for dyers to know what fibres are made of?

7. Find out how the burn test is important in police work.

POTTERY GLAZES

Fig. 6 *Do you know how to make pottery?*

Do you know how plates and cups are made? Clay is shaped into objects such as plates, cups, and saucers. When the objects have dried, they are placed in a heating oven called a **kiln**. The objects are heated to a high temperature. The chemicals making up the clay react to form a porous material, called **bisque-ware**. At this stage, the potter makes an insoluble glaze mixture. This is added to water to form a liquid that flows like cream. The porous pottery is dipped into the glaze mixture. The water is sucked into the pores of the bisque-ware and leaves the insoluble glaze chemicals on the surface of the object. The glazed object is heated in the kiln until the glaze and the clay become vitreous (glass-like). The kiln and its contents are allowed to cool, and the glazed pottery is ready for use.

Some of the chemicals that give colour to glazes are:

Metal oxide	Colour(s) of glaze
copper(II) oxide	blue, green
iron(III) oxide	brown, yellow
cobalt(II) oxide	blue
chromium(III) oxide	red, yellow, pink, brown, green
manganese(IV) oxide	purple, brown

12.5 Chemical Etching

The technique of chemical etching is used in the preparation of printing plates, in creating works of art and pieces of jewellery (Figure 7), and in making electronic circuits.

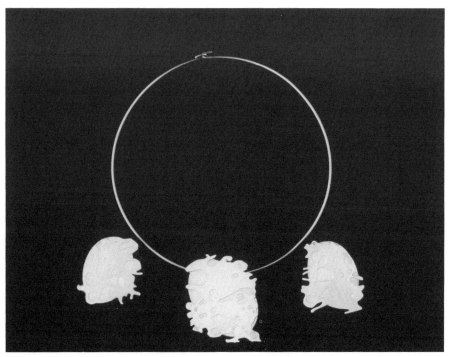

Fig. 7 *Chemical etching is used to make jewellery.*

To etch a metal, you first coat it all over with wax. Then you draw your design in the wax layer. The wax is removed along the lines you have drawn. When the metal is placed in an acid solution, the metal is eaten ("bitten") away at places not covered by wax, that is, along the lines you have drawn. You may use many things to draw through the wax, for example old record player needles.

In this experiment, you can make a piece of etched copper jewellery such as a ring, bracelet, earring, or pendant, or you can make a printing plate and print some wall prints or personal cards.

Materials

safety goggles
rubber gloves
flat-bottomed glass bowl, pie plate, or casserole (depending on the size of the metal)

plastic tongs
pointed piece of wood or old record player needle
glass rod
hotplate (if using beeswax)
100-mL beaker
acetone
alcohol
vinegar
copper piping cut into ring or bracelet sizes
copper jewellery shapes (available from art or craft supply stores)
highly polished zinc or copper plates, about 0.8 to 1.0 mm thick
   (available from art or craft supply stores)
salt
calcium carbonate fine powder
soft cloths
paint brush
yellow beeswax or a commercial metal protection material
6 mol/L nitric acid
fume hood or well ventilated work area

Method

I. *Copper Jewellery*

1. If the piece of copper is discoloured, use a soft cloth to clean the surface with a little vinegar and salt. Then clean the metal further by rubbing it with a little calcium carbonate powder and a soft cloth dipped in alcohol. Rinse the metal in water and dry with a clean soft cloth. *Do not touch the surface with your bare hands if possible.*

2. Melt the beeswax in a beaker on a hotplate and apply it with a paint brush to the whole surface of the piece of copper (Figure 8a). If you are using a commercial metal protector, apply it according to the instructions on the container. Allow the wax to cool and solidify on the metal surfaces. Remember, wherever there is no wax, the acid will attack the metal.

3. Use a pointed object to draw your design on the copper. Make sure you scratch the wax away down to the metal (Figure 8b). Check that there are no unwaxed areas on your piece of copper other than your design. If there are any uncovered spots, cover them with the wax or metal protector.

4. Pour nitric acid carefully into the glass bowl to a depth that will just cover your piece of copper. To avoid waste, use bowls just big enough to hold your piece when it is covered with acid.

Nitric acid is corrosive. Be careful!

Wear rubber gloves throughout this activity.

Carry out steps 4 and 5 in the fume hood. Do not inhale the fumes. They are toxic.

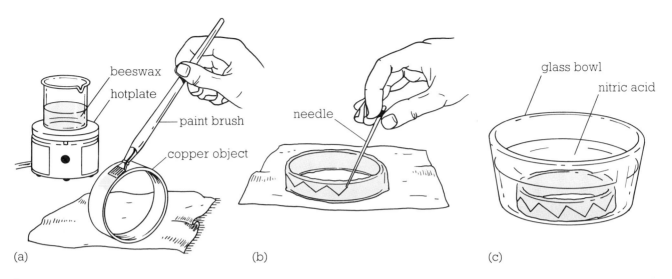

beeswax
hotplate
paint brush
copper object
(a)

needle
(b)

glass bowl
nitric acid
(c)

Fig. 8

5. Lower your piece of copper into the acid using the plastic tongs or a glass rod (Figure 8c). Allow it to stay in the acid bath until the metal has been eaten away to your satisfaction. You may want to remove the piece every now and again, rinse it, and inspect it to see if the etching has gone far enough. Time the length of each dipping so that eventually you can predict the time you need to get the desired effects.

6. When you are satisfied with the depth of the etched lines, remove the piece, rinse it in water, and dry it. Then remove the wax by using a solvent such as acetone.
(If you want to burn off the wax, you may be pleasantly surprised by the lovely colours on the metal surface. Place the piece on a wire gauze and heat it with a Bunsen flame. Be careful not to touch the piece until it has cooled.)

7. Take a photograph of your piece of copper jewellery, and submit the piece and the photograph to your teacher. The photographs of the whole class can be mounted to make a permanent display.

II. *Printing Plates*

1. Etch your copper or zinc plates by following steps 1 to 6 for copper jewellery. If you are using plates that already have a protective coat all over them, start at step 3. However, do *not* burn the coating off your plates. Use the acetone solvent.
Also remember to draw the *mirror image* of what you want to print (Figure 9).

Fig. 9 *The design you draw must be the mirror image of what you want to print.*

If you want this

then draw this on the plate

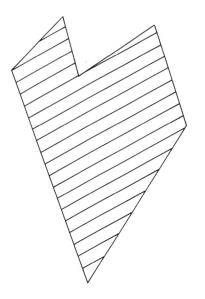 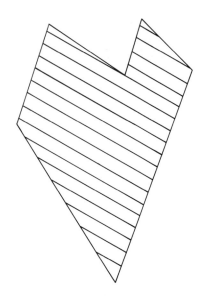

2. When the etched plate is cleaned, rinsed and dried, you have to use the printing press in the art room of your school.
   Ink your plate and remove excess ink. The ink will stay in the etched grooves. Then use the roller press in your art room to print your etching on nice paper. You should be able to produce 30 or more prints of your etching.

3. When your prints are dry, pick the best one. Frame it if it is a wall piece, or mount it if it is a card. Submit the print and the plate to your teacher. The prints of the whole class can be mounted to make a permanent display.

Follow-up

1. What did you observe when copper reacted with nitric acid?

2. List at least three precautions that you took during the etching process. Give a reason for each precaution.

3. Look up and write a short description of the compositions of inks used in printing.

4. Investigate and write a short description of another form of printing such as lithography.

292

- Chemicals play an important role in the art world.
- Artists must take safety precautions when working with any chemicals.
- Nature is a wonderful source of coloured dyes.
- Mordants are used to attach natural dyes to fibres.
- Synthetic dyes are more predictable than natural dyes and less likely to fade in sunlight.
- Burn tests are used to identify types of fibres.
- Potters make use of chemicals to colour their clays and to glaze their pottery.

R E V I E W · Q U E S T I O N S

1. Why must you never use dyeing equipment for cooking even after washing?

2. Many artists produce fine dust when working. What precautions should the artists take?

3. An aluminum or iron pot cannot be used for natural dyeing. Explain why.

4. What is the role of the mordant in natural dyeing?

5. Suggest a way to speed up the fading of new jeans.

6. Wool and silk are animal (protein) fibres. Cotton and linen are plant (cellulose) fibres. Why do dyes behave differently with each type of fibre?

7. Why should you wash new clothes, highly coloured T-shirts, and towels separately for the first few washes?

8. Which oxides would a potter use to make (a) blue glazes, (b) green glazes, (c) purple glazes?

9. Why must you etch metal in a fume hood or in a well ventilated room?

10. You have blue, red, and yellow stock dye solutions. Describe how you would combine them to obtain the following colours:
(a) orange   (b) purple   (c) green

11. Suggest two reasons why you would use a little vinegar in the rinse water when washing wool that has been dyed with acid dyes.

12. Think back to when you crafted something. What chemicals did you use? What precautions did you take? What precautions should you have taken that you didn't take?

13 CONSUMER CHEMISTRY

How would you assess the worth of a product?

CONTENTS

13.1 Buying, Selling, and Manufacturing

Why do you buy what you buy? Companies spend a fortune trying to answer this question. Sometimes you buy a consumer product because it is the cheapest on the market. Other times something else causes you to buy the product. Many factors can make a product attractive.

Bring in your favourite consumer product, preferably in its original packaging. If this is not possible, think of this product when you complete the questionnaire on the following page. Please do not write in the textbook.

Everyone of us is a consumer. Many of us will be working in the manufacturing sector. Look at the examples of careers related to manufacturing on pages 299 and 300. In addition to these, industry is highly dependent on many other employees who look after finances, production, and customer services. Accountants, lawyers, computer operators, salespeople, production line workers, quality controllers, engineers, shippers, secretaries, receptionists, and transporters all play vital roles.

Questionnaire

Part A: Product Characteristics

	Yes	No
1. Do you like the texture (feel)?		
Reason:		
2. Do you like the odour/fragrance (if any)?		
Reason:		
3. Do you like the taste (if this applies)?		
Reason:		
4. Do you like the colour?		
Reason:		
5. Do you like the container?		
Reason:		
6. Do you like the outer packaging (if any)?		
Reason:		
7. Are there sufficient directions for use (if needed)?		
Reason:		
8. Are the ingredients listed?		
9. If your answer to question 8 is yes, are any *active* ingredients specified?		
10. Is the size convenient?		
Reason:		
11. Does the size make comparison shopping easy?		
Reason:		
12. Does the product live up to the manufacturer's claims?		
Reason:		
13. Which of the 12 product characteristics above is/are important to you? _____		
Reason:		

Questionnaire

Part B: Product Marketing

1. Why did you first buy this product?

    (a) By chance.

    (b) Because your friends were buying it.

    (c) Because you liked the free sample.

    (d) Because you saw it advertised.

    (e) For other reasons. (Please specify.)

    _____

2. You have probably seen the product advertised.

    (a) What attracted you to the advertisement?

    _____

    (b) Where did you see it advertised?

    _____

3. What made you buy this product over a competing product?

    (a) Performance.

    (b) The characteristics described in Part A.

    (c) Price.

    (d) You had a coupon for it.

    (e) For other reasons. (Please specify.)

    _____

4. If this product was priced very much higher, but was still affordable (for you), would you still purchase it?

Yes	No

    Reason:

Packaging Designer: Designing packaging that is attractive, strong, and safe.

Research and Development: Developing new products that the consumer will buy.

Production: Making the product in bulk so that every batch is the same.

Marketing: Getting the consumer to choose the product.

Flavour Design: Creating flavours that make a product taste better.

Perfumery: Adding fragrances that make a product more desirable.

13.2 Flavour and Fragrance

Flavours are added to a lot of food. Animal foods contain them too. For example, farmers wean calves and pigs with foods that contain flavours similar to those in the mother's milk.

Fragrances are added to a great variety of products: perfumes, rubber shoes, erasers, detergents, shampoos, dolls, watches, cat litter, packaging, and candles. Some "no-odour" products in fact contain fragrances to mask the smell of the chemicals used to make the products. Odours in a product give the first impression. The impression may be of softness. Two identical samples of fabric softener with different fragrances can cause people to judge the softness of the wash as being different because one of them smells softer! Some people loyally buy a product because they like the smell.

A pleasant smell to one person may not be pleasant to another. Because it is difficult to know how people will react to a fragrance, manufacturers test a fragrance in a product on many people before they market it.

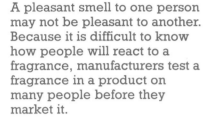

Fig. 1 *A variety of fragrances.*

Your sense of smell reaches into your subconscious memories much more quickly than do any of your other senses. Odours can bring back vivid memories of scenes that happened many years ago. Many people associate smells with events and feelings.

An artificial (or synthetic) flavour or fragrance is usually made by mixing as many as 50 or more compounds to match a desired flavour (such as ripe orange) or fragrance (such as rose). A natural flavour or fragrance is extracted from the source, for example, strawberry flavour from strawberries.

Artificial flavours are more often used than natural ones in processed foods. This is because artificial flavours are, in general, stronger and cheaper. For example, flavouring with natural strawberries costs a lot more than using artificial strawberry flavour. Also it is sometimes difficult to preserve the freshness of natural materials.

Fig. 2 *Artificial flavours are used in jellybeans.*

Imagine opening a bottle and finding a substance that smells and tastes exactly like green peppers, ripe bananas, chicken, peanut butter, marshmallow, or fresh baked bread! As a flavour technician you can work these wonders.

In a flavour applications laboratory, you would flavour new food products using the flavours produced by your company, and test different flavours in an unflavoured product. For example, you may have to try out a new chewing gum flavour by adding it to the unflavoured gum. You and others then taste-test the product. The flavour may have to be changed many times before you are satisfied with the results. You may also have to create a finished product at a client's request. Working with flavours is a unique occupation because you often work on new products and it requires a lot of creativity. The job demands very close cooperation with fellow laboratory personnel, and with the sales and marketing people. You are often called upon to attend presentations of your work to a client. You must be prepared to answer questions about the product, so keeping accurate and detailed records is essential.

High school chemistry is the minimum requirement. A laboratory technician course and a knowledge of cooking are helpful.

The Taste Bud Challenge

Design a taste-test investigation based on a certain type of product. The idea is to see if people are able to tell one brand of product from another just by tasting. Examples are:

two brands of chocolate chip cookies
Pepsi and Coke
Classic Coke and Diet Coke

Describe how you intend to carry out the test. Then carry it out on your classmates, friends, or family members, and report your findings. Do not do this in the chemistry lab for safety reasons!

As a fragrance marketer you would work for a fragrance company. Most of these companies sell artificial fragrances, but some still sell natural ones. Your job is to suggest fragrances to manufacturers that will suit their products. You must translate a client's ideas and requirements into something that the fragrance designer in your company understands. You work closely with a client's technical and marketing people. As a marketer of fragrances, you must be aware of competing products, new technologies, and regional, national, and international markets.

You need on-the-job training to understand the complex nature and limitations of perfumery. You need a good odour memory and a vivid imagination. Hands-on experience in a laboratory where you try out fragrances in many products would help you to be a good marketer. A formal education in basic chemistry, marketing and market research would be valuable. A knowledge of French and other languages helps too.

You are constantly working with clients, laboratory personnel, perfumers, other salespeople, and marketers. So you must get along well with people. You will gain a lot of satisfaction when "your" project is widely advertised and is successful in the marketplace.

How Good Is Your Odour Memory?

Bring in a selection of perfumes and colognes for men and women. Dip a blotter in each product and smell the blotter. Draw up a chart with the headings:

Name of perfume or cologne	Description of the fragrance

Under the second heading, write down anything that will help you identify the fragrance.

Have a partner place the bottles where you cannot see them.

Ask you partner to give you a ball of cotton batting with some fragrance on it.

Refer to your notes and try to name the fragrance. Repeat the test on the other fragrances.

How many fragrances did you get correct? Was any fragrance particularly appealing or particularly unpleasant? Explain why you found it appealing or unpleasant.

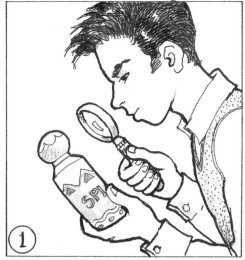

13.3 A Packaging Project

Remember it is often the packaging that first catches the eye of the consumer. Some people buy a perfume just to have the bottle!

The packaging for a product should be

- attractive
- easy to handle
- safe
- durable

In this project you will play the role of a packaging engineer investigating the container of a competitor. Choose one or more of the following aspects for your investigation.

1. Design
   (a) How well does the container work?
   (b) How good does the container look?

2. Operating characteristics
   (a) How does the container operate?
   (b) How can you improve the way the container operates?

3. Chemical and physical characteristics
   (a) Does the product react with the container?
   (b) How does the container behave under conditions such as heat or cold? For example, if you were examining a spray, you could look at:
      - comfort and feel of the spray in the hand
      - ease of action of the spray lever
      - the amount of material (number of grams) sprayed per stroke
      - what happens when the container bottle and spray are heated or cooled
      - how it operates with only a little product left in the bottle

You could even videotape the inside workings of the spray head! Present your findings and suggested improvements in a creative way.

Other types of products you could investigate are automatic toilet bowl cleaner dispensers, striped toothpaste dispensers, toothpaste pumps, and liquid soap dispensers.

If you have an eye for design and a sense of the theatrical, then packaging is for you! Many large companies have packaging departments which employ packaging engineers and technicians.

If you worked in a packaging department, you would constantly be evaluating the packages produced by your company and its competitors. Sometimes competing products are much the same, but one of them may sell better due to the attractiveness of the package and the ease with which the purchaser can handle the product.

You would carry out chemical and physical tests on packages. It is necessary to test a product in various containers to see if they react chemically. It is also important to check packages for leakage, for resistance to splitting when dropped, for deterioration over time, or for colour changes. You would also go to local stores and check for any defects in your packages such as peeling labels, leaking bottles, and dented containers. This information is important because any deterioration before a customer buys the product leads to a drop in sales.

At high school the most helpful courses are physics, chemistry, drafting, mathematics, computer science, English, art, and economics. A community college packaging diploma would be good preparation for your job. Packaging associations also run training courses.

Adding a plastic bumper ring to prevent breakage—the job of a packaging designer.

13.4 Making and Testing Liquid Soap

The Romans started making soap 3000 years ago. Soap became affordable to everyone near the end of the eighteenth century, when it was discovered that table salt could be used to make soap more efficiently. Whale oil can be used to make soap, but this source of fatty acid is gradually reduced due to the decline of whaling.

Let us now look at the manufacturing of some common consumer products. In pioneer times, soap was made in the home. Water washings of wood ash (containing a base) were boiled in a pot with some fat from the cooking of meats. As the boiling mixture was stirred, the soap separated out. In some cases, table salt was used to "salt out" the soap (that is, to get the solid soap to come out of solution). The soap was then rinsed and allowed to set. This soap was quite alkaline and crude.

You are now going to make soap using a fat and a base.

Fig. 3 *Pioneer women making their own soap. Today, soaps are still made from a fat and a base, but they contain other ingredients such as whiteners, preservatives, fragrances, and colouring.*

Potassium hydroxide solution is corrosive. Wear safety goggles at all times and clean up any spills immediately.

Materials

safety goggles
20 mL potassium hydroxide solution (2.5 mol/L or 137 g/L)
10 g melted D-coconut fatty acid
kerosene

two 100-mL beakers	balance
thermometer	test tube
sample vial	beaker tongs
pH papers	glass rod
hotplate	distilled water

Method

I. *To prepare the soap*

1. Weigh out 10 g of D-coconut fatty acid by pouring it down a glass rod into a clean, pre-weighed 100-mL beaker placed on a balance.

2. Pour 20 mL of potassium hydroxide solution down the cleaned glass rod into another clean 100-mL beaker.

3. Heat the potassium hydroxide solution on a hotplate. When it is at about 60°C, add the D-coconut fatty acid while stirring the mixture. Keep the mixture at about 60°C. Stir constantly until no droplets of the D-coconut fatty acid are visible and you have a uniform product. Do not overheat!

4. Remove the glass rod and allow the product on it to cool. Use your fingers to pick up a drop of the product from the end of the rod. Rub the drop between your fingers and try to wash it off with water. If no grease is left on your fingers, your soap is ready.

5. Cool the liquid soap. If a fragrance is available, stir some into the liquid soap.

6. Place a sample of your liquid soap in a vial. Label the vial with your name. Give your product a name (be creative!). Hand in the product.

II. *To test the soap*

1. Describe the appearance of the soap.

2. Place a tiny amount of the D-coconut fatty acid on your finger and rub it between your thumb and finger. What does it feel like?

3. Try to wash the D-coconut fatty acid off your fingers *with water only*. What happens?

4. Put a drop of your soap between your thumb and finger. Feel it and then try to wash it off with water only.

5. Place a drop of your soap in a clean test tube. Add distilled water to about one-third of a test tube. Shake. What quantity of suds do you get? Is your soap solution clear or cloudy?

6. Use pH paper to determine the pH of your soap solution in the test tube.

7. Place a few drops of oil (kerosene) in a test tube which is one-third full of distilled water. Add about five drops of your soap and shake. Does the oil disappear? What else do you see?

Follow-up

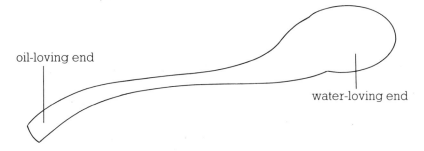 An emulsion is a uniform mixture formed from substances that would not normally dissolve in each other.

1. What evidence suggested that you changed the D-coconut fatty acid into soap?

2. Name the two substances that you used to make soap?

3. Is the soap you made efficient? How did you decide?

4. Why do you think soap is called an **emulsifying agent**?

5. What was the approximate pH of the soap solution? Is it basic, acidic or neutral?

6. A typical chemical equation for making soap from a fat and a base is shown below. Balance the equation.

$$C_3H_5(C_{18}H_{35}O_2)_3 \;+\; KOH \;\rightarrow\; K(C_{18}H_{35}O_2) \;+\; C_3H_5(OH)_3$$

      fat   base   soap   glycerin

Investigation

The term **emulsifying agent** is commonly used in the food and cosmetic industries. In other industries, the term **surfactant** (short for surface active agent) is used instead.

13.5 How Emulsifying Agents Work

Guess what soaps, egg yolk, ice cream, and chocolate have in common! Soaps are emulsifying agents, and all the other foods contain emulsifying agents.

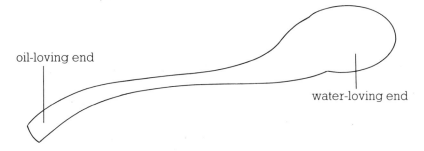

oil-loving end   water-loving end

Fig. 4 *An emulsifying agent is made up of long-chain molecules each with a water-loving end and an oil-loving end.*

Detergents contain molecules that resemble those of soap. So detergents remove grease in the same way that soap does. But detergents contain additives (for example, nitriloacetic acid) that prevent scum formation.

You learned in Chapter 7 that an emulsifying agent can join oil molecules and water molecules together. If you wash your clothes in water, the oil particles attached to your clothes do not dissolve in the water because oil and water do not mix. If you wash your clothes with soap, the soap enables the oil particles to dissolve in water, and the oil particles are then washed off the clothes (Figure 5).

Fig. 5 *The oil-loving ends of soap molecules dissolve in an oil particle (which is attached to clothes), leaving the water-loving ends sticking out. The oil particle is completely covered by water-loving parts, and the whole group dissolves in the wash water.*

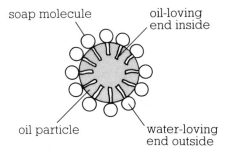

soap molecule   oil-loving end inside

oil particle   water-loving end outside

In ice cream, the emulsifying agent is usually the lecithin from egg yolk. It keeps the milk fat and water together to form a uniform mixture.

Chocolate is a mixture of sugar, cocoa butter, chocolate liquor, and milk. The sugar does not dissolve in oil and therefore does not move easily through the fat, so the chocolate may not flow well when pouring during production. Lecithin, made from soybeans and also present in egg yolk, is the emulsifying agent added to help the chocolate flow properly (Figure 6).

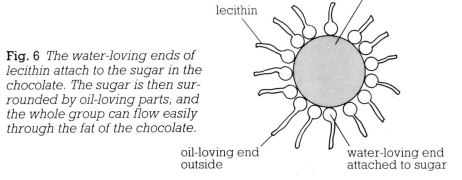

lecithin   sugar

Fig. 6 *The water-loving ends of lecithin attach to the sugar in the chocolate. The sugar is then surrounded by oil-loving parts, and the whole group can flow easily through the fat of the chocolate.*

oil-loving end outside   water-loving end attached to sugar

In the experiment below, you will investigate the effect of egg yolk as an emulsifying agent on oil and lemon juice.

Materials

safety goggles
2 egg yolks at room temperature
20 mL lemon juice (or vinegar)
1 mL salt
250 mL cooking oil
5 mL dry mustard powder
pepper
liquid measuring equipment
crackers for tasting
20 mL Ivory liquid detergent
blender

Method

1. Place all ingredients in the blender except the oil and the Ivory liquid. Blend them thoroughly.

2. With the blender running, add 250 mL of oil in a thin, steady stream. Blend until the mixture thickens.

In order to taste the product, do the experiment in a food science laboratory or at home, or with equipment brought from home and uncontaminated by laboratory chemicals.

3. Taste the creamy uniform product with crackers. If you have any hard boiled eggs, try some of your emulsion (mayonnaise) on egg slices on the crackers!

4. Repeat the process described in steps 1 and 2, but use 10 mL of Ivory liquid detergent instead of the egg yolks. *Do not taste this product*! It will not taste too good.

Follow-up

1. Oil and lemon juice do not normally stay mixed. Did the addition of the egg yolk produce an emulsion? Did the emulsion separate out?

2. Which was a better emulsifying agent, Ivory liquid or egg yolk?

3. How do you think the Ivory liquid works at cleaning your dirty dishes?

4. If you had oil and vinegar dressing that kept separating into two layers, how could you make an emulsion?

5. If you add a few drops of water to a cup of melted plain chocolate, the chocolate becomes very difficult to stir (Figure 7). Why?

6. Why must you dry the outside of fresh strawberries before dipping them in melted chocolate? (Try this. The results are scrumptious, especially served with whipped cream!)

Fig. 7 *When water is added to chocolate, the sugar attaches itelf to the water, and the lecithin is let go to some extent. The sugar and water are also repelled by the fat particles, so easy movement of particles past one another is prevented.*

(a) flow of melted chocolate

(b) flow of melted chocolate with a few drops of water added

ONE TECHNOLOGY LEADS TO ANOTHER!

The action of soap in most household water leaves a scum on the washed fabrics. If the clothes are sun dried, this scum traps a layer of water, so there are no static charges on the fabrics. However, if a detergent and hot tumble drier are used, the fabrics feel harsh and contain static charges, especially in winter. That's why fabric softeners were designed! These products may be added during or after the wash cycle, or even in the dryer, depending on the chemicals in the product.

Fabric softeners work by leaving a greasy layer on the surface of the fabrics, making them feel soft. This greasy layer also traps a layer of water, and this reduces the static charge on the clothes. However, if you use fabric softener with every wash, the greasy layer builds up and attracts grime, and the water absorbing ability of the fabrics (especially of towels) is lowered. It is therefore a good idea to do a wash without fabric softener every now and again.

Hair conditioners are like fabric softeners in many ways. Describe how you think they work. What disadvantages are there to using hair conditioners?

Charlie

"..And for those doing their laundry tomorrow, the Weather Bureau has issued a severe 'static cling' advisory..."

13.6 Determination of Sodium Hypochlorite in a Bleach

The active ingredients of laundry aids and cleaners such as bleaches, abrasive cleaners, and fabric softeners can be dangerous. Therefore, these products have to be checked before they can be sold. The correct concentration of a bleach, for example, must be shown on the label. If the concentration is too high, the bleach may be dangerous to use or it could damage the wash. If the concentration is lower than claimed, the manufacturer can be charged.

Household bleach, such as Javex, is a sodium hypochlorite solution. The percentage of sodium hypochlorite can be determined by carrying out a titration.

Acetic acid and the bleach are both corrosive. Never pipette by mouth. Use a pipette bulb or a syringe.

Materials

safety goggles
40% (volume/volume) acetic acid
10% (mass/volume) potassium iodide solution
Javex household bleach (diluted 1:10 with distilled water)
0.1 mol/L sodium thiosulfate solution
250-mL Erlenmeyer flask
25-mL or 50-mL burette
two 10-mL graduated cyclinders
100-mL graduated cyclinder
10-mL pipette with pipette bulb (or a 10-mL syringe)
white tile or paper to be placed under the titration flask

Method

1. Pipette 10.00 mL diluted bleach into the 250-mL Erlenmeyer flask using a pipette bulb.

2. Add 20 mL of distilled water to the contents of the flask.

3. Fill the burette with 0.1 mol/L sodium thiosulfate solution and record the initial volume reading.

4. Measure out 5.0 mL 10% potassium iodide solution into one of the graduated cylinders, and 5.0 mL 40% acetic acid into another graduated cylinder.

5. Add the potassium iodide solution to the flask, with swirling, and then immediately add the acetic acid with swirling. The dark yellow-brown colour of iodine appears.

6. Immediately titrate the contents of the flask with the sodium thiosulfate solution from the burette. The end point is reached when the yellow-brown colour just disappears, leaving a colourless solution. Record the final burette reading. Calculate the volume of sodium thiosulfate solution used by subtracting the initial volume reading from the final volume reading.

7. Repeat the titration from steps 1 to 6 until you have two consistent results. Record all your data in a chart.

Follow-up

1. For each trial, calculate the percentage of sodium hypochlorite in the bottle using the following formula:
   Percentage of sodium hypochlorite
   = volume of sodium thiosulfate solution (in mL) $\times$ 0.3725

2. If the results from two different trials were very different, what would this tell you? What would you do about it?

3. Compare your calculated percentage to that on the bleach bottle used to prepare your bleach solution. Explain any differences.

4. List at least three different uses of sodium hypochlorite.

5. There are precautions mentioned on the bleach bottle label, and in this experiment. List each precaution and give the reason(s) behind it. Also list any other precautions you took in this experiment together with the reason(s) for them.

6. Why is it important to read labels before using any product?

7. Why do you think some manufacturers do not list all the ingredients in their products?
   Should manufacturers be required to list all ingredients on product labels? Explain your answer.
   Should manufacturers be required to put the actual amount of each ingredient on product labels? Explain your answer.

8. Design and carry out an experiment to test the effect of a household bleach on dyed fabrics. You will have to decide on:
   (a) the fabrics or yarns you will test,
   (b) the concentration(s) of bleach to use,
   (c) the temperature of the bleach solutions,
   (d) the volume of bleach solution and quantity of fabrics to use,
   (e) the method of monitoring the changes in the fabrics and in dye colours,
   (f) the way of presenting your findings.

Before you start your experiment, check with your teacher to make sure that your method is safe. Also remember that you need enough fabric for tests and controls.

THE ACTION OF BLEACHES

Not all bleaches are the same. The bleach used on hair is hydrogen peroxide, and that used in some detergents is sodium perborate. Some bleaches are better for certain tasks. Household bleaches (3 to 6% sodium hypochlorite) damage protein fibres such as wool, hair, silk, cashmere, and angora, so hydrogen peroxide is often used for bleaching these fibres.

The most common household bleach is sodium hypochlorite. It is made by reacting chlorine and sodium hydroxide.

sodium hydroxide + chlorine →
    sodium hypochlorite + sodium chloride + water

Fig. 8 *Sodium hypochlorite is also used in water treatment plants and swimming pools.*

The active part of sodium hypochlorite is the hypochlorite ion, OCl^{1-}. It reacts with the staining material, which is either turned into a colourless material and so appears to be gone, or converted to a soluble compound that is flushed away by the wash water.

Sodium hypochlorite also kills bacteria. The hypochlorite ion can enter a bacterial cell where it reacts with the protein and kills the cell.

Bear the following facts in mind when using household bleaches:

1. A dilute bleach does not weaken cellulose fibres like cotton and linen, but a concentrated bleach will.

2. To remove stubborn stains, do not increase the volume of bleach you use. Rather bleach for twice the time, or repeat the wash with the same recommended volume of bleach.

3. Fast colours on fabrics are not bleached by sodium hypochlorite. Check the garment labels to see if a bleach may be used.

4. Do not use liquid swimming pool chlorine instead of household bleach. The former is twice as concentrated.

13.7 Determination of Available Chlorine in an Abrasive Cleaner

Fig. 9 *Bleaches are present in many cleaning products, such as abrasive cleaners, denture cleaners, and toilet bowl cleaners.*

You have probably used an abrasive cleaner such as Ajax. The following chart shows the composition of such a cleaner:

Ingredient	Role
detergent	emulsifies greasy dirt
trisodium phosphate (TSP), sodium carbonate (both are basic salts)	helps in removing grease
perborates (oxygen releasing) or hypochlorite or hypobromite bleaching agents	bleaches colouring materials kills bacteria
silica abrasive (about 90% of the mass of the cleaning powder)	helps to rub dirt free
perfume/colour	attracts the consumer

When water is added to an abrasive cleaner, hypochlorite ions are set free. The efficiency of the cleaner is measured by the "percentage of available chlorine." You can measure this percentage by doing a titration similar to the one used for household bleach. The differences are:

- you have a milky, insoluble material present throughout the titration,
- starch is added to make it easier to see the end point, when the colour changes from dark purple-blue to colourless.

If the abrasive cleaner has a blue dye, the colour change at the end point will be from dark purple-blue to pale blue.

312

Materials

safety goggles
abrasive cleaner such as Ajax
10% (mass/volume) potassium iodide solution
0.1 mol/L sodium thiosulfate solution
starch indicator solution (4 g/L)
3% (volume/volume) sulfuric acid
25-mL or 50-mL burette
100-mL graduated cylinder
50-mL graduated cylinder
10-mL graduated cylinder
250-mL Erlenmeyer flask
balance
white tile or paper to be placed under the titration flask

Method

1. Weigh 10.00 g of the abrasive cleaner into a pre-weighed 250-mL Erlenmeyer flask.

2. Fill the burette with the sodium thiosulfate solution and note the initial volume reading.

3. Pour 20 mL potassium iodide solution into the 50-mL graduated cylinder, 10 mL of sulfuric acid into the 10-mL graduated cylinder, and 50 mL of distilled water into the 100-mL graduated cylinder.

4. Quickly add the three solutions from step 3 into the flask containing the cleaner and swirl. A yellow colour will appear because iodine is set free.

5. Immediately titrate with the sodium thiosulfate in the burette. When the yellow colour of the iodine is almost gone, add about 5 mL of starch indicator solution. The solution will become dark purple-blue. Continue to titrate until the colour has just disappeared.
   Record the final burette reading. Calculate the volume of sodium thiosulfate used by subtracting the initial volume reading from the final volume reading.

6. Calculate the percentage of available chlorine in the abrasive cleaner by using the following formula:

$$\text{Percentage of available chlorine} = \frac{\text{volume of sodium thiosulfate (in mL)} \times 0.355}{\text{mass of abrasive cleaner (in g)}}$$

Be careful not to breathe the dust of the powdered abrasive cleaner.

If the abrasive cleaner has a blue dye, the colour will be yellow-green at this stage.

If the abrasive cleaner has a blue dye, the colour at the end point will be pale blue.

313

Activities

1. Do you expect an abrasive cleaner to be acidic, basic, or neutral? Design an experiment to find the pH of a 1% (mass/volume) mixture of abrasive cleaner and water.

2. Design an experiment to find the percentage of the abrasive material in Ajax. (Clue: The abrasive material is the insoluble part of the cleaner.)

For each activity:
- briefly describe your method (and ask your teacher to check it),
- show all your measured results in a chart,
- show your calculations,
- describe what you noticed about the appearance or properties of the abrasive material.

Investigation

Salt is widely distributed in food, and there is no need to add any salt to food. Scientists believe that too much salt causes high blood pressure and heart disease.

Do not get silver nitrate on your clothes or skin. After exposure to light it changes to black deposits of silver.

13.8 Determination of Salt in Butter

Some people have to watch the amount of salt that they consume. Therefore dairies are concerned about the amount of salt present in butter. They measure the amount of salt by titrating the butter with silver nitrate solution.

The test depends on the reaction of sodium chloride (salt) with silver nitrate to form a white precipitate of silver chloride:

sodium chloride + silver nitrate → silver chloride + sodium nitrate

Potassium chromate is used as the indicator. When all the sodium chloride is reacted, any extra silver nitrate reacts with the added potassium chromate indicator to produce a brown colour. This brown colour signals the end of the titration.

Materials

safety goggles
different brands of salted butter
0.05 mol/L silver nitrate solution
5% (mass/volume) potassium chromate solution in a dropper bottle
20-mL pipette
10-mL burette
balance
thermometer
500-mL graduated cylinder (100-mL will also do)
500-mL Erlenmeyer flask

Fig. 10 *Some people prefer unsalted butter for medical reasons.*

Fig. 11

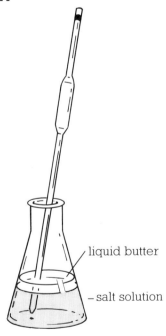

liquid butter

salt solution

100-mL Erlenmeyer flask
white tile or paper to be placed under the titration flask
hotplate

Method

1. Weigh exactly 10.00 g of a brand of butter into the 500-mL flask.

2. Measure out exactly 300 mL of distilled water which has a temperature of about 60°C. Add it to the butter in the flask. Be sure to wash down any butter on the inside walls of the flask.

3. Shake the flask to dissolve all the salt out of the butter. Then let the flask stand for two to three minutes to allow the fat to rise to the surface.

4. Insert a pipette below the fat layer and withdraw a 20.00 mL sample of the salt solution (Figure 11). Deliver this into the 100-mL Erlenmeyer flask.

5. Add 10 to 15 drops of the potassium chromate solution to the salt solution in the Erlenmeyer flask. A pale yellow colour will result.

6. Fill the burette with the silver nitrate solution and record the initial volume reading.

7. Titrate the salt solution in the Erlenmeyer flask with the silver nitrate solution from the burette. Stir constantly. A white precipitate will form initially, although it may look yellow. Continue the titration until the solution just turns a light brown colour. Record the final burette reading.
   Calculate the volume of silver nitrate solution used by subtracting the initial volume reading from the final volume reading.

8. Repeat the titration at least twice.

9. Record all your data in a chart.

Follow-up

1. For each trial, calculate the percentage of sodium chloride by mass (to one decimal place) present in butter using the following formula:
   Percentage of salt = volume of silver nitrate (in mL) × 0.44

2. Average the results from your trials.

RESEARCH AND DEVELOPMENT

COMPOUNDING

Many products sold on the market today are mixed by people called compounders. The compounders use standard "recipes" developed by other people working in research and development. Compounders have a great responsibility because an error on their part could cost their company a lot of money in wasted raw materials.

PACKAGING

Packaging are "silent salespersons"! They should provide protection, preservation, and promotion. Consider the following in package design:

EFFECTIVENESS. How well does it do its job?
EFFICIENCY. Can it be handled easily? Is the size suitable?
TYPES OF MATERIAL. Plastic, paper, metal, or glass?
LEGALITY. Does it obey government rules on packaging and labelling (for example, full and correct information in English and French)?

MARKETING AND ADVERTISING

To make people buy your product, you must first answer several key questions:

WHAT IS YOUR TARGET GROUP? Industry, commercial enterprises, or the consumer (age group, income level, gender)?
WHAT WILL YOU CALL YOUR PRODUCT? The name must suit the target group and the product.
WHERE WILL YOU SELL YOUR PRODUCT? In shops, at trade shows, or by mail order only?
HOW WILL YOU ADVERTISE YOUR PRODUCT? T.V., shop window displays, radio, magazines, newspapers, or free samples?
WHEN WILL YOU ADVERTISE YOUR PRODUCT? Christmas, summer, or back-to-school?

LAUNCHING A NEW PRODUCT

A PRESENTATION

Prepare a presentation for your company president and board.

1. You will need to have answers for each of the following questions.
   (a) What is the name of the product?
   (b) What is the target group?
   (c) What is the estimated cost of the product?
   (d) Where will you sell the product?
   (e) Why is the style and size of packaging chosen?
   (f) How will you advertise the product?
   (g) When will you advertise the product?

2. A brief description of how the product is made.

3. A sample of the package.

4. An advertisement.

INSTRUCTION

A product does not just appear on store shelves. A great deal of thought and work goes into the launching of each product. The five main stages are shown above. In this project, you are given the compounding recipes. Choose and prepare a product, design and make a package for it, develop a marketing and advertising campaign, and finally make a presentation for your company president and board (your teacher and classmates).

A. Aftershave Lotion

Materials

Ingredient	Mass (g)	Role
ethyl alcohol, denatured	50.0	acts as solvent
glycerin	2.5	helps retain moisture
perfume oil	0.5	attracts the consumer
boric acid	2.0	neutralizes basic soap residue
water	44.9	acts as solvent
menthol (optional)	0.1	relieves minor irritation
dye solution (optional)	as wanted	gives colour

safety goggles
two 250-mL beakers
balance
filter paper
bottle for the product
glass rod
filter funnel
boiling chip
hotplate with stirrer

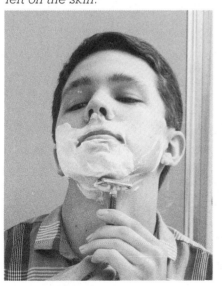

Fig. 12 *A good aftershave should refresh and cool the skin, act as a mild skin tightener, soothe minor irritations, and neutralize the soap left on the skin.*

Method

1. Weigh out and dissolve all the ingredients, except the water, in the ethyl alcohol in a 250-mL beaker. Then add the water. Stir well to prevent the less soluble materials (such as the perfume oil and menthol) from coming out of solution.

2. Stand the mixture in a refrigerator, until the poorly soluble portions of the perfume oil clump together. Set up a funnel with filter paper. While the mixture is still cool, filter it to obtain a clear solution.

3. If the lotion is to be coloured, add the dye to the clear solution *after* it has returned to room temperature.
   Re-filter without further chilling to obtain a brilliant clear product.

4. Bottle and label your product.

B. Aftershave Stick

Materials

Ingredient	Mass (g)	Role
ethyl alcohol, denatured	80.5	acts as solvent and carrier
sodium stearate	6.0	forms the gel
glycerin	4.0	helps retain moisture
propylene glycol	3.0	helps retain moisture
menthol	0.1	relieves minor irritation
water, demineralized	5.0	provides moisture
perfume oil	1.4	attracts the consumer
dye solution (optional)	as wanted	gives colour

safety goggles
round-bottomed flask
reflux condenser
beaker
hotplate with magnetic stirrer bar
thermometer
rod and clamps
mould

Method

1. Weigh out and put all the ingredients, except the perfume oil, into a round-bottomed flask.

2. Place the flask in a beaker of water on a hotplate.
   Introduce the magnetic stirrer bar into the flask.
   Fit the flask with a reflux condenser and clamp the equipment as shown in Figure 13. Make sure that cold water is running through the condenser and into the sink.

3. Heat the flask with stirring. The mixture will start to boil. The condenser cools the vapours back to a liquid, which falls back into the flask. Control the hotplate to keep the mixture *just* refluxing. Stir until all, or almost all, the ingredients completely dissolve.

The process of condensing vapour to liquid, thereby returning a product to the reaction mixture, is called **refluxing**.

Fig. 13

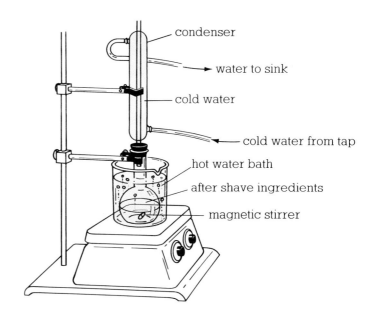

4. Make a mould out of foil, or clean an empty plastic stick deodorant or gel cologne container.

5. Disconnect the reflux condenser from the flask. Place a thermometer into the flask. Allow the temperature of the mixture to fall to about 60°C. Add the perfume oil, and pour the mixture into the mould to set.

6. Label your product.

C. Cleansing Cream

There are two types of cleansing cream:

- emulsified, or cold cream, type — usually emulsified by beeswax and borax
- translucent, or liquefying, type — made of a mixture of oils and waxes with no water

The beeswax-borax emulsified cleansing cream is the most common type. It is typically white, shiny, and smooth. Although it is firm, it liquefies on application and spreads on the skin with ease. It contains a high percentage of mineral oil for cleansing efficiency.

Many examples of this type of cream are oil-in-water (O/W) emulsions (Figure 14a). After these are rubbed on the skin, enough water evaporates to change the emulsion to a water-in-oil (W/O) emulsion (Figure 14b). The oil then becomes the outer layer. It acts as a solvent for efficient cleansing.

To test whether an emulsion is an oil-in-water (O/W) type or a water-in-oil (W/O type, apply it to your skin and try to wash it off with water. An O/W emulsion will come off with water, a W/O emulsion will not.

319

Fig. 14 *(a) oil-in-water (O/W) emulsion (b) water-in-oil (W/O) emulsion.*

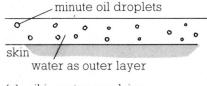 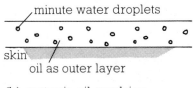

(a) oil in water emulsion   (b) water in oil emulsion

Materials

safety goggles
stirring rod
2 thermometers
100-mL glass beaker
250-mL glass beaker
hotplate with temperature control
balance
small sample bottles brought from home

The cleansing power of the cream is directly related to the percentage of mineral oil present. If the percentage exceeds 60%, the emulsion becomes unstable.

Materials in the 250-mL beaker		
Ingredient	Mass (g)	Role
beeswax, bleached white	16.67	interacts with borax to give soaps which emulsify oils
mineral oil	50.00	dissolves the oils and greases that bind grime and makeup to the skin.

Materials in the 100-mL beaker		
Ingredient	Mass (g)	Role
borax	0.83	converts the acids in beeswax to soaps
water	32.5	softens the product
perfume (optional)	0.5	attracts the consumer

Method

Increasing the amount of water softens the product, but the cleansing action is reduced.

1. Weigh out all the ingredients listed in the two tables above. Put them into their separate beakers.

2. Warm the two beakers separately to 70°C on the hotplate.

3. Hold the temperatures at 70°C and stir the contents of the 250-mL beaker vigorously with a rod.

4. While stirring rapidly, add all the contents of the 100-mL beaker drop by drop to the 250-mL beaker. Keep the temperature at 70°C until a uniform, opaque cream forms.

Slow stirring is required at this point or else the oil and water will separate.

5. Now stir more slowly until a temperature of about 40°C is reached. Then add the perfume.

6. Pour the cream into the sample bottles at about 40°C. Label your product.

Follow-up

1. Describe the product in as much detail as you can.

2. Put some on your skin and try to wash it off with water. Note your results and state what type of emulsion you have prepared.

3. Place some eye makeup or lipstick on your hand. Use a bit of your cream to remove it by working your cream over the makeup and wiping off with a tissue paper. Note how efficient your cream is and how your skin feels.

4. If you have a cleansing cream, bring in a sample and compare it with your preparation.

D. Bubble Blowing Liquid

Fig. 15 *Bubble making time!*

Materials

safety goggles
20 mL liquid detergent (preferably JOY)
50 mL glycerin
60 mL water
wire for making a bubble blowing loop
250-mL beaker
glass rod
glass jar for the product
100-mL graduated cylinder

Method

1. Use the graduated cylinder to measure each liquid ingredient.

2. Pour the ingredients into the beaker as they are measured out. Stir to blend the mixture. Add some food colouring to the mixture if you want the product to appeal to children.

3. Design your bubble blowing loop. Make sure that it fits into the jar you intend to use for your product.

4. Test your loop and your product outdoors. Dip the loop into the liquid and blow through the loop. Try various loop shapes.

- Many factors determine why a product is attractive.
- Flavours and fragrances are added to a lot of food and consumer products.
- Artificial flavours and fragrances, made by mixing many chemicals, are usually stronger and cheaper than natural ones.
- The packaging of a product should be attractive, easy to handle, safe, and durable.
- Soaps are made from a fat and a base.
- An emulsifying agent is a long-chain molecule with a water-loving end and an oil-loving end.

- Fabric softeners form a greasy layer on clothes; this layer traps water and reduces static electricity.
- Household bleach and abrasive powder often contain hypochlorite ions.
- Cleansing cream is divided into emulsified (cold cream) type and translucent (liquefying) type.
- Many beeswax-borax cleansing creams are oil-in-water emulsions.
- Marketing, packaging, and advertising are all important in promoting a product.

SUMMARY·CHART

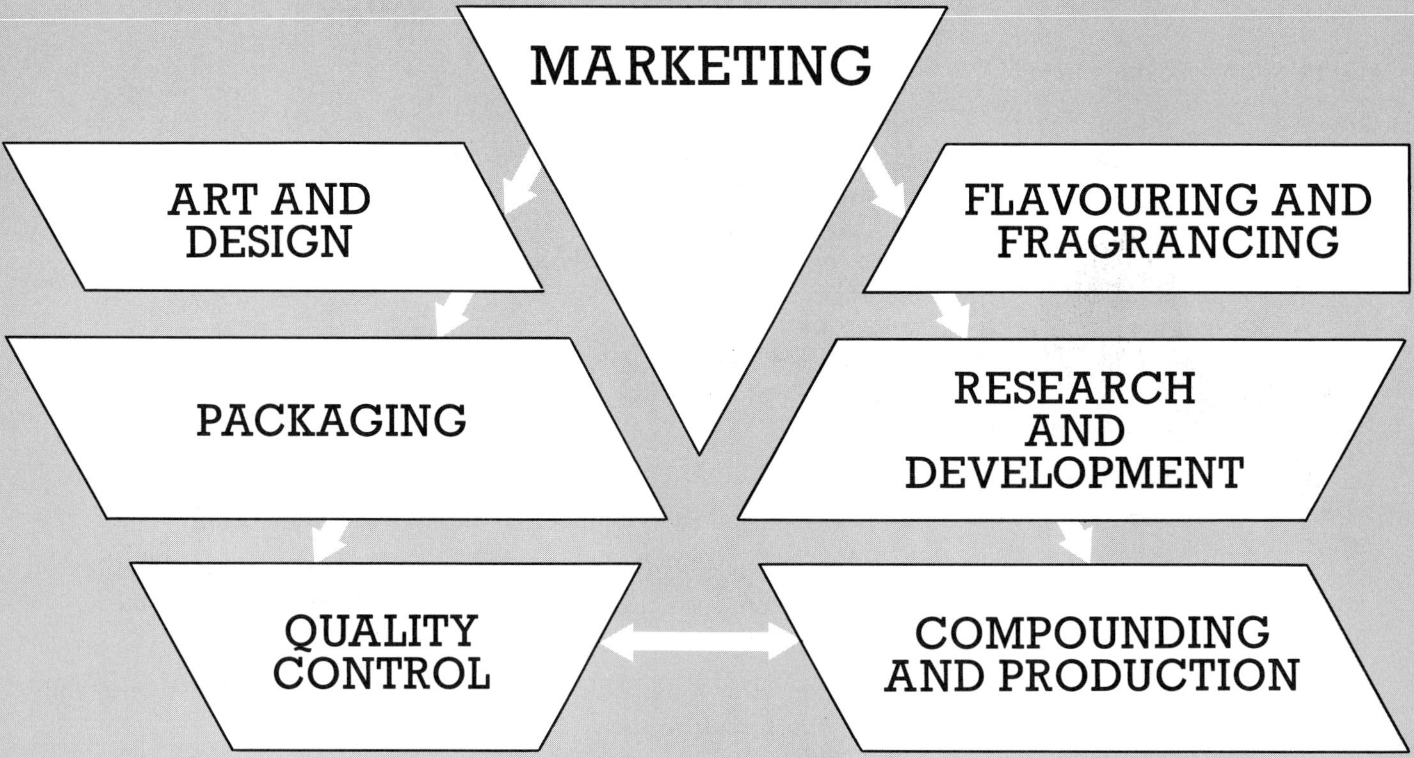

MARKETING

ART AND DESIGN

FLAVOURING AND FRAGRANCING

PACKAGING

RESEARCH AND DEVELOPMENT

QUALITY CONTROL

COMPOUNDING AND PRODUCTION

1. Pick any two of the following roles, and describe why each role is so important in a manufacturing company.
   quality control technician
   flavour technician
   research and development technician
   packaging designer
   packaging technician
   fragrance technician
   compounder
   marketing manager

2. Why do you think artificial flavours and fragrances have to be approved by government before they can be used?

3. Soap is an emulsifying agent. How does it work?

4. If a cream emulsion does not wash off your hand with water, what type of emulsion is present?

5. Why is it a good idea to blindfold people when they are doing a taste test?

6. Why do a lot of label instructions on personal care products suggest you try the product on a small part of your skin first?

7. Why must you never pipette bleach by mouth?

8. "New and Improved" is a slogan often used when advertising a product.
   What do the advertisers want you to believe about their product?
   Should you always believe advertising hype?

9. Select your favourite dessert mix, ice cream, jello, or packaged food. Write down the ingredient listing from the label.
   The first mentioned ingredient makes up the greatest percentage in the mixture.
   Whereabout are flavours found in the listing? What does that tell you about the quantity of flavouring in your favourite product?

10. Describe your favourite product advertisement on television. Do you buy the product being advertised? Does anyone in your family buy the product?

11. Describe a television advertisement that irritates you. What is the product being advertised? Why does the advertisement irritate you?

12. Advertising flyers come to your home either by mail, with the newspapers, or by hand delivery.
    (a) Do you like this kind of advertising? Why?
    (b) Do you think this kind of advertising is effective? Why?
    (c) Do you see any problems for our environment? Why?

13. "All Natural" is used to suggest that a product is good for you. Is this necessarily the case?

14. What is your favourite fragrance? Why do you think it attracts you?

15. If you had to choose one of the careers in a manufaturing company, which career would you choose? Why?

16. What are the "three P's" of packaging success? Explain the role of each of the P's.

14 THE CHEMISTRY OF METALS

Metals are everywhere.

CONTENTS

14.1 Things You Would Just Hate to Give Up!

In a small group, discuss and list all objects that you like and use every day. Through group consensus, include only those items that you would hate to lose. Compare your list to those of the other groups. Add or delete items so that the class ends up with one list which is representative of the people in the class.

Organize your list of items into groups with common characteristics. Some examples could be:

(a) items made from a special type of material
(b) items that require energy to work
(c) items that require energy to produce

Place an item under more than one heading if necessary.

You will find that many things that are important to you are metallic (such as jewellery, means of transportation, kitchen appliances, and compact discs). Some of the items in your list require electrical energy to produce them or make them operate (for example, music systems, televisions, and kitchen appliances).

In earlier chapters we dealt with the structure of the atom, how atoms can lose or gain electrons, and how ions in solution are good conductors of electricity. This would all suggest that there might be some connection between chemical reactions and electricity. In this chapter we will explore this idea further.

Canadians spend approximately a billion dollars a year on jewellery. The jewellery industry involves not only retail sales but also design and manufacture. Most of the people who do well in this industry have some business, administrative, and financial ability. They should also understand the craft of jewellery making. A skilled jewellery maker must know the properties of gems and metals.

Sandra Noble-Goss and Andrew Goss are two creative jewellery makers who live and work in Owen Sound, Ontario. They work mostly with silver, brass, copper, stainless steel, and gold. Their speciality is the **patination** of metals to produce beautifully coloured jewellery. (Patination is the process of discolouring the surface of an object using chemicals or heat.) They use a variety of chemicals and employ waxes and acrylics to protect their jewellery.

Sandra and Andrew were married in 1969. Their ambition was to be self-employed, live in the country, and travel as much as possible. They discovered that they both had a talent for jewellery making, so they took a night course in jewellery making at Central Technical School in Toronto. Later, they went to England to study jewellery making for one year at Hornsey College in London. When they returned to Canada, they studied jewellery making at George Brown College in Toronto for two more years. They then went into business as jewellery makers. In the early 1980s a woman came to work with them. She had studied patination techniques with another jeweller. Sandra and Andrew started to experiment with patination and have made many outstanding pieces of patinated jewellery (shown below).

Both Sandra and Andrew studied chemistry at high school and Andrew had one year of science at university. They therefore have a fair knowledge of handling chemicals safely, and they are able to use their knowledge to experiment further with the technique of patination. Sandra says that she wishes she had had more opportunity to study applied chemistry at school.

At first Sandra and Andrew worked without a break. Now they take August off to renew their creative juices and enjoy their family. Their satisfaction with their lives stems from the fact that they are able to spend time with their children, that they are successful at what they do, that they have established their names in the jewellery field, and that they are making a living from the work they enjoy. Their work has not stagnated. Rather it has developed and evolved over the years.

Patinated jewellery made by Sandra Noble-Goss and Andrew Goss.

14.2 Electrical Energy and Reactivity of Metals

In Chapter 5, you used single displacement reactions to determine an order of reactivity for certain metals. In this investigation you will use pairs of different metals to generate electricity. By studying a series of metal pairs, you can also determine an order of reactivity.

Materials

safety goggles
250-mL beaker
1 mol/L sodium chloride solution
electrical leads fitted with clips at one end and plugs or clips at the other end
voltmeter (reading to at least 1.5 V)
emery paper or fine steel wool
aluminum
copper
iron
lead
magnesium
nickel
tin

Method

1. List as many different metal pairs as you can form from the supply provided.

2. Draw up a chart with the following headings:

Metal attached to positive terminal of voltmeter	Metal attached to negative terminal of voltmeter	Voltmeter reading (V)

3. Clean each metal surface thoroughly with emery paper or steel wool.

4. Place 100 mL of sodium chloride solution in the 250-mL beaker.

5. Place the first pair of metals in the solution at opposite sides of the beaker (Figure 1).

Fig. 1

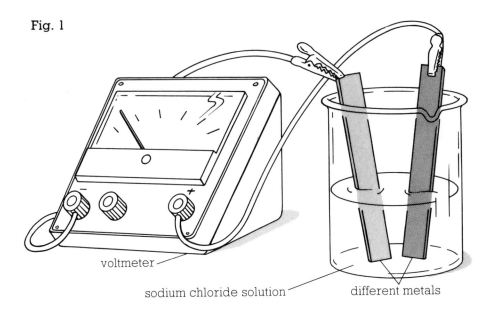

voltmeter

sodium chloride solution   different metals

6. Connect the metals to the voltmeter with the electrical leads. If the needle deflects below zero, then reverse the leads.

7. If the voltmeter has more than one scale setting, select the one that will give the largest needle deflection. Record the highest reading obtained for the pair of metals.

8. Repeat steps 5 to 7 for all the other possible metal pairs.

Follow-up

1. From your results, select the metal that was attached to the negative terminal of the voltmeter the *most frequently*. This is the most reactive metal that you used. Continue until you have listed all the metals from most reactive to least reactive. If you have difficulty deciding between any two metals, repeat the experiment with the two metals in questions.

2. Look at your results from the displacement experiments carried out in Chapter 5. Does the order of reactivity from those experiments agree with your results now? Suggest a possible cause if the results are not in agreement.

Oxidation and Reduction

The process of losing electrons and becoming more positively charged is called **oxidation**:

$$Zn \rightarrow Zn^{2+} + 2e^{1-}$$

The reverse process where a substance gains electrons and becomes less positively charged is called **reduction**:

$$Zn^{2+} + 2e^{1-} \rightarrow Zn$$

An electrolyte is any substance, such as an ionic compound, that will form a solution which conducts electricity.

When two different metals are placed in an electrolyte solution, the more reactive metal is oxidized, that is, it loses electrons. The electrons flow from this metal to the negative terminal of the voltmeter and then from the positive terminal to the other metal (Figure 2). In your experiment, the greater the voltmeter reading, the greater the difference in reactivity of the two metals.

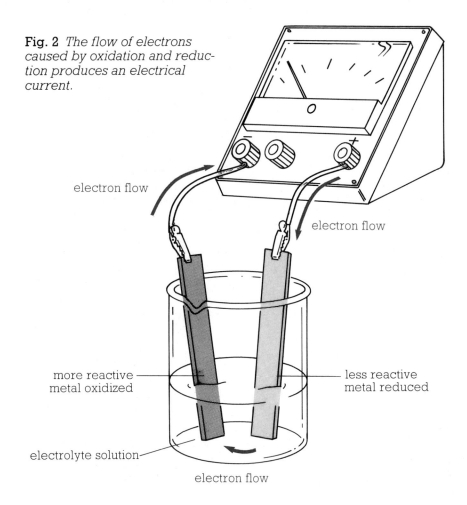

Fig. 2 *The flow of electrons caused by oxidation and reduction produces an electrical current.*

electron flow

electron flow

more reactive metal oxidized

less reactive metal reduced

electrolyte solution

electron flow

14.3 Reacting Magnesium With Water

By observing many different reactions, chemists can list the metals, from most to least reactive. This list is called the **activity series**. It can be used to predict the products of single displacement reactions.

Of interest in this list is the inclusion of hydrogen. Hydrogen is not a metal. It does not conduct electricity. It can, however, be oxidized to positive hydrogen ions. In this way, it is like a metal.

To place hydrogen in the activity series, you will have to find which metals can and which cannot displace hydrogen. From your work in Chapter 5, do you remember which metals can displace hydrogen from hydrogen oxide (water)?

Magnesium does not appear to react with cold water. Does it mean that magnesium is less reactive than hydrogen? Perhaps the reaction with cold water is too slow to be observed over a 5 min period. You will now investigate the reaction of heated magnesium with steam.

The reaction of magnesium with steam should be demonstrated by the teacher.

Materials

safety goggles
magnesium ribbon
250-mL Erlenmeyer flask
hotplate
Bunsen burner
retort rod, ring clamp and gauze
boiling chips
emery paper or fine steel wool
tongs
matches

Method

1. Clean a 5-cm strip of magnesium ribbon with emery paper or steel wool until the surface is shiny.

2. Place the Erlenmeyer flask containing about 50 mL of water on a hotplate.

3. Add two boiling chips and bring the water to the boil.

4. When a strong stream of steam exits from the Erlenmeyer flask, place the magnesium ribbon in the steam for 2 to 3 min. Carefully check the surface of the magnesium and record your observations.

5. Place a burning match in the steam coming out of the Erlenmeyer flask. Record what happens to the match.

6. Heat the magnesium strip in the Bunsen flame until it just ignites. Quickly place the burning magnesium in the steam. Record your observations.

Do not look directly at the flame of burning magnesium.

Follow-up

1. What evidence suggests magnesium reacts with steam in step 4?

2. Does steam support the combustion of the match?

3. What gas supports combustion?

4. Does steam support the combustion of magnesium? Where does the burning magnesium get the gas needed for combustion?

5. Write a balanced chemical equation showing the reaction between magnesium and water.

6. In Chapter 9 you learned that oxides of metals react with water to produce a base. Write a balanced chemical equation showing how magnesium oxide reacts with water to produce magnesium hydroxide.

7. Based on your work in Chapter 5, draw up a chart showing how lithium, sodium, potassium, calcium, and magnesium react with water.

Lithium	Sodium	Potassium	Calcium	Magnesium

14.4 Reacting Metals With Acid

Many metals which cannot displace hydrogen from water can displace hydrogen from an acid solution. In the following experiment, you will once again be looking for relative activity of the metals used.

Materials

safety goggles
calcium, magnesium, aluminum, zinc, iron, and copper (one small piece of each)
emery paper or steel wool
six medium sized test tubes
dilute hydrochloric acid (2 mol/L)

Method

1. Clean each piece of metal with emery paper or steel wool.

2. Pour approximately 5 mL of dilute hydrochloric acid into each test tube.

3. Place each piece of metal into a test tube containing hydrochloric acid.

4. Record all observations. Note the speed with which bubbles of gas form. Use this as an indication of the activity of the metal.

Follow-up

1. What evidence suggested that some of the metals reacted with the hydrochloric acid?

2. Based on your observations, list the six metals in order from most to least reactive.

3. Write balanced chemical equations for all the reactions studied in this investigation. Use a slash through the equation arrow for the metals that did not react.

4. Based on this experiment and your previous experiments of reacting metals with water and steam, list, in order from most to least reactive, the elements aluminum, calcium, copper, hydrogen, iron, lithium, magnesium, potassium, sodium, and zinc.

14.5 A New Look at the Activity Series

Taking all the experimental evidence into account, chemists have placed the metals in an order of reactivity. The order may not agree with your experimental observations. For example, when reacting with cold water, potassium appears to be more reactive than lithium. According to the activity series, lithium is more reactive than potassium. Chemists believe that the results are not inconsistent. It is just that we are comparing different things. Lithium remains solid when reacting with water, whereas potassium melts, and reacts as a liquid. The liquid is easier to break apart, has a larger surface area, and therefore reacts more quickly.

Found in nature only as compounds	Li K Ba Ca Na	Displace hydrogen from cold water
	Mg Al Mn Zn Cr Fe	Displace hydrogen from steam
	Co Ni Sn Pb	Displace hydrogen from acids
Found in both compounds and as free elements	H Cu Ag Hg	
Found only as free elements	Pt Au	Do not displace hydrogen from acids

As we move up the activity series, each metal is more reactive than the ones below it. The series allows us to predict which metals will react in single displacement reactions. For example, magnesium is more reactive than copper and the following reaction is therefore possible:

$$Mg_{(s)} + CuSO_{4(aq)} \rightarrow MgSO_{4(aq)} + Cu_{(s)}$$

We refer to 100% gold as 24 karat gold. The common purities of gold used in jewellery are 10 kt (10/24 or 42%), 14 kt (14/24 or 58%), and 18 kt (18/24 or 75%).

Fig. 3 *The gold mask of Tutankahun. It has been estimated that all the gold ever refined would occupy a cube measuring approximately 15 m on each side.*

But if a piece of copper is placed in a solution of magnesium sulfate, there will be no reaction.

The more reactive a metal is, the less likely that it can be found in nature as a free element. Gold is the least reactive metal, and it exists as a free element. Gold was therefore one of the earliest metals discovered. Because of its scarcity, its beautiful colour, and its resistance to corrosion, gold has always been prized for decorative purposes. It was often used in objects of worship by earlier civilizations. Today it is still almost universally accepted as a monetary standard. In reality, pure gold is not a very useful metal. It is too soft for use as coinage or jewellery and must be mixed with other metals.

Questions

Write balanced chemical equations for the following reactions. Place a slash through the arrow ($\nrightarrow$) if a reaction is not possible:
(a) tin in a solution of zinc sulfate
(b) magnesium in a solution of aluminum chloride
(c) nickel in sulfuric acid solution
(d) gold heated in steam

14.6 Hydrogen—The Most Abundant Element in the Universe

Fig. 4 *Astronomers believe that our sun and other visible stars are composed mostly of hydrogen. The energy we get from the sun results from a nuclear fusion process in which hydrogen is converted into helium.*

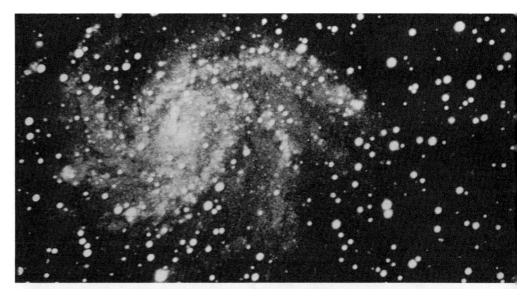

Fig. 5 *In 1766, Henry Cavendish proved that the gas obtained when metals were added to acid solution was an element and produced only water when burned in air. The name hydrogen means "water maker."*

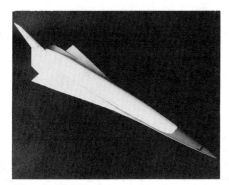

Fig. 6 *This hypersonic transport plane, still under development, uses hydrogen as fuel.*

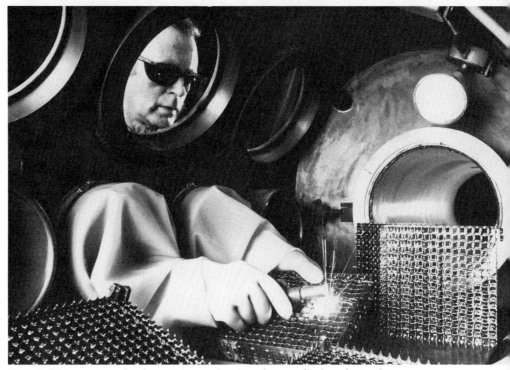

Fig. 7 *The oxygen-hydrogen reaction can be explosive, but when controlled, is used in the oxyhydrogen blowtorch (with temperatures up to 3000°C). The atomic-hydrogen welding torch can burn at 4000°C.*

Fig. 10 *As the lightest material known, hydrogen was used to fill balloons. The first recorded air battle was between two hydrogen-filled balloons in the Franco-Prussian War in 1870. The worst airship disaster occurred in 1937 when the airship Hindenburg exploded and burned at Lakehurst, New Jersey. The use of hydrogen in balloons ended with the discovery of helium.*

(a) copper(II) oxide   (b) copper

Fig. 8 *Hydrogen is a good reducing agent in that it can remove oxygen from certain metallic oxides leaving the free metal. The picture shows black copper(II) oxide (left) and metallic copper (right).*

Fig. 9 *With nickel as a catalyst, hydrogen is used to change animal and vegetable oils into solid fats for baking and cooking. Margarine is made this way.*

Fig. 11 *Hydrogen is used as a rocket fuel and will likely be used commercially as an alternative to fossil fuels. Technology must now solve the problem of efficiently storing the hydrogen and then releasing it on demand.*

14.7 Electrochemical Cells

A previous section shows that it is relatively easy to make an **electrochemical cell**: a device for obtaining electrical energy from a chemical reaction. However, the simple cells that you made from pairs of metals were unlikely to give stable voltmeter readings for a long time. Researchers and technologists have designed more reliable batteries consisting of one or more cells.

There is much interest today in electrically operated cars and trucks (Figure 13). If conventional lead-acid batteries are used, many of them would be required and they would be too heavy.

Fig. 12 *Count Alessandro Volta produced the first battery in the late eighteenth century. The volt, the unit of electrical potential, is named after him.*

Fig. 13 *There has been a lot of research in the production of electric cars and vans.*

Scientists are constantly looking for light, high powered batteries. A Toronto company is now working on a litium-iron(II) sulfide battery which is as powerful as the lead-acid battery but is only about one third as heavy. A recently made plastic, called polyacetylene, with a suitable chemical added, is a good conductor of electricity. Batteries made from polyacetylene, with lithium perchlorate as the electrolyte, are light and can be recharged and reused almost indefinitely. The materials do not deteriorate as they do in lead-acid batteries. A Vancouver company is planning to produce lithium-molybdenum(IV) sulfide batteries for consumer electronics products. These are rechargeable batteries and should last twice as long as nickel-cadmium batteries. Research continues.

Fig. 14 *Can you list some of the appliances for which these batteries are used?*

337

All electrochemical cells work on the same principle (Figure 15). Two different electrodes are needed. Ions are exchanged from one electrode to the other through an electrolyte solution. If the cell is connected in a circuit, the movement of ions in the solution and electrons through the circuit will produce an electrical current.

Fig. 15 *The principle of an electrochemical cell—a Daniell cell.*

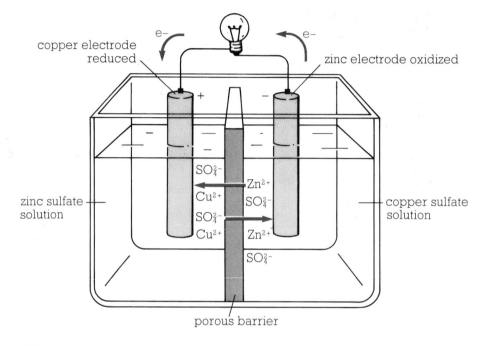

Materials

safety goggles
250-mL beaker
two 100-mL beakers
U-tube or thick string or porous cup
voltmeter
Bunsen burner
emery paper or fine steel wool
cotton batting
saturated potassium chloride solution
strip of copper
strip of zinc
carbon rod
carbon strip
manganese(IV) oxide powder
1 mol/L copper(II) sulfate solution
1 mol/L zinc sulfate solution
saturated ammonium chloride solution
tongs

I. *Daniell Cell*

1. If a porous cup is not available, use a "salt bridge." The salt bridge can be constructed in two ways. Fill the U-tube with saturated potassium chloride solution. Plug each open end with a large piece of cotton batting. If U-tubes are not available, then soak a thick piece of string in saturated potassium chloride solution for about 5 min. The salt bridge is used to form a continuous circuit between the two solutions.

2. Clean the surface of the copper and the zinc.

Fig. 16 *Set-up for the Daniell cell.*

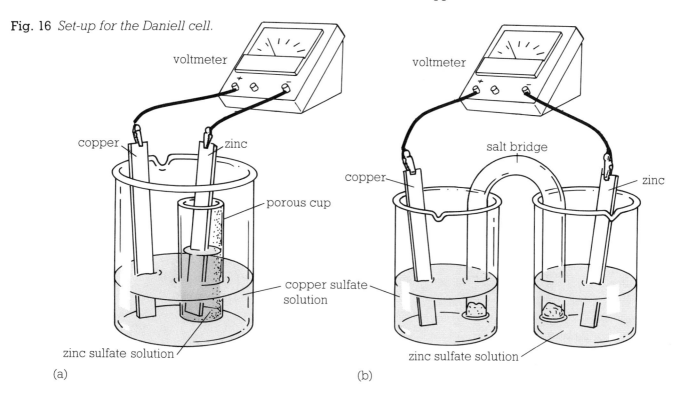

3. Set up the apparatus as in Figure 16a if you have a porous cup. If you are using the salt bridge, follow Figure 16b. Quickly invert the U-tube and place the open ends beneath the surface of the liquids in each beaker. if you are using the string instead of the U-tube, lift it out of the saturated potassium chloride solution and drape it over the two beakers, with one end in each liquid.

4. Connect the metal electrodes to the voltmeter.

5. Record the voltmeter reading and observe what happens to this reading over a 5 min period.

II. *Wet Sal Ammoniac Cell*

1. Place some saturated ammonium chloride solution in the beaker (Figure 17).

Fig. 17 *The wet sal ammoniac cell.*

2. Use a clean piece of zinc metal as one electrode.

3. Heat the carbon rod to red heat for about 5 min to drive off any impurities. Allow it to cool before placing it in the solution as the second electrode.

4. Attach the electrodes to a voltmeter. Record the voltmeter reading and observe what happens over a 5 min period.

III. *Dry Sal Ammoniac Cell*

1. Soak a piece of cotton batting in the ammonium chloride solution.

2. Place the cotton batting between a zinc strip and a carbon strip.

3. Connect the two electrodes to the voltmeter (Figure 18) and record the reading. Note what happens over a 5 to 10 min period.

The dry sal ammoniac cell is used in many non-rechargeable or non-alkaline batteries. If you have such a battery at home, you can dissect it to see what is inside. Do not get any chemicals on yourself and thoroughly clean any equipment you use.

Fig. 18 *A simulation of the dry sal ammoniac cell.*

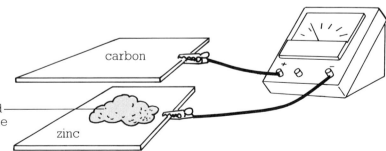

4. Use tongs to coat the cotton batting with manganese(IV) oxide powder. Repeat steps 1 to 3. Is the voltmeter reading more stable over the 5 to 10 min period?

Follow-up

1. What happened to the voltmeter reading for the wet sal ammoniac cell? Can you suggest how the cell could once more be rejuvenated?

2. The wet sal ammoniac cell and the Daniell cell are not often used today. How would you use these cells to provide sufficient power to operate a small portable radio or cassette deck? Try it.

FUEL CELLS

Fuel cells are batteries into which a fuel is continuously fed and from which electricity is continuously drawn off. To turn off the fuel cell, you stop the flow of fuel. Some of the most common fuels used are hydrogen, methane, ammonia, hydrazine, and glucose. Oxygen is most often used as the oxidizer with these fuels. This type of cell is used as an auxiliary power supply in spacecraft and in submarines (Figure 19). Research is underway to produce a fuel cell for heart pacemakers. The cell would draw glucose and oxygen directly from the blood and would never have to be replaced.

Fig. 19 *Fuel cells are often used in submarines.*

14.8 Electrolysis

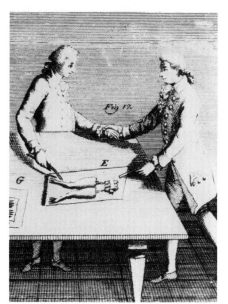

Fig. 20 *Galvani's experiment.*

In 1786, Luigi Galvani attached a piece of copper to a nerve, and a piece of iron to a muscle in a frog's leg. He noted that the frog's leg could be made to twitch if contact was made between the two metals. Ten years later, Allesandro Volta demonstrated that electrical energy could be produced from a chemical reaction. He separated two different metals with a piece of hide moistened with salt solution. This arrangement produced an electrical current when the metals were brought into contact. To increase the intensity of the electrical current, Volta stacked pairs of the two different metals on top of each other. This became known as the **voltaic pile**. In 1800, William Nicholson and Anthony Carlisle showed that electrical current from a voltaic pile could be used to decompose water into hydrogen and oxygen. In 1807, Sir Humphrey Davy discovered the elements potassium and sodium. These elements were produced when an electrical current was used to decompose two different solid materials. This electrolytic process is still used today to obtain pure forms of elements such as chlorine, aluminum, hydrogen, and oxygen. The process is also used in the electro-plating and electroforming industry.

Electrolysis is the process in which an ionic compound or water is decomposed by means of an electrical current (Figure 21). The ionic compound is dissolved in water to form the electrolyte solution. Two electrodes are placed in the solution and an external battery is used to pass electrical energy through the solution. The positive electrode is called the **anode** and the negative electrode is called the **cathode**. Negative ions in the solution move to the anode. There they lose electrons and are oxidized. Positive ions move to the cathode. There they gain electrons and are reduced.

Fig. 21 *The process of electrolysis.*

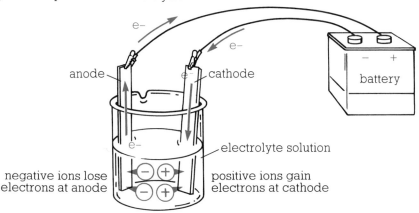

The products obtained in this process depend on a number of factors such as:

(a) the concentration of the electrolyte
(b) the type of electrolyte
(c) the strength of the applied electrical current
(d) the type of electrodes

Let us first look at a simple example of electrolysis — that of a solution of copper(II) chloride. In solution, the copper(II) chloride breaks up into copper(II) ions and chloride ions:

$$CuCl_2 \rightarrow Cu^{2+} + 2Cl^{1-}$$

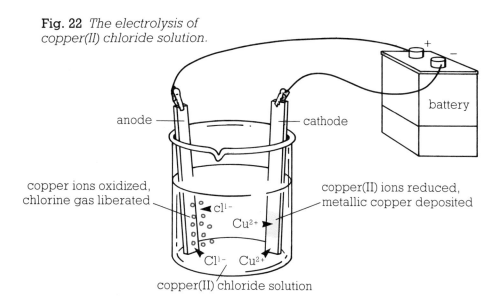

Fig. 22 *The electrolysis of copper(II) chloride solution.*

When the electrodes are placed in the solution and the battery connected, the positive copper(II) ions will move to the cathode. There they accept two electrons and are reduced to metallic copper:

$$Cu^{2+} + 2e^{1-} \rightarrow Cu$$

The negative chloride ions move to the anode. There they lose electrons and are oxidized to chlorine molecules:

$$2Cl^{1-} \rightarrow Cl_2 + 2e^{1-}$$

The electrolysis of a saturated sodium chloride solution, however, produces hydrogen gas at the cathode and chlorine gas at the anode.

When sodium chloride dissolves in water, we get sodium ions and chloride ions:

$$NaCl \rightarrow Na^{1+} + Cl^{1-}$$

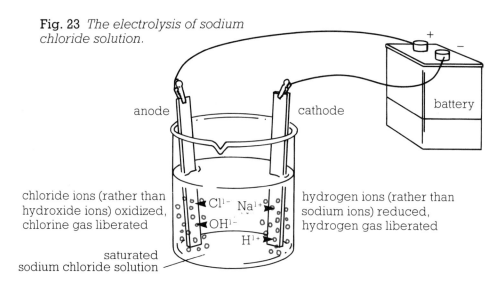

Fig. 23 *The electrolysis of sodium chloride solution.*

anode

cathode

battery

chloride ions (rather than hydroxide ions) oxidized, chlorine gas liberated

Cl^{1-} Na^{1+}
OH^{1-}
H^{1+}

hydrogen ions (rather than sodium ions) reduced, hydrogen gas liberated

saturated sodium chloride solution

Chorine gas forms at the anode as in the electrolysis of copper(II) chloride. But why does hydrogen gas form at the cathode? At first chemists believed that two reactions were taking place at the cathode.

(a) The positive sodium ions each gained an electron to become metallic sodium atoms:

$$Na^{1+} + 1e^{1-} \rightarrow Na$$

(b) The metallic sodium, being more reactive than hydrogen, then displaced hydrogen from water, forming sodium hydroxide and hydrogen:

$$2Na + 2H_2O \rightarrow 2NaOH + H_2$$

Some chemists do not agree with the above explanation because there is no evidence that sodium forms in this way. They have suggested an alternative way of producing hydrogen gas. Neutral water contains a very small concentration of hydrogen ions and hydroxide ions:

$$H_2O \rightarrow H^{1+} + OH^{1-}$$

The water remains neutral because the concentrations of these ions are equal. When the electrodes are placed in the sodium chloride solution and a battery is connected, positive sodium and hydrogen ions move to the cathode. There hydrogen ions can gain electrons more easily than sodium ions can. The hydrogen ions are therefore changed into hydrogen gas, leaving the sodium ions in solution:

$$2H^{1+} + 2e^{1-} \rightarrow H_2$$

Since sodium is more reactive than hydrogen, sodium is more easily oxidized to sodium ions than hydrogen to hydrogen ions. In the reduction process, the reverse is true. Hydrogen ions are more easily reduced than sodium ions.

Chloride and hydroxide ions move to the anode. There the situation is a little more complicated. At very low concentrations of chloride ion, the hydroxide ion loses electrons and is changed into oxygen gas:

$$4OH^{1-} \rightarrow 2H_2O + O_2 + 4e^{1-}$$

With high concentrations of chloride ion, such as in a saturated solution, the chloride ion loses electrons and is converted into chlorine gas.

Questions

Titanium is a fairly abundant metal but it is very expensive to produce from its ores. Gram for gram it is stronger than steel and many other metals. All we need now is a cheap way to produce it.

1. Some metals, such as titanium, are produced using displacement reactions. Other metals, such as aluminum, are prepared by electrolysis. If you were a manufacturer, where would you locate your plant for producing metals using electrolysis? Explain your answer.

2. Aluminum cans require more energy to produce than steel cans. The aluminum cans, however, are lighter and take longer to corrode. Aluminum also requires less energy to recycle. Make a case for the use of aluminum or steel cans and indicate why you think they are, or are not, being used in Canada today.

Investigation

14.9 Electrolysis of Potassium Iodide

In this experiment you will be electrolyzing a potassium iodide solution. Careful observation will enable you to identify the products formed at each electrode.

Materials

safety goggles
1 mol/L potassium iodide solution
starch indicator solution
phenolphthalein indicator solution
2 carbon electrodes
12-V battery
electrical leads
U-tube
retort stand and clamp
alligator clips

Starch indicator in the presence of iodine turns a blue-black colour. Phenolphthalein is red in a basic solution and colourless in an acidic solution.

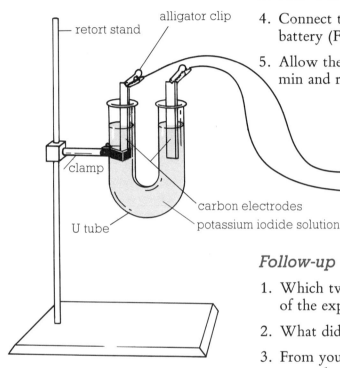

Fig. 24 *Set-up for electrolysis of potassium iodide solution.*

- retort stand
- alligator clip
- clamp
- U tube
- carbon electrodes
- potassium iodide solution
- 12 volt battery

Refer to test N2 in Chapter 11 Qualitative Analysis.

Method

1. Add a few drops of starch indicator solution and phenolphthalein indicator solution to the potassium iodide solution.

2. Fill the U-tube with this mixture until it is almost full.

3. Place a carbon electrode in each arm of the U-tube.

4. Connect the carbon electrodes to the terminals of the 12-V battery (Figure 24).

5. Allow the current to pass through the solution for about 5 to 10 min and record all your observations.

Follow-up

1. Which two positive ions are present in solution at the beginning of the experiment?

2. What did you observe at the cathode (negative electrode)?

3. From your observations, which positive ion gained electrons and was reduced at the cathode?

4. Write the equation showing what happened at the cathode.

5. Which two negative ions are present in solution at the beginning of the experiment?

6. What did you observe at the anode (positive electrode)?

7. From your observations, which negative ion lost electrons and was oxidized at the anode?

8. Write the equation showing what happened at the anode.

9. When zinc bromide solution is electrolyzed, a fine black metallic material deposits on the cathode. The liquid around the positive electrode turns brown. When some of this brown liquid is shaken with aqueous chlorine solution and 1,1,2-trichloro-1,2,2-trifluoroethane (TCTFE), the TCTFE layer turns yellow. Write equations to show what happened at each of the electrodes.

14.10 Electroplating

Electroplating uses an external source of electrical energy to coat an object with a particular metal (Figure 25). The most common metals used for plating are chromium, nickel, cadmium, tin, silver, copper, and gold.

All electroplating is done in essentially the same way. The electrolyte used must be an ionic compound containing the metal ion to be used for plating. The anode is also made from the metal that is being used for plating. The cathode is the object to be plated. The object must conduct electricity and is therefore usually metallic.

Copper plating can be used as an example. The electrolyte solution is a mixture containing copper(II) sulfate. The anode is a clean piece of copper. The cathode is the metal object you wish to plate.

Successful electroplating depends on the cleanliness of the object being plated, the purity of the electrolyte solution, the strength of the electrical current, and the time taken.

Fig. 25 *Electroplating is used to produce an attractive and durable finish on many products.*

Many toxic chemicals are used in the cleaning and plating processes of electroplating. The wastes from electroplating plants must be carefully handled to avoid polluting the environment.

Prepare the copper(II) sulfate solution by dissolving 70 g of copper(II) sulfate pentahydrate in 500 mL of distilled water, then adding 25 mL of ethanol and 15 mL of concentrated sulfuric acid.

Materials

safety goggles
strip of copper
small object to be plated
variable voltage direct current source
ammeter if available
rheostat if available
emery paper or fine steel wool
dilute hydrochloric acid (2 mol/L)
two 250-mL beakers
electrical leads
copper(II) sulfate solution
tongs

Method

1. Roughly estimate the area (in cm²) of the surface of the object being plated.

2. Clean the object by dipping it into the hydrochloric acid and then rinsing thoroughly with water. Polish the surface with emery paper or steel wool. Then avoid handling the object with your fingers.

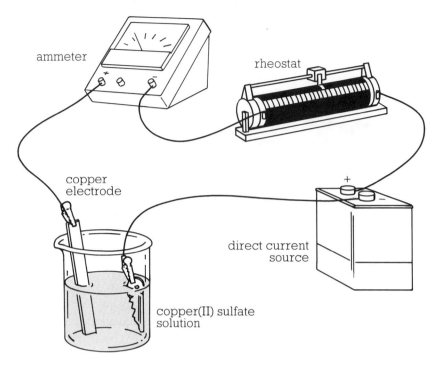

Fig. 26 *Set-up for electroplating.*

ammeter

rheostat

copper electrode

direct current source

copper(II) sulfate solution

3. Set up the apparatus as in Figure 26.

4. Start with a low electrical potential (1.5 to 3 V) and adjust the rheostat until the ammeter gives a reading of about 0.002 A for every square centimetre of object to be plated. If you are not using an ammeter and rheostat, then use 1.5 V and keep the two electrodes as far apart as possible in the 250-mL beaker. Make sure the copper plates on *slowly*. If it goes on too quickly, it will not be shiny and will easily rub off. Try a larger beaker if this happens.

5. If your object does not plate well the first time, repeat the procedure but lower the electrical current. The slower the process, the better the appearance of the final product.

Follow-up

1. Suggest a possible electrolyte and specify the anode needed to plate an object with:
   (a) nickel
   (b) silver
   (c) chromium
   (d) gold

2. The object to be plated must be free of any surface dirt or corrosion. Explain why.

14.11 Corrosion and the Environment

Corrosion is the destruction of metals caused by reactions with gases or liquids in the environment. Different metals are affected differently but very few will not corrode with time. Each year millions and millions of dollars are spent trying to control the problem of corrosion.

Corrosion involves oxidation and reduction. Two electrode sites are needed for corrosion to occur: the anode where oxidation takes place, and the cathode where reduction occurs. If the cathode and anode are connected by an electrolyte solution then corrosion begins.

The rusting of iron is a typical example of corrosion. The iron atoms are oxidized to iron(II) ions at the anode site:

$$Fe \rightarrow Fe^{2+} + 2e^{1-}$$

Oxygen in the presence of water at the cathode site is changed into hydroxide ions:

$$O_2 + 2H_2O + 4e^{1-} \rightarrow 4OH^{1-}$$

The iron(II) ions then combine with the hydroxide ions to form iron(II) hydroxide:

$$2Fe^{2+} + 4OH^{1-} \rightarrow 2Fe(OH)_2$$

This is further oxidized to iron(III) oxide, Fe_2O_3, which we call rust.

Materials

safety goggles	three 250-mL beakers
fine steel wool	spatula
5 medium sized test tubes	plastic wrap
distilled water	acetone
sodium chloride	long eye dropper
hotplate	thermometer
tongs	

Method

1. Pour about 100 mL of distilled water into the 250-mL beaker and bring it to the boil. Allow it to simmer for 5 min. Remove the beaker from the hotplate, cover it with plastic wrap and allow it to cool to room temperature.

2. Remove any grease on the steel wool by dipping it in acetone contained in a beaker. Allow the steel wool to dry and tear off five pieces of equal size. Each piece should fill a 2-cm depth in a test tube. Place a piece in each of the five test tubes (Figure 27).

Fig. 27

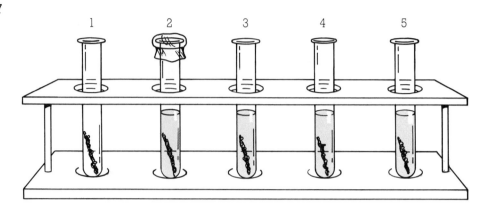

There is no air dissolved in the boiled distilled water.

3. Test tube 1: Keep as is.
   Test tube 2: Cover the steel wool with boiled distilled water from step 1. Seal the test tube with plastic wrap.
   Test tube 3: Cover the steel wool with regular aerated distilled water.
   Test tube 4: Cover the steel wool with regular aerated distilled water.
   Test tube 5: Dissolve a spatula full of sodium chloride in about 20 mL of distilled water. Cover the steel wool with this solution.

4. Place test tube 4 in a beaker of water at about 40°C and maintain it at this temperature.

5. Aerate the liquid in test tubes 3, 4, and 5 every 5 to 10 min by bubbling air through each liquid with a long eye dropper.

6. Continue the experiment for as long a period of time as possible. Record all your observations.

Follow-up

1. List the factors that appear to affect the rate at which steel wool corrodes.

2. Did the steel wool corrode faster in test tube 3 or test tube 4?

3. What effect did the dissolved salt have on the rate of corrosion of the steel wool?

4. How did aeration affect the rate of corrosion?

5. Why do cars parked in heated garages in the winter corrode faster than cars parked outside?

6. Explain why an iron nail can be kept on the shelf in a store for many days without showing signs of rust, but rusts quickly when placed in aerated water.

Investigation

14.12 Other Factors That Affect Corrosion

Materials

Galvanized means covered with zinc.

safety goggles
4 iron nails (non-galvanized)
2 petri dishes with lids
agar
distilled water
potassium ferricyanide solution (0.2 mol/L)
magnesium ribbon
copper wire
pair of pliers
250-mL beaker
hotplate
acetone
emery paper or steel wool

Method

1. Clean four iron nails with steel wool or emery paper. Rinse each nail in acetone to remove grease. Allow to dry.

2. Nail 1: Leave alone.
   Nail 2: Bend in the middle several times and then leave bent.
   Nail 3: Wrap copper wire tightly around just the head portion of the nail.
   Nail 4: Wrap magnesium ribbon tightly around most of the length of the nail.

There must be tight contact between the nail and the metal wrapped around it.

3. Heat 100 mL of distilled water to boiling, add 1 g of agar and stir for 3 min. Add 10 drops of potassium ferricyanide solution. Allow the mixture to cool to room temperature without hardening.

351

4. Place nails 1 and 2 in one petri dish and nails 3 and 4 in a second petri dish (Figure 28). Cover the nails with the cool agar solution. Cover each petri dish and allow to stand overnight.

5. Draw labelled diagrams of your results. Use shading or coloured pencils to indicate where corrosion was found.

Fig. 28

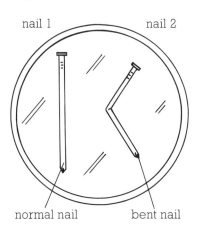
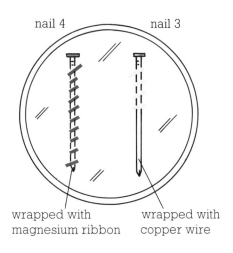

Potassium ferricyanide gives a blue colour when iron(II) ions are present. This colour indicates where the nail is rusting. Potassium ferricyanide gives a white colour in the presence of magnesium ions, which are formed when magnesium oxidizes.

Follow-up

1. Where does corrosion form most rapidly on nail 1? Why do you think this part of the nail corrodes first?

2. Does nail 2 confirm your answer to question 1? Explain.

3. Did the iron nail wrapped in the copper wire show any signs of corrosion? Did the copper wire itself show any signs of corrosion?

4. Did the iron nail wrapped in the magnesium ribbon show any signs of corrosion? Did the magnesium itself show any signs of corrosion?

5. Use the activity series to explain the result when copper and magnesium are attached to the iron nail.

6. Explain why magnesium rods are sometimes placed in hot water tanks.

14.13 Preventing Corrosion

With so much money needed to repair corrosion damage, many companies have expensive research programs to find ways of combatting corrosion. One of the easiest methods is to paint the metal or coat it with oil. This method prevents contact with moisture but can only be carried out if you have easy access to the metal.

Access can be difficult in such cases as metal ships, hot water tanks, septic tanks, and underground pipes. The use of a more reactive metal as a sacrificial anode often helps in such cases. The metal to be protected is attached to a more reactive metal. The more reactive metal corrodes and is sacrificed to keep the less reactive metal free of corrosion. The magnesium used in the above experiment was a sacrificial anode. Magnesium or zinc plates are welded onto the hulls of many steel ships and are replaced when necessary. The steel is partially protected from corrosion and need not be repaired as frequently.

Fig. 29 *A lot of effort has been spent on repairing the corrosion damage to the Statue of Liberty. The restored face is shown on the left.*

The 46-m high Statue of Liberty in New York was built in 1886 with copper as the surface metal (Figure 29). To support this copper outer layer, the builders used a web-like series of iron bars. The iron web was riveted to the copper. With lots of sea air and moisture available, corrosion was fairly rapid. The iron bars, being more reactive than copper, acted as the sacrificial anode. One hundred years later, some of the iron bars were only one third of their original thickness. The whole structure was in danger of collapse. So the support structure was rebuilt using special stainless steel bars.

Corrosion of copper usually produces a green oxide layer called a **patina**. This layer adheres very strongly to the copper surface and prevents further corrosion. However, the patina on the surface of the Statue of Liberty has recently been damaged by acid rain. A similar problem occurred in the 1979 nuclear accident at Three Mile Island. Zirconium metal is used in the nuclear reactor and comes into contact with water. Zirconium is more reactive than hydrogen and would displace hydrogen from water. Like copper, zirconium forms a protective oxide layer and under normal circumstances does not react with water. In the accident, the coolant escaped and the reactor reached a very high temperature. The heat caused the protective oxide layer to break off. The zirconium metal then reacted with water, and hydrogen gas was produced. The hydrogen could have exploded had there been a spark. Fortunately it did not.

In the 1970s, rusted out cars were thrown into the sea off the Hawaiian coast. Platinum salts are naturally found in sea water. Because iron is more reactive than platinum, the cars are now coated with crusts of platinum.

In the 1960s, disposable aluminum pencil sharpeners were available. The manufacturers correctly believed that aluminum would not corrode. Like copper, aluminum has a protective oxide layer. However, the manufacturers used iron blades in the pencil sharpeners. Since aluminum is more reactive than iron, the aluminum slowly corroded, leaving a rust-free blade. Some automobile manufacturers made the same mistake. They bolted aluminum water pumps directly to cast-iron engine blocks. The water pumps frequently sprung leaks.

Galvanizing, tin plating, and chromium plating (Figure 30) are often used to prevent iron from corroding. Galvanized pipe is iron or steel coated with zinc. ''Tin cans'' are iron cans coated with a thin layer of tin to protect the iron from oxygen and moisture. But tin is less reactive than iron, so if the tin surface is broken, the exposed iron rusts. A similar problem occurs when a galvanized pipe is joined to a copper pipe. Zinc is more reactive than copper and corrodes, thus exposing the iron. The iron is also more reactive than the copper and it too corrodes.

An electrical method can now be used to prevent cars from corroding. A special device passes a very low current through the body of the car. It is claimed that the electricity counteracts the flow of electrons in the oxidation and reduction processes of corrosion. Does it work? Time will tell.

Fig. 30 *Chromium plating protects iron from rusting because chromium has a protective oxide layer. However, there are often tiny holes in the chromium layer and the iron rapidly rusts beneath. For this reason, scientists coat the iron with nickel before applying the chromium. The nickel does corrode, but fortunately oxidized nickel is not as unsightly as oxidized iron.*

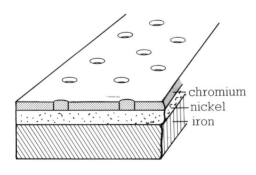

chromium
nickel
iron

14.14 Removing Tarnish From Silverware

The tarnishing of silverware (Figure 31) is caused by the reaction of silver with hydrogen sulfide in the air to form silver sulfide:

$$4Ag + 2H_2S + O_2 \rightarrow 2Ag_2S + 2H_2O$$

Tarnishing can be controlled by storing the silver in air-tight plastic bags. The silver can also be wrapped in paper that has been specially treated with chemicals that absorb hydrogen sulfide.

In the following procedure for removing tarnish from silverware, the silver sulfide layer is first removed and then the silver is replated onto the article. The equation for the reaction is:

$$2Al + 3Ag_2S + 6H_2O \rightarrow 6Ag + 2Al(OH)_3 + 3H_2S$$

Materials

Do not use articles which are coated with only a very thin layer of silver.

piece of silverware
fresh egg
two 100-mL beakers
sodium hydrogen carbonate
aluminum pie pan or aluminum foil
glass dish (large enough to hold the pie pan or foil and the
  silver object)
tablespoon
hotplate

Method

1. Separate the yolk from the white of an egg into two beakers.

2. Warm the egg white until it is semi cooked.

3. Dip the piece of silver in the egg white and rub it over the surface.

4. Set the piece of silver aside for 10 to 15 min.

5. Gently wash the piece of silver with cold water and record any observations.

6. Dissolve about 10 tablespoons of sodium hydrogen carbonate in 2 L of water.

7. Place the solution in the large glass dish.

8. Place the pie pan, or aluminum foil, in the dish so that it is covered by the solution.

9. Heat the solution slowly. Do not boil it.

10. Turn off the heat and immerse the tarnished silver in the hot solution such that the silver touches the aluminum.

11. If the solution does not appear to remove the tarnish, add more sodium hydrogen carbonate.

12. When the silver is clean, remove it and rinse with cold water.

Follow-up

1. After you rubbed egg white on the silverware, what evidence suggested that the silver had tarnished?

2. How is silverware normally cleaned?

3. Suggest how you can adapt the technique used in this experiment for use in your home.

4. Why should care be taken using this technique with articles made from very thin silverplate?

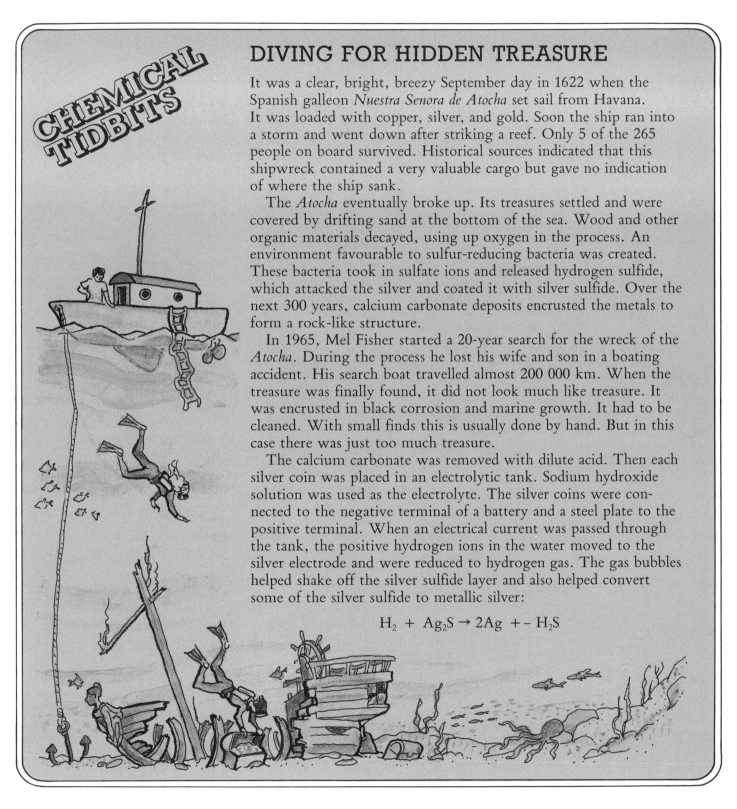

DIVING FOR HIDDEN TREASURE

It was a clear, bright, breezy September day in 1622 when the Spanish galleon *Nuestra Senora de Atocha* set sail from Havana. It was loaded with copper, silver, and gold. Soon the ship ran into a storm and went down after striking a reef. Only 5 of the 265 people on board survived. Historical sources indicated that this shipwreck contained a very valuable cargo but gave no indication of where the ship sank.

The *Atocha* eventually broke up. Its treasures settled and were covered by drifting sand at the bottom of the sea. Wood and other organic materials decayed, using up oxygen in the process. An environment favourable to sulfur-reducing bacteria was created. These bacteria took in sulfate ions and released hydrogen sulfide, which attacked the silver and coated it with silver sulfide. Over the next 300 years, calcium carbonate deposits encrusted the metals to form a rock-like structure.

In 1965, Mel Fisher started a 20-year search for the wreck of the *Atocha*. During the process he lost his wife and son in a boating accident. His search boat travelled almost 200 000 km. When the treasure was finally found, it did not look much like treasure. It was encrusted in black corrosion and marine growth. It had to be cleaned. With small finds this is usually done by hand. But in this case there was just too much treasure.

The calcium carbonate was removed with dilute acid. Then each silver coin was placed in an electrolytic tank. Sodium hydroxide solution was used as the electrolyte. The silver coins were connected to the negative terminal of a battery and a steel plate to the positive terminal. When an electrical current was passed through the tank, the positive hydrogen ions in the water moved to the silver electrode and were reduced to hydrogen gas. The gas bubbles helped shake off the silver sulfide layer and also helped convert some of the silver sulfide to metallic silver:

$$H_2 + Ag_2S \rightarrow 2Ag + - H_2S$$

CHEMICAL TIDBITS

14.15 Removing Rust From Iron Objects

Fig. 32 *Restoring corroded objects is a laborious task. Before and after photos of a pistol restored by the Conservation Department of the Royal Ontario Museum.*

Restoration of ancient metallic articles is very important if those articles are to be kept for future generations. Much of this work is done by museums. Once a metal has corroded away, it is difficult to restore its original shape. Most restoration programs remove existing corrosion and then prevent further corrosion from taking place.

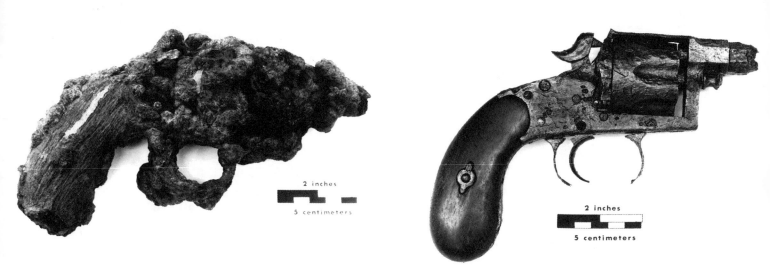

Materials

safety goggles
rubber gloves
a small rusted iron object
glass container (large enough to hold the rusted object)
a sheet of zinc to fit into the glass container
5 mol/L sodium hydroxide solution
two 400-mL beakers
2 hotplates
low-melting paraffin wax
steel brush
thermometer
tongs
oven
hair dryer

To avoid breathing in any
fumes, carry out the experiment in a fume hood.

Method

1. Use a steel brush to remove any loose corrosion from the iron object.

2. Place a clean sheet of zinc on the bottom of the glass container.

3. Carefully pour sufficient sodium hydroxide solution into the container to cover the object.

4. Warm the container on a hotplate and maintain at about 50°C.

5. Use tongs to place the iron object in the solution. The object should make as much contact with the zinc as possible.

6. Leave the object in the solution for about 30 min or until the corrosion is completely removed.

7. While waiting, boil distilled water in a 400-mL beaker. There should be enough to cover the object. Place cold distilled water in another 400-mL beaker.

8. Remove the object with tongs and rinse it with distilled water. Dip the object in the hot water bath and then immediately in the cold water bath. Alternate between hot and cold water at least five times.

9. Without touching the object with your hands, dry it with a hair dryer.

10. Without touching the object with your hands, place the object in the oven and leave it at 105°C overnight.

11. Use a hotplate to melt the paraffin wax in a 400-mL beaker.

12. Without touching the object with your hands, dip it into the molten wax for a few minutes.

13. Use tongs to remove the object. Allow excess wax to drain onto some paper towel or use the hair dryer to remove excess wax. Allow the wax to solidify before handling the object.

Follow-up

1. It was essential not to touch the object with your hands in steps 9 through 13. Explain why.

2. The hot and cold water baths removed any salts from the object. Why was this essential before coating the object with wax?

3. Refer to the activity series of metals and suggest why zinc was used in the sodium hydroxide bath.

14.16 Anodizing Aluminum

Aluminum rapidly forms an oxide layer which sticks to the surface so strongly that further corrosion of the metal cannot take place. It is therefore an ideal metal to use in places where it will be exposed to the environment. However, with time, the oxide layer becomes very dull and unsightly.

Anodizing the aluminum is an electrical process which prepares the surface of the aluminum so that coloured dyes can be applied. What happens is that the aluminum surface is first coated with a layer of porous oxide in an electrical process; the oxide layer can accept dye, which is then sealed to the surface on boiling. This gives a better looking and longer lasting product. Anodized aluminum is frequently used in household products, including aluminum siding and jewellery (Figure 33).

Steps in anodizing aluminum:

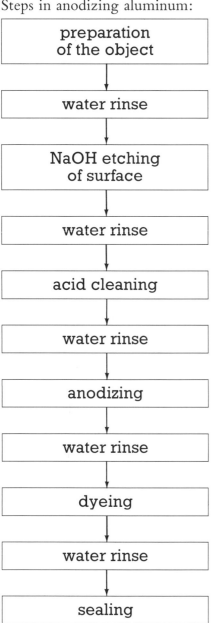

- preparation of the object
- water rinse
- NaOH etching of surface
- water rinse
- acid cleaning
- water rinse
- anodizing
- water rinse
- dyeing
- water rinse
- sealing

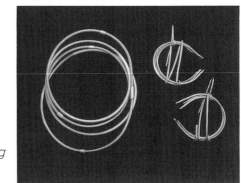

Fig. 33 *Jewellers use the anodizing process to produce beautifully coloured aluminum jewellery.*

Materials

safety goggles	15-V battery
rubber gloves	emery paper
1-L beaker	clean cloth
two 400-mL beakers	thermometer
glass rods	2 mol/L sulfuric acid
electrical leads	5 g of aluminum nitrate crystals
1 mol/L sodium hydroxide solution	hotplate
1 mol/L nitric acid	1.25 g of commercial aluminum
three 250-mL beakers	dye powder
copper rod	spatula
two pieces of aluminum	balance
aluminum hook	wash bottle
aluminum object	soap solution
copper wire	tongs

Method

I. *Preparing the Dye Solution*

1. Place 1.25 g of dye powder in a 400-mL beaker.

2. Use a glass rod to mix the powder with 2 mL of distilled water. Then add small amounts of water slowly until the powder dissolves.

3. Add water to give a final volume of about 250 mL. Mix well.

4. Warm the mixture on a hotplate to about 50°C.

II. *The Anodizing Process*

Since toxic fumes may be present, carry out this process in a fume hood.

1. Pour 800 mL of the sulfuric acid solution into a clean 1-L beaker. Add the aluminum nitrate and stir to dissolve.

2. The aluminum object to be anodized should be no larger than a $1 coin. Polish the surface with emery paper, wash with soap solution, and then rinse with distilled water.

3. Use tongs to place the object in sodium hydroxide solution in a 250-mL beaker for 15 min. Remove and rinse with distilled water.

4. Place the object in nitric acid solution in a 250-mL beaker for 3 min. Remove and rinse with distilled water. After this, the object should only be handled with gloved hands.

5. Attach the object to the aluminum hook (which has been cleaned with emery paper), ensuring good contact. The aluminum hook can be tightly twisted around the object if necessary.

6. Set up the apparatus as in Figure 34.

Fig. 34 *Set-up for anodizing aluminum.*

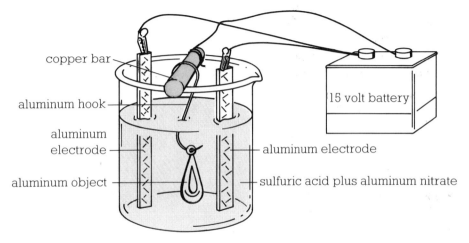

copper bar

aluminum hook

aluminum electrode

aluminum object

15 volt battery

aluminum electrode

sulfuric acid plus aluminum nitrate

To avoid electric shock, do not touch the apparatus once the current is on.

7. Using a 15-V battery, apply an electrical current for about 30 to 45 min. The longer the time, the more intense the final colour will be.

8. Pour 200 mL of distilled water into a 250-mL beaker. Bring to the boil on a hotplate. While waiting, continue with step 9.

9. Switch off the current, remove the object, and rinse it with distilled water.

10. Remove the beaker of dye from the hotplate. Immediately place the object in the dye solution for 5 to 10 min. For pale colouring use a shorter time and a cooler dye mixture. For more intense colours use a longer time and a warmer dye mixture.

11. Remove the object and rinse with distilled water.

12. Using tongs, place the object in the boiling water for 15 min. This seals in the colour.

13. Remove the anodized object with tongs and rinse with distilled water. Pat dry with a clean cloth.

14. If you repeat the process with a new object, then use a new aluminum hook.

P O I N T S · T O · R E C A L L

- An electrolyte is a substance which dissolves in water to form a conducting solution.
- Oxidation is a loss of electrons.
- Reduction is a gain of electrons.
- An electrochemical cell is made from two different electrodes and an electrolyte solution.
- The greater the difference in reactivity between the two metals making up the electrodes, the greater the voltage reading in an electrochemical cell.
- In an electrochemical cell, the more reactive metal electrode is attached to the negative terminal of the voltmeter.
- The activity series is used to predict the outcome of a single displacement reaction.
- Most metals are found in compounds in nature.

- Gold and platinum are two metals found only as free elements in nature.
- Hydrogen can be prepared from the reaction of very active metals with water or of active metals with acids.
- Hydrogen is usually prepared commercially by the electrolysis of water.
- Hydrogen forms an explosive mixture with oxygen.
- All commercial batteries use chemical reactions to produce electrical energy.
- During electrolysis, electrical energy decomposes an ionic compound or water.
- The products obtained from electrolysis depend on the concentration and type of electrolyte used, and on the applied electrical potential.

- Positive ions move to the negative electrode (cathode) where they are reduced.
- Negative ions move to the positive electrode (anode) where they are oxidized.
- Electroplating uses electrical energy to cover a metal object with a film of another metal.
- In electroplating, the object to be plated is the cathode, and the electrolyte must contain ions of the plating metal.
- With some metals, corrosion produces protective surface coats. With other metals, corrosion is an unwanted electrochemical reaction.
- Metals corrode quickest at points of strain such as bends and cracks.
- Coating a metal with paint or oil protects the metal from corrosion.
- More reactive metals attached to less reactive metals protect the less reactive metals from corrosion.

R E V I E W · Q U E S T I O N S

1. Explain the following terms:
   (a) electrolyte   (b) oxidation   (c) reduction
2. Give an example of:
   (a) oxidation   (b) reduction
3. Sketch a typical voltaic cell. Explain how it produces electrical energy.
4. Which cell would produce a greater electrical potential, one with magnesium and copper electrodes, or one with zinc and copper electrodes? Explain your answer.
5. In each of the cells in question 4, which metal would be connected to the negative terminal of the voltmeter?
6. Which of the following metals
   (a) displace hydrogen from cold water: K, Ca, Al, Zn, Cu?
   (b) displace hydrogen from steam: Na, Mg, Cr, Sn, Ag?
   (c) do not displace hydrogen from an acid: Zn, Pb, Cu, Pt?
7. Museums exhibit many ancient copper, silver, and gold objects but very few ancient iron objects. Is this proof that iron was unknown in early times? Explain your answer.
8. Why is hydrogen no longer used in balloons?
9. How is hydrogen used in the preparation of margarine?
10. Why is gold such a valuable metal?
11. List two metals that displace cobalt from its compounds.
12. Write a balanced chemical equation to show what happens when copper is added to silver nitrate solution.
13. When copper (II) sulfate dissolves in water, there are two positive and two negative ions present in the solution. List them.
14. The electrolysis of copper(II) sulfate solution produces copper and oxygen. Write equations showing what happens at each electrode.
15. Sketch the general set-up used for nickel plating an iron object.
16. What factors speed up the corrosion of iron?
17. Why does a coat of paint on metal slow corrosion?
18. Cars are sprayed with salt all winter yet only appear to start rusting in the spring. Explain.
19. If the surface of a tin-plated can is scratched, the can rapidly rusts. Explain why.

15 ORGANIC CHEMISTRY

Oil rig off Newfoundland coast. Oil is the source of raw materials of many chemical industries.

CONTENTS

Investigation

15.1 A Treat From Your Past

Materials

safety goggles
400-mL beaker
100-mL graduated cylinder
hotplate
balance
metal spatula
scrap paper
beaker tongs
pulverized plant middlings
sodium chloride
potassium tartrate
cold water
vegetable oil
food dye (your choice)
plastic bags (Ziplock)

Method

1. Add 75 g of pulverized plant middlings, 35 g of sodium chloride, and 14 g of potassium tartrate to a clean 400-mL beaker.

As the product of this experiment is edible, use new apparatus.

2. Stir the ingredients thoroughly with a metal spatula. Continue stirring while you add 125 mL of cold water, 8 mL of vegetable oil, and 5 drops of food dye.

3. Place the beaker on the hotplate and, stirring constantly with the metal spatula, heat the mixture for 3 to 5 min, or until the product becomes semi-solid and very difficult to stir.

4. Remove the beaker from the hotplate, and allow the product to cool.

5. Sprinkle a piece of scrap paper with some pulverized plant middlings. Scrape the product out of the beaker with the metal spatula and place the product on the paper.

6. Pat the product into a pancake shape and fold the edges inwards. Use your hand to work it into a ball on the paper. A few minutes of working the product on the paper should produce a smooth, non-sticky, product.

7. Place your product into a plastic bag. It will last for weeks if the bag is sealed.

Follow-up

1. Think back to your childhood. What is your product? What memories does this product bring to mind? Discuss your answers with your classmates.

2. You have made a product from organic materials such as plant middlings, vegetable oil, a tartrate, and dyes. What do you think the term ''organic'' means?

15.2 The "Vital Force"?

As you know, food, clothing, means of transportation, everyday implements, and the human body are composed of chemicals. A large number of the chemicals you use are **organic** chemicals. Some organic chemicals that you may have heard of are proteins, vitamins, aspirin, hormones, gasoline, carbohydrates, dioxins, and PCBs (polychlorinated biphenyls).

Fig. 1 *PCBs (polychlorinated biphenyls) are dangerous organic compounds that must be disposed of properly. The picture shows the removal of soil contaminated with PCBs near Halifax.*

Wöhler, a German chemist, produced an organic compound, urea, from an inorganic compound, ammonium thiocyanate.

People used to think that organic chemicals could only be produced by living organisms, which possess "vital force." This idea was disproved by Wöhler in 1828. Organic chemicals have a carbon "skeleton." Carbon is very special because it is able to form very strong carbon-to-carbon bonds and these bonds stay strong even when the carbons are joined with other elements. The other elements which may also be present in organic compounds are hydrogen, oxygen, phosphorus, nitrogen, chlorine, bromine, and iodine. The structural formulas of some organic compounds are given below:

ethanol   glucose   chloroform   methyl isocyanate

Fig. 2 *In 1985, a pesticide plant in Bhopal, India, accidentally released methyl isocyanate into the air. Many people were killed or blinded by this organic compound. The picture shows protesters in Bhopal.*

The chief source of starting materials for making organic chemicals in the laboratory or in industry is petroleum. Crude oil is distilled in refineries and separated into commercially important components as shown in the chart below. Molecules of roughly the same formula mass distill at about the same temperature.

Fig. 3 *Distillation of crude oil is carried out in the fractional distillation towers of oil refineries.*

Component	Distillation temperature	Number of carbon atoms in molecule	Uses
gases	less than 20°C	1 to 4	heating, cooking
liquid petroleum	20 to 60°C	5 to 6	solvents
gasoline	40 to 200°C	4 to 8	motor fuel
kerosene	175 to 275°C	10 to 16	aircraft fuel
fuel oil, diesel oil, lubricating oils	200 to 400°C	15 to 20	fuel, lubricants
greases, vaseline petrolatum	above 300°C	18 to 22	pharmaceutical preparations, cosmetics
paraffin wax (hard)	above 300°C	20 to 30	candles, wax paper
asphalt	does not distil	20 and above	road paving

THE HIBERNIA OIL FIELD

The discovery of oil in the relatively shallow Grand Banks off Newfoundland occurred in 1979. It was estimated the field contained about 5.6% of Canada's oil reserves. In 1988, Prime Minister Brian Mulroney and Newfoundland Premier Brian Peckford signed the Hibernia oil agreement. The Hibernia off-shore oil field is about 300 km off the east coast of Newfoundland. The drilling structure will be enormous, about the size of a very tall skyscraper, and will cost about $5.2 billion! The Hibernia platform will be anchored to the floor in the stormy North Atlantic. The developers expect to be in operation in 1995.

Many people are excited at the job prospects for the people of Newfoundland. The building of the development is supposed to create employment for 14 500 people for one year. Once Hibernia is operating, 1100 people will have permanent employment.

Many other people are extremely worried. They remember the 166 deaths that occurred when the Ocean Ranger drilling rig sank in 1982, and the great loss of life in 1988 when another off-shore rig exploded in the North Sea off the coast of the British Isles.

Environmentalists are also concerned. They believe that an oil leak in the cold waters of the North Atlantic could have devastating effects on sea and shore life.

The federal government is providing a grant of up to $1.04 billion, and a guaranteed bank loan for $1.66 billion to the developers. In 1988, the price of a barrel of oil was US$15. For Hibernia to break even, oil will have to be about US$20. Many taxpayers are asking some hard questions about the development. It may be years before the government sees any royalties from Hibernia, and the taxpayers are meanwhile footing the bill.

Do you think we should go ahead with this development?

Fig. 4 *The Hibernia development requires an investment of billions of dollars.*

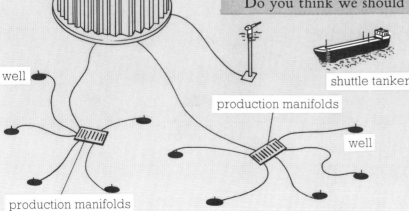

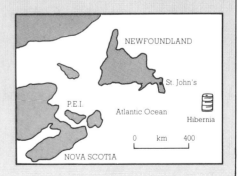

15.3 Distillation of Crude Oil

Materials

safety goggles
retort stand
wooden splint
test tube clamp
Bunsen burner
5 test tubes, one 20 × 200 mm size and 4 smaller ones
100-mL beaker
glass wool
thermometer that can read to about 300°C
crucible or metal can cut off to look like a petri dish
crude oil

This experiment may be extremely dangerous if any of the openings in the apparatus become clogged or if you heat too fast. Use *small* quantities — do not use larger quantities than specified.

Fig. 5 *Set-up for distilling crude oil.*

Method

1. Place a small loose ball of glass wool in the bottom of the large test tube.

2. Add about 2 mL of crude oil to this test tube.

3. Set up the apparatus as shown in Figure 5.

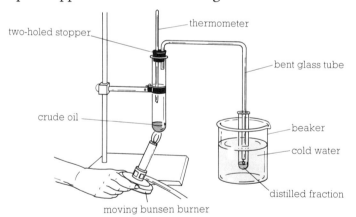

4. Heat the test tube carefully until liquid drops start to appear in the side test tube. Collect four liquid samples, called **fractions**, in four different test tubes when the temperature is
   (a) below 70°C
   (b) 70 to 120°C
   (c) 120 to 170°C
   (d) 170 to 220°C
   A black thick material will be left in the original test tube.

Some of the products from the distillation of crude oil can be changed into important chemicals such as benzene, toluene, and other materials used in dye and drug industries. Substances that contain 6 to 10 carbon atoms are mixed with excess hydrogen gas and passed over a platinum catalyst at high temperatures (900°C) and pressures. This process is called **catalytic reforming**.

5. Note the colours of the fractions.

6. Pour a few drops of each fraction in turn onto the metal can or crucible, and light the sample with a lit wooden splint. Note how easily the fractions pour, and the results of the burning.

7. Draw up a chart that shows for each fraction: the temperature range, how easily it pours, the colour, and flammability (if and how it burns).

Follow-up

1. What were the major differences between the fractions?

2. List the uses for the substances found in each of the four fractions.

3. In what way would your life change if we were to run out of crude oil?

4. Canada has large reserves of crude oil in the Athabasca oil sands in Alberta (Figure 6). Find out what problems are associated with extracting oil from the sands.

Fig. 6 *The cost of producing crude oil from the Athabasca oil sands in Alberta is very high.*

15.4 Hydrocarbons

Organic chemicals are named in a very organized way and the name endings tell you a lot about the structure of the chemicals. Once you have learned the rules of naming, you can write the formula for many organic chemicals directly from the name. The naming system depends on the names of the simplest organic compounds, the **hydrocarbons**.

The name "hydrocarbons" tells you that the only elements in these compounds are hydrogen and carbon. But how do you know how many carbon atoms and how many hydrogen atoms there are in one molecule?

The *first part* of the name of a hydrocarbon tells you the *number of carbon atoms* in a molecule, while the *second part* tells you the types of carbon-to-carbon bonds present (single C–C, double C=C, or triple C≡C). The number of carbon atoms, and the type(s) of bonds present, determine the number of hydrogen atoms.

Hydrocarbons with only single C–C bonds have the maximum number of hydrogen atoms possible and are called **saturated** hydrocarbons. Hydrocarbons containing double C=C, or triple C≡C bonds have less than the maximum number of hydrogen atoms, and are called **unsaturated** hydrocarbons. If there are many double or triple bonds in a molecule, then the hydrocarbon is called a **poly-unsaturated** hydrocarbon.

Number of carbon atoms	First part of name	Second part of name		
		-ane (contains C–C)	*-ene* (contains C=C)	*-yne* (contains C≡C)
1	meth-	methane	—	—
2	eth-	ethane	ethene	ethyne
3	prop-	propane	propene	propyne
4	but-	butane	butene	butyne
5	pent-	pentane	pentene	pentyne
6	hex-	hexane	hexene	hexyne
7	hept-	heptane	heptene	heptyne
8	oct-	octane	octene	octyne

Fig. 7 *Ethene (ethylene), an unsaturated hydrocarbon, is very important industrially. It is used to make many organic chemicals and polyethylene (a widely used plastic).*

Fig. 8 *The structure of (a) ethane, (b) ethene, and (c) ethyne. Their names begin with eth- because they have two carbon atoms each. Remember that carbon has four bonds, oxygen two, and hydrogen one.*

a

b

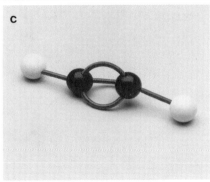

c

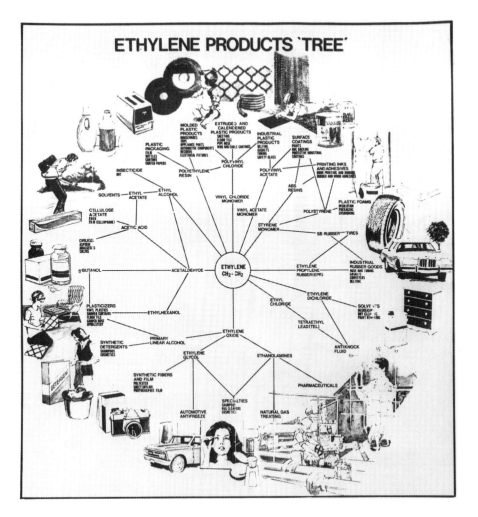

ETHYLENE PRODUCTS 'TREE'

The three different types of hydrocarbons, **alkanes**, **alkenes**, and **alkynes**, each show characteristic properties. Once you know how a hydrocarbon behaves, you know that other hydrocarbons of the same type behave in a similar way. This is like the behaviour of families in the periodic table of the elements.

Questions

Draw structural formulas for propane C_3H_8, pentene C_5H_{10}, hexane C_6H_{14}, octane C_8H_{18}, ethyne C_2H_2, and butane C_4H_{10}.
(In some cases you will find that the same formula gives more than one structure. You learned in Chapter 7 that substances with the same molecular formula but different structures are called **isomers**. Each isomer has its own characteristic properties.)

WHAT DOES "CRACKING" HAVE TO DO WITH YOU?

Before cars were developed, most crude oil was distilled to produce kerosene which was used as lamp fuel. When the demand for gasoline increased, chemists discovered they could convert non-gasoline molecules into ones that would work efficiently in the internal combustion engines of cars. The conversion process, called **cracking**, involves heating the petroleum to about 500 to 600°C. This process breaks large saturated hydrocarbon molecules into smaller molecules. Gasoline from the cracking process burns more smoothly at high pressure. When the gasoline-air mixture burns too rapidly, or pre-ignites, in the car's combustion chamber, a small explosion is heard. This is called "knocking." This sound warns a car owner of trouble. If knocking is not corrected, it causes breakdowns. Gasolines often contain anti-knocking agents such as tetraethyllead, $(C_2H_5)_4Pb$. This lead compound is highly poisonous and gasolines containing it is coloured to warn consumers of its presence. Lead-free gasoline is available today to prevent lead pollution of the environment.

Other important products of cracking have molecules with one to four carbon atoms: methane, ethane, ethene, propane, propene, butane, butene, and iso-butene. These products are used in the preparation of a huge number of commercial products.

Fig. 9 Unleaded gasoline does not contain tetraethyllead as the anti-knocking agent.

15.5 Alkanes and Alkenes

In this experiment you will compare the chemical behaviour of alkanes and alkenes. The chemicals used are liquids at room temperature.

For safety, your teacher will add the sulfuric acid for you.

Materials

safety goggles
2 medicine droppers
2 test tubes
test tube rack
concentrated sulfuric acid
cyclohex*ane* (an alkane)
cyclohex*ene* (an alkene)
acidified potassium permanganate solution (1% mass/volume)

Method

1. Pour 2 mL of potassium permanganate solution into each of the clean, rinsed test tubes.

2. Using a dropper, add two drops of cyclohex*ene* to one of the test tubes. Shake well. Record your observations.

3. Using the other dropper, add two drops of cyclohex*ane* to the other test tube. Shake well. Record your observations.

4. Clean and rinse the test tubes.

5. Add two drops of cyclohex*ene* to one of the test tubes. Ask your teacher to add one drop of concentrated sulfuric acid to the test tube. Record your observations.

6. Add two drops of cyclohex*ane* to the other test tube. Ask your teacher to add one drop of concentrated sulfuric acid to the test tube. Record your observations.

Cyclohexane	Cyclohexene

Follow-up

1. What are the chemical differences between alkanes and alkenes?

2. The structures for cyclohexane and cyclohexene are:

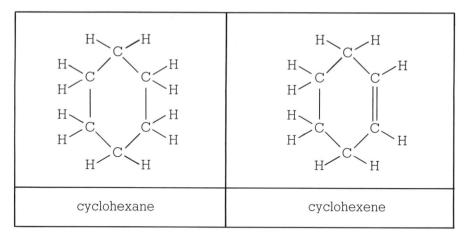

| cyclohexane | cyclohexene |

What do you think the term "cyclo" means?
Try to draw the structure for cyclopentane, and cyclobutene, and write the formulas for these too.

3. Give at least two examples of the use of propane in your everyday life. What commercial use is made of butane?

4. Look up the physical properties (such as melting point, boiling point, density) of methane, ethane, propane, and butane in a chemical dictionary. Draw up a chart showing the values for these substances.

5. If you go camping in warmer countries than Canada, butane is used in camp stoves and camping lamps rather than propane. Why do you think this is so?

6. Benzene is another hydrocarbon with a ring structure. It is known as a cancer-causing agent. Find out about the industrial uses of benzene.

Petroleum and coal tar are the sources of many materials we take for granted. The chemicals refined from these sources are the starting materials for plastics, synthetic fibres, detergents, pesticides, herbicides, and drugs.

Chemists design and prepare new organic molecules all the time. Often they try to change an existing molecule, such as a drug, to make it more effective. Aspirin is an organic compound that you have already prepared in the laboratory. You will now make and purify another organic compound, iodoform. This compound has disinfectant properties.

Materials

safety goggles
10-mL graduated cyclinder
two 100-mL graduated cylinders
boiling chip
100-mL or 250-mL Erlenmeyer flask
100-mL beaker
100-mL round-bottomed flask
condenser
watchglass
hotplate and hot water bath (or heating mantle)
retort stand with small ring clamp
funnel
filter paper
vial
labels
balance
oven
thermometer (that can read to above 120°C)
propanone (acetone)
ethanol
mineral oil
potassium iodide solution (10% mass/volume)
sodium hydroxide solution (10% mass/volume)
household bleach such as Javex (sodium hypochlorite solution)

Bleach can damage clothing and skin. Be careful not to get any on you. If you do, immediately rinse with cold water.

Method

1. Using separate graduated cylinders, measure out 1 mL of propanone (acetone), 40 mL of the potassium iodide solution, and 16 mL of the sodium hydroxide solution. Pour each of these solutions into the clean Erlenmeyer flask.

2. Add 40 mL of household bleach to the contents of the flask. Swirl the contents of the flask well so that thorough mixing occurs. Yellow crystals of iodoform will begin to separate out of solution almost immediately.

3. Let the mixture stand at room temperature for about 10 min. Collect the crystals by passing the mixture through a funnel fitted with a filter paper.

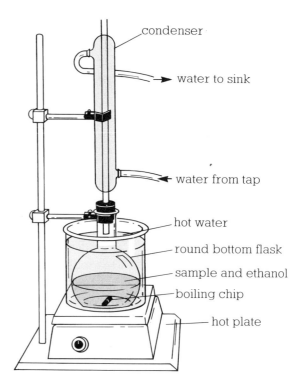

Fig. 10 *Set-up for recrystallizing.*

condenser

water to sink

water from tap

hot water

round bottom flask

sample and ethanol

boiling chip

hot plate

4. Recrystallize the product. Place the crude crystals in a small round-bottomed flask that can be fitted with a condenser. Add 5 mL of ethanol to the flask, add a boiling chip, and fit the condenser as shown in Figure 10. Turn on the water to the condenser, then heat the contents of the flask using *either* a hot water bath on a hotplate *or* a heating mantle. When the liquid boils, carefully add 0.5 mL amounts of ethanol down the condenser until all the iodoform just dissolves.

Fig. 11 *Set-up for filtering.*

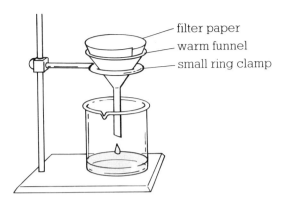

5. Warm the filter funnel, fit it with filter paper, and place it in the funnel holder (Figure 11). Filter the hot solution through filter paper directly into the small beaker, and allow the contents to cool to room temperature. The iodoform quickly crystallizes. Filter off the pure crystals, and dry on a watchglass in the oven set at about 105°C. Transfer your sample to a clean, dry, weighed, and labelled vial.
Determine the mass of your sample, and record the mass on the label on the vial.

6. Determine the melting point of the dried crystals. Use a thermometer that reads to above 120°C. Your heating liquid will have to be mineral oil, not water. The melting point should be 120°C. If it is not, repeat the recrystallization.

Follow-up

1. Why did you need to put a condenser on the flask when you were recrystallizing?

2. Why did you weigh your sample? Why would a manufacturer be very interested in the mass of the product?

3. Iodoform was once used as an external disinfectant. Make a list of household disinfectants with which you are familiar.

4. The structure of iodoform is:

$$I - \overset{\displaystyle I}{\underset{\displaystyle I}{C}} - H$$

Build a molecular model of iodoform. Take a (Polaroid) photograph of the model, or make a three dimensional drawing of the model. Submit your drawing or photograph, together with your sample, to your teacher.

DIRECT LINK BETWEEN ILLNESS AND AN AGRICULTURAL CHEMICAL

In 1985 in British Columbia, about 140 people vomited, and had diarrhea and dizziness after eating long English cucumbers. The Health Protection Branch in Ottawa ordered a recall on all long English cucumbers available in provinces west of Ontario. The Vancouver office of the Federal Health Protection Branch traced the source of the cucumbers to a food company. Laboratory tests showed that cucumbers from the company contained traces of an organic pesticide, aldicarb. This pesticide is restricted by law to use on potatoes and beets. The company was convicted of violating the Federal Food and Drugs Act and fined $5000. The owner of the company was jailed for one month.

Fig. 12 *Dumping English cucumbers contaminated with an agricultural pesticide.*

15.7 Famous Families of Organic Chemicals

When a hydrogen atom in a hydrocarbon molecule is replaced by a group containing atoms such as oxygen, nitrogen, and phosphorus, the compound is no longer a hydrocarbon. The new attached group is called a **functional group**. Each functional group has different properties and is named in a special way.

H atom is removed → C atom has free bond → an O—H functional group is attached

Name of functional group	Structure of functional group	Example		
		Structural formula	Name	Use
alcoh**ol**	—O—H	H | H—C—O—H | H	methan**ol**	solvent
ether	| | —C—O—C— | |	H H H H | | | | H—C—C—O—C—C—H | | | | H H H H	diethyl **ether**	anesthetic
aldehyde	—C=O | H	H—C=O | H	methan**al** (formaldehyde)	preservative
ket**one**	| | —C C=O —C |	H | H—C | C=O H H—C | | H H	propan**one** (acetone)	solvent
acid	O // —C \ O—H	H | O | // H—C—C | \ H O—H	ethan**oic acid** (acetic acid)	vinegar

ester	O
	//
	—C
	\
	O—C—
	|
		H O
		| //
		H—C—C H H
		| \ | |
		H O—C—C—H
		           | |
		           H H
			ethyl ethan**oate**
			(ethyl acetate)
				solvent in nail polish

amine	H / —N \ H	H H | | H—C—N | \ H H	methyl**amine**	drug manufacture

The name of a compound shows the number of carbon atoms and the nature of the functional group. For example, in the name *diethyl ether*, $C_2H_5–O–C_2H_5$:

- *di-* shows two side chains
- *-ethyl* shows that each side chain has two carbon atoms
- *ether* shows a C–O–C bonding in the compound

As you can see in the above table, the name ethanoic acid shows that a molecule of this substance contains two carbon atoms. The name ends in *-oic acid* because this is the ending for organic acids.

Fatty acids are organic acids with long hydrocarbon chains. Some examples are:

(a) palmitic acid

$$H–O–\overset{\overset{\textstyle O}{\|}}{C}–(CH_2)_{14}CH_3$$

(b) stearic acid

$$H–O–\overset{\overset{\textstyle O}{\|}}{C}–(CH_2)_{16}CH_3$$

Many chemists still use an older form of naming that was often related to how a substance was made. For example, formic acid (correctly called methanoic acid) was originally named after the German word for ants because it was produced by distilling ants.

Questions

1. What is the correct name of $CH_3CH_2CH_2CH_2COOH$?

2. What type of organic compound is methyl methanoate?

3. Write the formula for ethyl methyl ether.

4. Write the formula for butanoic acid.

5. Build a molecular model for C_3H_8O. How many different structures can you build?

15.8 Alcohols

When you read about alcohol abuse, it sounds as if there is only one kind of alcohol. In fact, there are hundreds. Some common alcohols are shown in the chart below.

Structural formula	Correct name	Common name
H | H—C—O—H | H	methanol	methyl alcohol or wood alcohol
H H | | H—C—C—O—H | | H H	ethanol	ethyl alcohol or grain alcohol
H H | | H—O—C—C—O—H | | H H	ethan-1,2-diol	ethylene glycol or antifreeze
H | H—C—O—H | H—C—O—H | H—C—O—H | H	propan-1,2,3-triol	glycerol or glycerin

Fig. 13 *Methanol is being tested as a possible fuel for transportation.*

Fig. 14 *Drinking and driving is dangerous because ethanol affects the centres of the brain that control behaviour and ability to react.*

The breathalyser test solution used by the police contains potassium dichromate, sulfuric acid, and silver nitrate. When alcohol is breathed into the orange-coloured mixture, the alcohol is oxidized, and the dichromate ion is reduced, producing a green-coloured solution.

Guess what smelly socks and camembert cheese have in common? They both contain methyl thiol, the chemical responsible for the smell. Methyl thiol, CH_3SH, is similar to methanol, CH_3OH, except that the oxygen atom is replaced by a sulfur atom.

Methanol is called wood alcohol because it was originally made by heating wood chips and collecting the liquid distilled from it. It is a deadly poison, and causes permanent blindness or death. Some alcoholics have become permanently blind and some have died by drinking methanol-based consumer products such as mouthwash. They thought these products contained ethanol.

Ethanol is what most people associate with the word alcohol. It is made by the fermenting of many sugar-containing substances such as fruit juices, corn, and rice. Ethanol is poisonous. If its concentration in the blood of a person exceeds 0.4%, death may result. Because the ethanol molecule is small, it readily passes through the stomach lining, and about 93% of it is absorbed into the bloodstream within an hour. Carbon dioxide, present in such drinks as champagne, whiskey and soda, rum and coke, and gin and tonic, speeds up the absorption of alcohol by the stomach. This means that you will feel the effects of the alcohol faster than if the carbon dioxide were not present.

More than one alcohol group may be attached to the carbon chain, as in ethylene glycol and glycerin. Ethylene glycol is the main ingredient in most antifreeze products. Glycerol is used in making drugs, cosmetics, nitroglycerin, and many other products.

Nitroglycerin is used in explosives, but it has another important use. People with the heart complaint called angina take nitroglycerin to ease their chest pains. The tablets of nitroglycerin should be stored in a tightly closed bottle. If they are left in an open container, nitroglycerin escapes from the tablets, making them weaker. These tablets should never be stored in a container with other tablets because the nitroglycerin can escape and contaminate the other pills.

15.9 Some Wonderful Smells

Many esters have wonderful smells. The esters in rum, pineapple, apple, and banana are such examples. Esters are made by the reaction between an organic acid and an alcohol.

For example,

methanol + ethanoic acid → methyl ethanoate + water
       (acetic acid)   (methyl acetate)

$$H-\underset{\underset{H}{|}}{\overset{\overset{H}{|}}{C}}-O-H + H-O-\underset{\overset{||}{O}}{C}-\overset{\overset{H}{|}}{\underset{\underset{H}{|}}{C}}-H \longrightarrow H-\underset{\underset{H}{|}}{\overset{\overset{H}{|}}{C}}-O-\underset{\overset{||}{O}}{C}-\overset{\overset{H}{|}}{\underset{\underset{H}{|}}{C}}-H + H-O-H$$

The preparation of an ester requires the use of a dehydrating agent, which is a chemical that removes water from molecules. Usually concentrated sulfuric acid is used as the dehydrating agent. The product can be isolated in a pure form but that requires fairly sophisticated apparatus. You will be able to tell that you have made the ester by comparing the smell of the reactants to the smell of the product.

Materials

safety goggles
plastic gloves
methanol
isopentanol (3-methylbutanol)
salicylic acid
glacial acetic acid
concentrated sulfuric acid
retort stand with test tube clamp
10-mL graduated cylinders
4 test tubes
250-mL beaker
hotplate

Method

1. Set up a water bath by filling the 250-mL beaker two-thirds full of water and heating it on a hotplate. Bring the water to the boil and keep the water simmering.

Glacial acetic acid is pure acetic acid with less than 1% water. It is used as a solvent for oils. Both glacial acetic acid and concentrated sulfuric acid can burn you!

Fig. 15

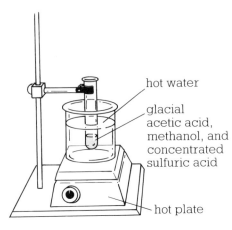

hot water

glacial acetic acid, methanol, and concentrated sulfuric acid

hot plate

2. Using a clean, dry graduated cyclinder, pour 1 mL of glacial acetic acid into a clean, dry test tube. Use a second clean, dry graduated cylinder to add 2 mL of methanol to the acetic acid.

3. Ask your teacher to add two drops of concentrated sulfuric acid to the contents of the test tube. Carefully smell the contents of the test tube. Note the result in a chart.

4. Heat the test tube containing the mixture in the beaker of boiling water (Figure 15) for about 5 min. Remove the test tube and carefully smell the contents. Describe the odour of the product, methyl ethanoate, in your chart.

5. Repeat steps 2 to 4 but use 2 mL of isopentanol (3-methylbutanol) instead of methanol. Use 1 mL of glacial acetic acid and two drops of sulfuric acid as before. The product is named 3-methylbutanyl ethanoate (or isopentyl acetate).

6. Repeat steps 2 to 4 but use about one-tenth of a test tube of salicylic acid crystals instead of the acetic acid. Use 2 mL of methanol and two drops of sulfuric acid as before. The product is named methyl salicylate.

Follow-up

1. What evidence do you have that a reaction occurred in each case?

2. What is the role of the concentrated sulfuric acid?

3. Why do the test tubes and graduated cylinders all have to be dried before the chemicals are added?

4. Describe the smell of each of the esters you prepared?

5. What general use can you see for esters?

6. Write a chemical equation for the reaction between:
   (a) isopentanol and ethanoic acid
   (b) methanol and salicylic acid

Fig. 16 *Remember the hand-waving technique for smelling chemicals.*

WHAT ARE FATS?

A fat (or oil) is the ester of glycerol (an alcohol) and a fatty acid. For example, when glycerol reacts with stearic acid, a fat called glycerol tristearate forms:

$$CH_2-O-H \quad + \quad HO-\overset{\overset{\displaystyle O}{\|}}{C}-(CH_2)_{16}CH_3$$

$$CH-O-H \quad + \quad HO-\overset{\overset{\displaystyle O}{\|}}{C}-(CH_2)_{16}CH_3 \quad \rightarrow$$

$$CH_2-O-H \quad + \quad HO-\overset{\overset{\displaystyle O}{\|}}{C}-(CH_2)_{16}CH_3$$

$$CH_2-O-\overset{\overset{\displaystyle O}{\|}}{C}-(CH_2)_{16}CH_3$$

$$CH-O-\overset{\overset{\displaystyle O}{\|}}{C}-(CH_2)_{16}CH_3 \quad + \quad 3H_2O$$

$$CH_2-O-\overset{\overset{\displaystyle O}{\|}}{C}-(CH_2)_{16}CH_3$$

glycerol + stearic acid → glyceryl tristearate + water

Animal fats such as butter, lard, and chicken fat contain saturated fat molecules and cholesterol. Liquid vegetable oils are thought to be better for your health because they contain polyunsaturated fats, and no cholesterol. High cholesterol diets may lead to heart disease. Saturated fat molecules do not contain double and triple carbon bonds, while unsaturated and polyunsaturated fat molecules contain many of these bonds. Vegetable oils can be made into solid margarines by reacting the oil molecules with hydrogen (hydrogenating them) to make them more saturated. The more saturated the margarine, the harder it is.

Fig. 17 *To avoid saturated fats, buy liquid vegetable oils and soft margarine.*

CHEMICALLY SPEAKING

387

CHEMICAL TIDBITS

A DIETER'S WISH

In 1979, a food scientist, Norman Singer, was working in the laboratory of Labatt's Ltd. in London, Ontario. He and his co-worker, Shoji Yamamoto, were working on whey, a bi-product of cheese manufacture. They were whipping the whey and heating it to see if it coagulated or collapsed. The product looked like styrofoam, but tasted like 35% cream cheese! Singer recognized, after a few experiments, that whey could be made into a new natural fat substitute. In 1984, Nutrasweet in the U.S.A. obtained a licence to use the technology from Labatt's. Singer was hired by Nutrasweet and this company has produced a product, Simplesse®, with half the amount of butter fat and no cholesterol. Simplesse® ice cream cannot be distinguished from top quality ice cream. Simplesse® can also be used in salad dressings, yogurt, coffee whiteners, sour cream, and other similar applications. The product cannot be used in frying because it coagulates like egg whites when heated to high temperatures.

Fig. 18 *Simplesse® products.*

15.10 Polymers

The word polymer comes from the Greek words *poly* (many) and *meros* (parts). The word plastic comes from the Greek word *plastikos*, which means "able to be moulded."

Polymers are giant molecules made by bonding a large number of smaller molecules together. The small building block molecules are called **monomers**.

Rubber (obtained from the rubber tree) and silk are examples of naturally occurring polymers. Today, synthetic polymers are more important than natural polymers. Plastic pipes, bags, car steering wheels, seat covers, false eyelashes, wigs, paints, pens, and synthetic fibres for clothing are just a few of the products made from synthetic polymers.

A common polymer is polyethylene, which is used for plastic bottles and bags. It is made by bonding many ethene (ethylene) molecules together. The double bond of the monomer opens up during reaction and the units can bond together into long chains.

many $\quad$ $\underset{H}{\overset{H}{>}}C=C\underset{H}{\overset{H}{<}}$ $\longrightarrow$ $\left[\begin{array}{cccc} H & H & H & H \\ | & | & | & | \\ -C & -C & -C & -C- \\ | & | & | & | \\ H & H & H & H \end{array}\right]$ many

many $\quad$ $CH_2{=}CH_2$ $\longrightarrow$ $[-CH_2-CH_2-]_{many}$

monomer $\qquad\qquad\qquad\qquad$ polymer

ethene (ethylene) $\qquad\qquad\qquad$ polyethylene

Another well-known polymer is polymethylmethacrylate or Plexiglas. It is a transparent solid used for aircraft domes, lighting fixtures, optical instruments, and surgical appliances. Plexiglas is made up of many units of methyl methacrylate.

many $CH_2\!\!=\!\!CCH_3COOCH_3$ $\longrightarrow$ $[-CH_2CH_2CH_3COOCH_3-]_{many}$

monomer   polymer

methyl methacrylate   polymethylmethacrylate

"It's not cotton, honey. It's nylon quilted to polyester. The leaves and trim are twenty per cent acrylic and eighty per cent modacrylic, and the flowers are acetate. The backing is polypropylene. Go to bed."

(Drawing by Booth; copyright 1978 The New Yorker Magazine, Inc.)

389

WHAT SUBSTANCES IN THEIR FIFTIES ARE STILL GOING STRONG?

In the 1930s, the era of synthetic fibres and plastics began. Two important polymers, nylon (of women's stocking fame) and Teflon (of non-stick cookware fame), were discovered by the E. I. du Pont de Nemours Company in 1938.

Nylon was first used as toothbrush bristles, and **Teflon** was listed in the Guinness Book of World Records as the most slippery substance in the world. Du Pont described nylon as being made from coal, water, and air. It could be made into fine, shiny threads that were as strong as steel and yet more elastic than common natural fibres. During World War II, nylon was used for parachutes, tents, and aircraft tire cord. Famous women auctioned their nylon stockings to sell war bonds and women rioted to buy postwar nylon stockings. Today nylon is used in many items such as computer circuit boards, fishing lines, surgical thread, clothes, carpets, fire hose, and ropes. Although consumers hear of Teflon on cookware, the largest use of Teflon today is as wire and cable insulation.

Since plastics cannot easily be decomposed, plastic wastes remain in the environment. Julian Hill, the only surviving member of the team that developed nylon, is worried about the growing threat of plastic products to the environment. ''I don't think it is all good,'' he says, ''I think the human race is in danger of being smothered in its own plastics.''

What do you think?

Fig. 19 *Nylon is strong enough to make cables, yet soft enough to make women's stockings.*

Fig. 20 *Teflon is best known for its use on non-stick cookware.*

CHEMICAL OPERATOR

Charlie Hill is a chemical operator at Rohm and Haas Canada Inc. He has a Grade 12 education and auto re-finisher papers. He joined the company 20 years ago. His first position involved moving stores needed in the production of acrylics. Over the years Charlie gained wide experience. He has worked on all aspects of production, from the loading up of the reaction tanks to packaging of the finished acrylic product. Charlie has been part of the technological changes that occurred in production. When he started, the tanks were gravity fed with chemicals. Today the company operates computerized stainless steel reaction tanks, called kettles. Because of his knowledge of production, Charlie worked along with the computer specialists and chemical engineers to improve the computerization of the manufacturing process. Originally he did not know much about chemistry but, over time, he picked up chemical information from company experts. Company chemists have given Charlie mini-courses in the chemistry of acrylics to make his job more interesting and to help prevent chemical accidents. Safety is very important and the company makes sure that Charlie and his fellow workers are fully trained in safety procedures. A high school graduate could probably still start off in the chemical industry the way Charlie did. But, Charlie predicts that as companies modernize, community college courses and computer awareness will be needed to work in chemical production. Today Charlie still enjoys his job. He says it is a lot cleaner than when he started out, and a lot more challenging. What he really enjoys is sharing his knowledge by training new chemical operators on the new computerized reaction tanks.

CAN A CHEMICAL COMPANY BE A GOOD NEIGHBOUR?

Rohm and Haas Canada Inc. has environmental control programs designed to reduce or eliminate waste and harmful plant emissions. Air pollution is reduced when exhaust gases are cleaned by passage through scrubbing devices. Water pollution and waste are reduced or eliminated through recycling or improved methods of production. Incineration is used for any remaining waste disposal. A key part of environmental control is regular testing and analysis of air and groundwater samples. Rohm and Haas carry out such testing to ensure that the company operations do not harm the community or the environment.

Chemical plants such as Rohm and Haas Canada Inc. produce fertilizers, pesticides, and synthetic polymers used to make common products.

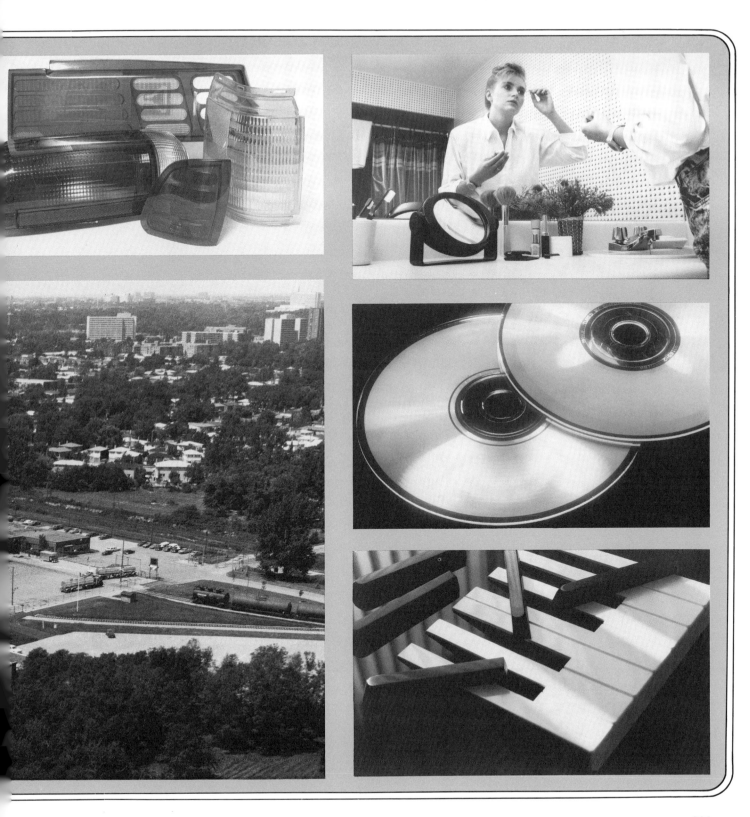

Fig. 21 *Canadians James Guillet and Harvey Troth invented a biodegradable plastic.*

15.11 Research Project

From the following list, select an organic chemistry topic which interests you. Explore the topic, using whatever resources you can — people, libraries, films, and so on.

- cancer-producing chemicals
- famous organic chemist(s), such as a Nobel prize winner
- food additives: pros and cons
- hallucinogenic drugs
- herbicides or pesticides: pros and cons
- medical applications of organic chemicals
- oil pollution
- organic dyes
- perming or dyeing of hair
- plastics
- plastics and the mounting garbage dilemma
- synthetic fibres
- dwindling oil supplies: economic, political, and practical problems

Present your findings in any form other than an essay. Some possible forms are:

advertisement	magazine article	role play
board game	paintings	scrap book
cartoons	photo sequence	skit
collage	poem	audio cassette
comic strip	poster	video tape

POINTS · TO · RECALL

- Organic chemicals all contain carbon atoms.

- Hydrocarbons are organic compounds which contain only carbon and hydrogen.

- Hydrocarbons are named using the number of carbon atoms in their molecules.
- Hydrocarbons may be saturated (alkanes), or unsaturated (alkenes and alkynes).

- The distillation of hydrocarbons produces many important organic chemicals.
- When functional groups bond to hydrocarbons, a great variety of different organic substances may be formed.
- Some important families of organic chemicals are: alcohols, ethers, aldehydes, ketones, acids, esters, and amines.
- Organic chemicals that have the same molecular formula, but different structural formulas, are called isomers.
- Polymers are giant molecules made by chemically linking small molecules together.
- Organic molecules play a very important role in our bodies and in our lives.

R E V I E W · Q U E S T I O N S

1. What are organic chemicals? Why are they so important to your lives?
2. In all the organic substances you studied, how many bonds did each carbon atom have?
3. Petroleum is the starting material for many organic chemicals. Go to your resource centre and find out where petroleum is found in Canada. Show your findings on a map of Canada.
4. What is a hydrocarbon?
5. What is an unsaturated hydrocarbon?
   If your doctor told you or a family member to avoid eating saturated fats, what products would you avoid?
6. What types of oils and margarines would be healthier for you to eat?
7. Draw one structural formula for each of the following hydrocarbons, and name them:
   (a) C_4H_{10} (b) C_3H_6
8. Lead compounds were added to gasoline to prevent "knocking."
   Why are governments trying to stop the sale of leaded gasoline?
9. Why are hotplates used instead of Bunsen burners when working with most organic solvents?
10. Organic esters sometimes have wonderful odours. What industries do you think make use of such esters?
11. Draw the two possible structural formulas for the molecular formula C_2H_6O (two isomers are possible).

Look at the table of functional groups and decide on the type of organic material you have drawn. Write down the names under your structures. Does anything interesting strike you about the uses of these two isomers?
12. Why must you never drink wood alcohol?
13. Working on your own or in small groups, draw up a three column chart as shown below.
    (a) List all the foods and/or drinks that you have for breakfast in the first column.
    (b) Other than water, list other chemicals that are part of you.
    (c) Add to your list ice cream, salad dressing, cheese spread, and at least three other packaged instant foods that you have at home.

   The chemical ingredients of many of the items on your list will be found on the labels of their containers. For each product in your list, write these ingredients in the column next to the products. Use a check mark to show which chemicals are organic. Discuss your findings as a class.

Product	Chemical ingredients	Check (✓) if the chemical is organic

16 NUCLEAR CHEMISTRY

CONTENTS

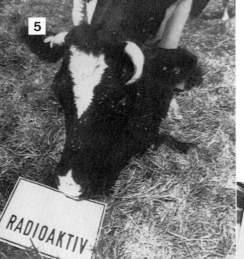

16.1 How Concerned Are You About Nuclear Matters?

Working in pairs, react to Figures 1 to 6. Write down your positive and negative feelings about the nuclear world we live in. Discuss your feelings and concerns as a class.

Fig. 1 *The ultimate weapon!*

Fig. 2 *A nuclear power plant.*

Fig. 3 *Some food, such as this cookie, is preserved by nuclear irradiation.*

Fig. 4 *Gamma radiation is used as a diagnostic tool in medicine.*

Fig. 5 *Cattle in West Germany affected by nuclear fallout from Chernobyl. It is a pity the cow can't read.*

Fig. 6 *Radiation can be used to determine the thickness of metal sheets.*

16.2 The Birth of the Nuclear Age

You have learned that the atom consists of negatively charged electrons and a positively charged nucleus. The electrons are involved in ordinary chemical reactions. The nucleus can also undergo changes. The study of the atomic nucleus and its reactions is called **nuclear chemistry**.

In the mid 1800s and early 1900s a number of important discoveries were made about the atom and the nucleus. You will now research one aspect of the early development of atomic structure and nuclear chemistry.

1. Work in *home groups* of six. Each home group member will be given a topic to research. The topics are shown in Figures 7 to 12.

Fig. 7 *Röntgen, who discovered X-rays.*

Fig. 8 *Becquerel, who discovered radioactivity.*

Fig. 9 *Marie and Pierre Curie, who discovered two radioactive elements, polonium and radium.*

2. Everyone working on the same topic will form an *expert group* to share information. Make notes during your discussion sessions. Write a summary of your information to take to your home group.

3. Each member of the home group will teach the others in the group what they learned in their expert groups.

4. Each home group must prepare and present a brief paper (preferably typed), describing the development of the nuclear atom model.

1 2 3 4 5 6	1 2 3 4 5 6	**HOME GROUPS**
1 2 3 4 5 6	1 2 3 4 5 6	

1 1 1 1	2 2 2 2	3 3 3 3	**EXPERT GROUPS**
4 4 4 4	5 5 5 5	6 6 6 6	

Fig. 10 *Rutherford, who developed the nuclear model of the atom.*

Fig. 11 *Bohr, who proposed a model of electron arrangement.*

Fig. 12 *Chadwick, who discovered the neutron.*

16.3 Radioactivity

When the nucleus of an atom is *unstable*, it splits apart producing other nuclei, particles, rays, and a great deal of heat energy. The new nuclei formed are called **daughter nuclei**. The particles and rays given off are called **radiation**. The property of giving off radiation is called **radioactivity**.

The three common forms of radiation are shown in the following chart:

Radiation type	Symbol	Charge	Nature	Penetrating power
alpha, α, particles	$^4_2$He	2+	Helium nuclei	stopped by one sheet of paper
beta, β, particles	$^0_{-1}$e	1−	high energy electrons	stopped by 1 cm thick sheet of aluminum
gamma rays	γ	0	very high energy electromagnetic waves	stopped by very thick sheets of lead, steel or concrete

Fig. 13 *The three types of radiation differ in ability to pass through various thicknesses of substances.*

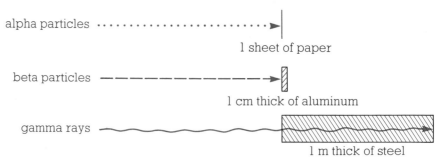

alpha particles ....➤ | 1 sheet of paper

beta particles — — — — — — —➤ ▨ 1 cm thick of aluminum

gamma rays ∿∿∿∿∿∿∿➤ ▨▨▨ 1 m thick of steel

X-rays are penetrating electromagnetic waves produced by a stream of high-speed electrons bombarding a metal plate in a vacuum. The nucleus is usually not involved in the process.

Cosmic rays are electrons and the nuclei of atoms, mostly hydrogen, that fall on the earth from outer space.

The three types of radiation are highly energetic. They ionize the materials through which they pass, and they can change or destroy molecules. Cells of living organisms exposed to radiation may be badly damaged or die.

Everyone is exposed to low levels of radiation from our natural environment. This is called **background radiation** and is mainly due to:
- cosmic rays from space
- radioactive isotopes produced by cosmic rays
- naturally radioactive isotopes (such as uranium, thorium, and potassium) in the ground and in building materials
- naturally radioactive isotopes in drinking water and food
- radon gas found indoors

Skin cancer, bone cancer, thyroid cancer, leukemia, or other cancers are produced when a person is exposed to too much radiation. Gamma rays are particularly harmful because they can readily pass through the human body.

The units used to measure radiation are the **gray** and the **sievert**. The gray (symbol Gy) is the basic unit used to measure the radiation absorbed by a certain mass of body tissue. The sievert (symbol Sv) is the unit of radiation dose which is related to the biological damage done to body tissue.

The immediate effect from a large dose of radiation (acute radiation) is the death of a very large number of cells in a short time. The chart below shows the effect of acute radiation.

According to the Atomic Energy Control Board of Canada, the maximum allowable annual radiation dose for a person is 5 mSv, that for an occupational worker is 50 mSv.

Dosage (mSv)	Effects
250 to 1000	Temporary changes in the blood. Some people may experience nausea at more than 750 mSv
2500 to 4000	Temporary blood changes, diarrhea, nausea and weakness. Death unlikely from these effects.
2500 to 4000	As above, but more severe. Death may occur in a few cases within several weeks.
4000 and above	As above, but with increased likelihood of death in a shorter period of time.

To minimize the effects of radiation, follow three principles:

- *shielding* (use paper or foil for alpha particles, 2 or 3-cm thick sheet of metal for beta particles, 0.5-m thick block of concrete for gamma rays)
- *distance* (keep as far away as possible from the source of radiation)
- *time* (reduce the time of exposure as much as possible)

So far only external radiation has been mentioned. If a radioactive material is taken into the body, then the radiation given out can be very dangerous. Gamma rays cause fairly widespread damage; alpha and beta particles cause damage in a very local area of tissue. A radioactive element may accumulate in a certain part of the body. For example, radioactive calcium-45 deposits along with normal calcium in bones, and radioactive iodine-131 is concentrated in the thyroid gland.

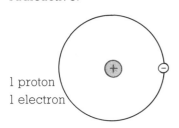

1 proton
1 electron

(a)   hydrogen – 1

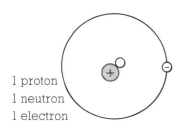

1 proton
1 neutron
1 electron

(b)   hydrogen – 2
        deuterium

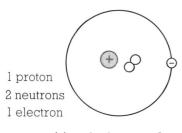

1 proton
2 neutrons
1 electron

(c)   hydrogen – 3
        tritium

In a physical or chemical change, elements never become new elements. In a nuclear change, however, new elements are formed.

16.4 Radioactive Isotopes

Are all isotopes of an element radioactive? The answer must be no! There are three isotopes of the simplest element, hydrogen (Figure 14). Only one of the three is radioactive. The isotopes of hydrogen are very important because of their differences in physical properties. They have been given their own symbols even though they are the same element.

Isotope	Symbol	Special name
hydrogen-1	H	hydrogen
hydrogen-2	D	deuterium
hydrogen-3	T	tritium (radioactive)

Relatively few radioactive isotopes (**radioisotopes**) are found in nature. Except for tritium and carbon-14, most radioactive isotopes are atoms with heavy nuclei. These atoms are of elements with atomic numbers greater than 81. A large number of radiosotopes that do not exist in nature can be synthesized.

16.5 Nuclear Equations

When a nucleus splits and gives out radiation, we say that the nucleus has undergone **nuclear decay** or it has **disintegrated**. Scientists use nuclear equations to show what happens when a nucleus changes. These equations include mass numbers and atomic numbers, as shown below.

The nucleus of uranium-238 splits to produce a thorium-234 nucleus and an alpha particle. The nuclear equation is:

$$^{238}_{92}\text{U} \rightarrow \ ^{234}_{90}\text{Th} + \ ^{4}_{2}\text{He}$$

Similarly, when tritium decays it produces helium-3 and a beta particle:

$$^{3}_{1}\text{1H} \rightarrow \ ^{3}_{2}\text{1He} + \ ^{0}_{-1}\text{e}$$

The two sides of a balanced nuclear equation have the same total mass numbers and atomic numbers. For example, in the equation for the disintegration of uranium-238:

	Left side of arrow	Right side of arrow
Sum of mass numbers (top numbers)	238	234 + 4
Sum of atomic numbers (bottom numbers)	92	90 + 2

Questions

Complete and balance the following nuclear equations:

(a) $^{12}_{6}\text{C}$ + $^{4}_{2}\text{He}$ →

(b) $^{87}_{37}\text{Rb}$ → ? + $^{0}_{-1}\text{e}$

Remember the symbol of the nucleus formed is determined by the atomic number.

16.6 Nuclear Fission and Fusion

A **fission reaction** is a nuclear reaction in which an unstable nucleus splits into two nuclei (Figure 15). During this process, a great deal of energy is released. The following nuclear equation shows one of the many possible fission reactions for uranium-235:

$$^{235}_{92}\text{U} + ^{1}_{0}\text{n} → ^{89}_{35}\text{Br} + ^{145}_{57}\text{La} + 2^{1}_{0}\text{n} + \text{energy}$$

Fig. 15 *Fission of heavy nuclei releases large amounts of energy.*

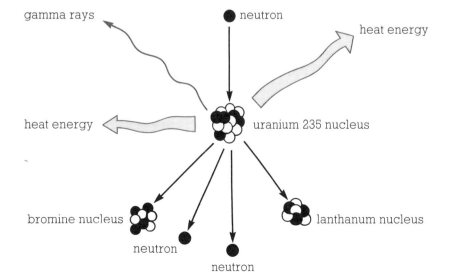

403

In the above example, when a nucleus of uranium-235 is struck by a neutron, $^1_0$n, it undergoes fission. The two neutrons from this disintegrating nucleus collide with two other uranium-235 nuclei, causing them to undergo fission. The result is a self-sustaining series of fission reactions called a **chain reaction** (Figure 16).

Fig. 16 *A chain reaction.*

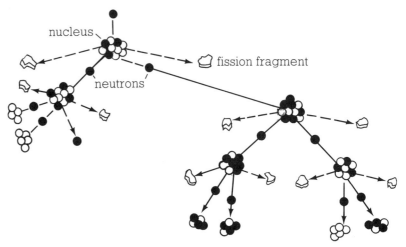

A nuclear (or atomic) bomb produces energy by the fission of uranium-235 or plutonium-239. A hydrogen bomb produces even more energy by the fusion of deuterium and tritium. A nuclear bomb is used to detonate a hydrogen bomb.

The symbol $^0_{-1}$e is given to a particle called a **positron**. It has the same mass as an electron but it has a positive charge ($+1$).

Enormous quantities of energy are produced in fission reactions. The fission of 1 g of uranium-235 gives about the same quantity of energy as is released when three tonnes of coal is burned!

The joining of two light nuclei to form a heavier nucleus is known as a **fusion reaction** (figure 17). A fusion reaction gives off even more energy than a fission reaction. It is very difficult to start a fusion reaction, and temperatures as high as millions of degrees are needed. The heat and light produced by the sun come from fusion reactions. An example of one of the series of reactions is:

$$^1_1H \ + \ ^1_1H \ \rightarrow \ ^2_1H \ + \ ^0_{+1}e$$

$$^2_1H \ + \ ^1_1H \ \rightarrow \ ^3_2He$$

$$^3_2He \ + \ ^3_2He \ \rightarrow \ ^4_2He \ + \ 2^1_1H$$

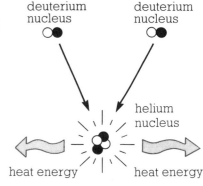

Fig. 17 *Fusion of light nuclei, under extremely high temperatures, releases very large amounts of energy.*

16.7 Harnessing Nuclear Energy

Fig. 18 *A nuclear power plant uses nuclear reactions to produce steam. Other power plants produce steam in other ways.*

Nuclear power plants are already part of our lives. As seen above, nuclear fission produces great amounts of heat. This heat is used to turn water into steam. The steam drives turbines and results in the generation of electrical energy (Figure 18).

(a) nuclear power plant

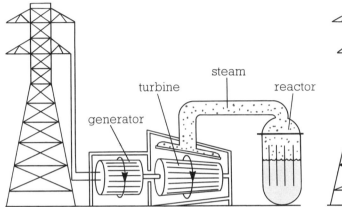

(b) coal power plant

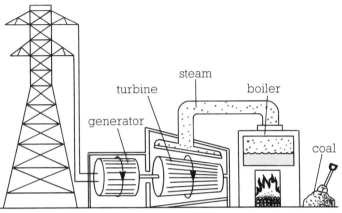

A **nuclear reactor** (Figure 19) is designed to hold a quantity of nuclear fuel, maintain a *controlled* nuclear reaction, and provide for the removal of the heat produced. In a controlled reaction, not too many nuclei are allowed to undergo fission at any one time, and so the energy output is controlled.

The main parts of a reactor (Figure 20) are: nuclear fuel, moderator, coolant, and control rods.

Fig. 20 *The main parts of a reactor.*

Fig. 19 *Working on a nuclear reactor.*

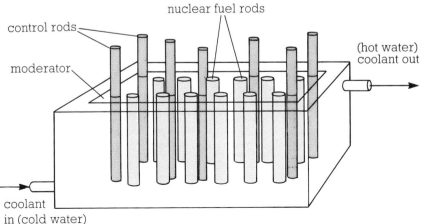

405

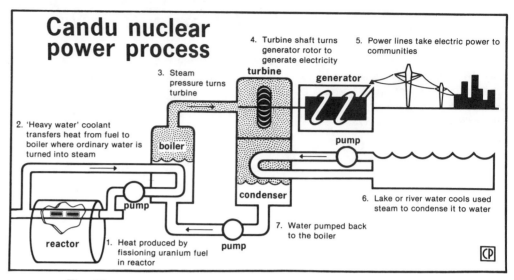

Fig. 21

Natural uranium contains 99.3% uranium-238 and 0.7% uranium-235. Uranium-235 is fissionable but uranium-238 is not.

The **critical mass** is the quantity of a fissionable material required to keep a chain reaction going.

The hydrogen in heavy water is the hydrogen-2 isotope, not the hydrogen-1 isotope found in ordinary water. Chemically, heavy water and ordinary water behave in the same way.

The **nuclear fuel** varies depending on the type of reactor. Reactors in Canada use uranium isotopes.

Neutrons produced by the fuel must be absorbed by other fuel nuclei. For this to happen, there must be a sufficient mass of fissionable material, and the neutrons must be slowed down to improve their chance of being absorbed by nearby fuel nuclei. The material that slows the neutrons down is called the **moderator**.

The **coolant** takes the heat from the reactor to the heat exchanger. In a heat exchanger the coolant gives up its heat to water in a separate boiler system and this water is turned into steam.

If all the neutrons formed from fission set off other fissions, then the reactor would get out of control. Rods that absorb some of the neutrons are inserted into the reactor to slow down the chain reaction. These are called **control rods**.

The **CAN**adian **D**euterium oxide natural **U**ranium (**CANDU**) nuclear reactors were developed by Canada. In the CANDU reactor, natural uranium is used as the fuel, and heavy water (deuterium oxide, D_2O) is used as the moderator and coolant.

Uranium-235 is the actual fissionable material that gives out energy. When uranium-238 in the reactor absorbs a neutron, it does not undergo fission but decays into plutonium-239, which is highly radioactive and very dangerous. Used fuel from the CANDU reactor therefore contains, among other radioisotopes, plutonium-239. The used fuel is housed in giant cement "swimming pools." These pools are sealed off from other parts

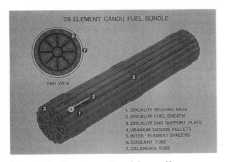

28 ELEMENT CANDU FUEL BUNDLE

END VIEW

1. ZIRCALOY BEARING PADS
2. ZIRCALOY FUEL SHEATH
3. ZIRCALOY END SUPPORT PLATE
4. URANIUM DIOXIDE PELLETS
5. INTER - ELEMENT SPACERS
6. COOLANT TUBE
7. CALANDRIA TUBE

Fig. 22 *Nuclear fuel bundle.*

of the power plant. The water in the pools absorbs the heat and radiation produced by the radioactive materials. Eventually, long term storage sites, or safe uses, will have to be found because the radiation hazard of the wastes lasts for hundreds of centuries. Major problems lie in the location of a waste site and the transportation of the wastes to the chosen site.

Plutonium-239 is used to make nuclear weapons. For this reason Canada has to be very careful about the countries to which it sells CANDU reactors.

Although a reactor has the components of a nuclear bomb, it cannot explode like a nuclear bomb. The reactor is usually protected by thick concrete structures. But if the reactor building does crack open, huge amounts of radiation would be released and scattered over a large area. This causes a major hazard as the radioactive particles settle. This settling is called **nuclear fall-out**. It contaminates soil and water, and gets into the food chain. Living organisms may have deformed offspring, and livestock and crops contaminated by radioisotopes must be destroyed.

Fig. 23 *Transporting heavy water from the Pickering nuclear power station to the Darlington tritium removal facility.*

Questions

1. List the various ways electrical energy can be produced. List the risks associated with each of these methods of energy production.

2. Does our need for energy warrant the risks associated with nuclear power plants?

3. Imagine an energy crisis. Oil is in very short supply and is mainly being used to make medicines and other essential products. In this situation, nuclear reactors are one of the main sources of energy for power corporations. How would you feel and react if a nuclear dump site were proposed for a site near your home?

4. Draw a simple diagram of a CANDU reactor and describe the function of each part.

5. In a **breeder reactor**, non-fissionable uranium-238 is converted into fissionable uranium-239, which is then used as the nuclear fuel. This kind of reactor produces more fissionable material than that you started with. List the differences between a CANDU reactor and a breeder reactor.

VICTIMS OF CHERNOBYL

In April 1986, more than 100 000 Russians were exposed to high levels of radiation when an explosion occurred in the nuclear power plant at Chernobyl (Figure 24). People were evacuated, leaving nearby cities deserted. There were increased radiation levels in Scandinavia within three days of the accident. This accident was the first well-publicized experience the world has had of an uncontained major nuclear accident. As the days went on, doctors in Russia saw patients with vomiting, diarrhea, jaundice, loss of hair, confusion, and high fevers. Some went into a coma and died.

A fireman who had entered the reactor site suffered radiation burns which caused his skin to blister and peel. His worst burns were on his hands because he had handled radioactive water. Within ten days he lost all his hair. His life was saved by a bone marrow transplant carried out by a joint American and Russian surgical team. Time will tell the final toll that this accident will take!

Fig. 24 *The destroyed reactor at Chernobyl.*

16.8 The Bomb!

The nuclear bomb that exploded over Hiroshima on August 6, 1945 contained uranium-235. Two days later, a bomb containing plutonium-239 was dropped on Nagasaki.

The first nuclear bombs used in warfare were dropped on two Japanese cities, Hiroshima and Nagasaki, at the end of World War II (Figure 25). Many survivors of the bomb still suffer the effects of the radiation and have horror stories to tell. Many of these people had to watch while loved ones died of radiation sickness.

Fig. 25 *The ruins in Hiroshima after the nuclear explosion.*

Radiation sickness occurs when a living organism is exposed to a high dose of radiation. If a person gets a lethal dose of radiation, then an ugly sequence of events occurs:

1. diarrhea and vomiting

2. ulceration of the linings of the stomach and intestines

3. physical weakness

4. breakdown of normal blood production

5. weakening of defences against bacteria

6. lowered production of bone marrow

7. destruction of body cells

8. damage to blood clotting abilities, likely to result in internal hemorhaging

Death can occur six weeks after exposure. Most die within 30 days. For those who survive, leukemia or other cancers are common, as are birth defects in offspring.

The major world powers have many nuclear weapons and are producing more. The threat of nuclear war is very real. Should countries continue to develop nuclear weapons?

Investigation	# 16.9 The Nuclear Decay Analogy

Not all radioisotopes remain radioactive over the same period of time. How long their radioactivity lasts depends on the size of the sample and which radioisotope is present.

You will use one cent coins to represent the nuclei in a radioactive sample. At the start all the coins represent "radioactive" nuclei. In this investigation the product formed is assumed to be non-radioactive.

When the coins are tossed in the air, some will land heads up, while others will land tails up.

- Those that land heads up are considered to represent nuclei that are still radioactive.
- Those that land tails up represent nuclei that have disintegrated, that is, they are non-radioactive.

Materials

a box of 100 pennies per group

Method

1. Divide into seven groups, A to G.

2. Divide 100 pennies as equally as possible among the members of each group.

3. Make up a chart for your results and those of the other groups in the class.

Throw number	Number of radioactive nuclei (Number of heads up)							Average
	A	B	C	D	E	F	G	
0	100	100	100	100	100	100	100	100
1								
2								
3								
4								
5								
6								
7								
8								
9								

4. Within a group, toss the coins and allow them to land on a large flat surface. Count the number of coins that have landed heads up. Record this number across from throw number 1 under your group's column. Put all the "tails up" coins into the box out of the way.

5. Repeat step 4, entering the number across from throw number 2.

6. Repeat step 4 until there are no more heads-up coins.

7. Calculate the average across all the groups for all the throws.

8. Plot the average results by placing throw number on the x-axis, and the number of heads-up coins on the y-axis. Draw the best *smooth* curve through the points.

Follow-up

1. From your graph find the number of heads-up coins at each throw.

2. Compare the numbers from:
   (a) throw 1 with throw 0,
   (b) throw 2 with throw 1,
   (c) throw 3 with throw 2, and so on.
   Do you notice a pattern?

16.10 Half-Lives

The time it takes for half of the nuclei in a sample of a radioactive isotope to decay is called the **half-life** of the isotope. If an isotope has a half-life of 10 min, then a sample of 1000 radioactive nuclei should give the following data:

Time (in min)	Number of radioactive nuclei left
0	1000
10	500
20	250
30	125

This decay pattern continues until there are no radioactive nuclei left in the sample. As you can see, each throw of the coins in the previous investigation represented one half-life. It doesn't mean that all radioactive nuclei of this isotope wait for a given time and then suddenly decay. Figure 27 shows that the number of radioactive nuclei is dropping all the time.

Fig. 27 *A half-life graph.*

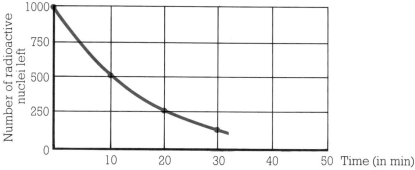

The following chart shows the half-lives of some radioisotopes.

Isotope	Half-life
uranium-238	4.51×10^9a
uranium-235	0.713×10^9 a
carbon-14	5730 a
iodine-131	8.05 d
cobalt-60	5.27 a
potassium-40	1.30×10^9 a

a = years
d = days
10^9 = billion

Because radioactivity decreases in such an orderly way, we can make use of it to date very old objects.

Radioactive carbon-14 is constantly being taken in by living things from the atmosphere and undergoing radioactive decay. Eventually, the carbon-14 concentration in a living thing reaches a constant value. As soon as a living thing dies, carbon-14 is no longer taken in. As the carbon-14 already in the sample decays, the radioactivity it produces decreases. Therefore, if the rate of decay of the carbon-14 in a sample of wood is carefully measured, it is possible to tell when the tree died. This method—called **carbon-14 dating**—has been used to date materials found on archaeological sites (Figure 29). For dating rocks, other radioisotopes, such as potassium-40 have to be used.

Carbon-14 is continuously formed in the atmosphere when neutrons from cosmic rays react with nitrogen-14. Carbon-14 decays back into nitrogen-14.

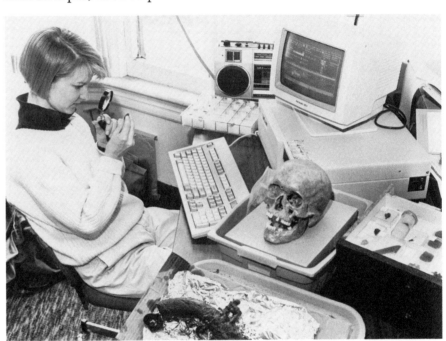

Fig. 28 *Carbon-14 dating is a method used to determine when an animal or plant died.*

Fig. 29 *The Dea Sea Scrolls are found to be two thousand years old using the carbon-14 dating method.*

1. The following data show the decay rate (number of disintegrations per minute per gram) of carbon-14:

Time (years)	Decay rate	Time (years)	Decay rate	Time (years)	Decay rate
0	15.30	6500	6.97	1300	3.17
500	14.40	7000	6.56	13500	2.99
1000	13.56	7500	6.18	1400	2.81
1500	12.76	8000	5.81	14500	2.65
2000	12.01	8500	5.47	15000	2.49
2500	11.31	900	5.15	15500	2.35
3000	10.64	9500	4.85	16000	2.21
3500	10.02	10000	4.56	16500	2.08
4000	9.43	10500	4.30	17000	1.96
4500	8.88	11000	4.04	17500	1.84
5000	8.36	11500	3.81	18000	1.73
5500	7.87	12000	3.58		
6000	7.40	12500	3.37		

(a) Graph the above data. Plot time on the x-axis, and decay rate on the y-axis.

(b) From your graph, estimate the time it takes for a sample of carbon-14 to reach half of its original level of radioactivity. That is, estimate the half-life of this isotope.

(c) Two fossils containing carbon-14 produced decay rates of
 (a) 8.62 disintegrations per min per g
 (b) 4.15 disintegrations per min per g
 From your graph, how old would you estimate these fossils to be?

2. Could you date an item that had a carbon-14 decay rate close to, or equal to, zero? Explain.

16.11 Beneficial Uses of Radioisotopes

What with nuclear fall-out and nuclear waste disposal problems, there seems to be little to recommend the use of radioactive isotopes! But these materials help us in many ways.

Pipeline blockages can be traced by sending a radioactive object (tracer) down the pipe and detecting the radiation. The tracer will be located at the blockage (Figure 30).

Fig. 30 *Radioactive tracers are used to locate blockages in pipelines.*

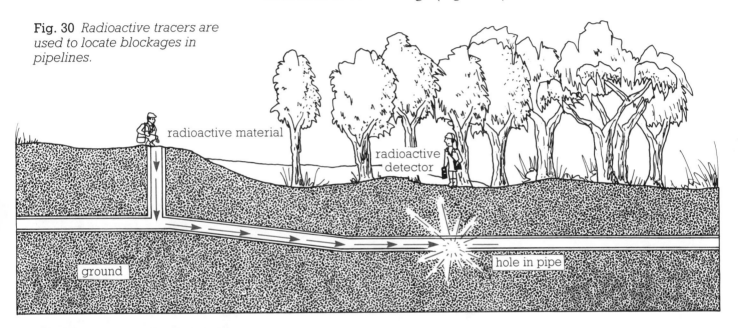

radioactive material

radioactive detector

ground

hole in pipe

Fig. 31 *Irradiation of potatoes prevent sprouting. Compare untreated potatoes (left) with irradiated potatoes (right) ten weeks after treatment.*

Foods may be irradiated to kill bacteria, delay ripening, and prevent spoilage. Ottawa approved the irradiation of potatoes for sale in Canada in the 1960s. Many people believe that irradiation is a good alternative to the addition of chemical preservatives in foods. Some people are against the practice. Would you eat food that you knew had been irradiated?

Some gemstones are irradiated so that they change colour, making them more desirable.

Radiation has been used in insect control. For example, screwworm flies, which cause a lot of damage to livestock, are bred in captivity and the adult flies are sterilized with radiation. These flies are then released to mix with normal flies. Mating results in a high proportion of sterile eggs, so very few flies hatch and the next generation of flies is practically eliminated.

Much use is made of radioisotopes in medicine. Most hospitals now have nuclear medicine units. The radiation from some radioisotopes, such as cobalt-60 and radium-226, can be used to destroy

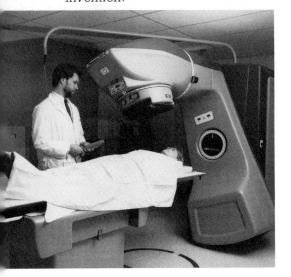

Fig. 32 *The cobalt-60 bomb used to treat cancer is a Canadian invention.*

cancer cells (Figure 32). Other short-lived radioisotopes are used to diagnose internal problems (Figure 33), as shown in the chart below:

Isotope	Use
chromium-51	determining total blood volume
iron-59	measuring how fast red blood cells form and how long they live
arsenic-74	locating brain tumours
iodine-131	detecting and treating defective thyroid glands
phosphorus-32	detecting skin cancer
sodium-24	detecting narrowing or blockage of blood vessels
hydrogen-3 (tritium)	determining total body-water

Fig. 33 *Radioisotopes are also used to help doctors in diagnosis. The picture shows a nuclear gamma camera for diagnostic imaging of the human body.*

416

16.12 The Nuclear Debate

Choose one of the following topics for research:

- Radioactive isotopes in medicine
- Radioactive isotopes in industry
- Radioactive isotopes in energy production
- Radioactive isotopes in food growing or preparation
- Radioactive isotopes in weapons
- Nuclear energy in ships
- Neutron-activation analysis in forensics
- Nuclear waste disposal
- Nuclear fall-out: short and long-term effects
- A nuclear scientist (Create a mock interview between yourself and the scientist.)

Fig. 34 *The first nuclear-powered vessel is the submarine* Nautilus *built in 1954. Now there are other ships driven by nuclear energy.*

You may obtain information on the topic you have chosen from many places and by interviewing people. Some places to try are the school resource centre, public libraries, government agencies, anti-nuclear agencies, and so on. Present your findings to the class in any form *other than an essay.*

Now that you have a fair knowledge of nuclear matters, you can debate nuclear issues such as:

- Nuclear weapons in space
- Limited nuclear war is possible
- Nuclear dump sites
- Can countries be totally nuclear free?

Pick one of the above topics. Select two teams: a pro-nuclear team and an anti-nuclear team. Hold a debate and at the end vote to see which team wins.

NUCLEAR TECHNICIAN

The idea of a Chemical Technology graduate with the job title technician may conjure up images of a worker peering through a test tube at some curious liquid. In fact, paperwork and computers are the main work tools of Randy Andrews, a **nuclear technician** at Ontario Hydro's Pickering power plant.

Randy's responsibilities involve monitoring the heavy water used as a coolant and moderator in the **CANDU** reactors. This unique Canadian reactor uses a cheaper grade of uranium fuel than U.S. and European systems, but requires heavy water which is expensive to produce. Control of the input, output, inventory and purity of this material is very important. Randy does not actually test the water himself, but prepares daily, weekly, and monthly reports on all aspects of the heavy water system, including all the pipes and pumps. The field workers send their test results to Randy who must identify and report any abnormalities. To prepare a report, Randy processes the raw information using computer software—spreadsheets, databases, word processing—to tabulate data and perform statistical analysis on it. The reports are part of Hydro's insistence on thorough and frequent communication between departments. Randy's recommendations are used to designate the stocks of heavy water to be used, purified, stored, or taken out of service.

Besides this important day-to-day activity, Randy Andrews is also responsible for preparing manuals for the process operators who do the hands-on running of the plant. As well, he is highly involved in any plant expansion or modification that involves the heavy water system—and most do!

The training period for this position is longer than most technician jobs. When Randy was in elementary school, a news report of an incident at a nuclear reactor at Chalk River had fired his imagination with the idea of working in this new and exotic field. Nonetheless, Randy attended high school in Malton, Ontario without any particular career goals. After high school, he completed three years at Humber College to gain his diploma in Chemical Engineering Technology. He worked briefly for a tobacco company before securing the job at Hydro. A strict basic training period of four months in Ralston, Ontario was followed by more specific on-site training in Pickering where Randy worked his way through four grade levels in order to qualify as a Nuclear Technician.

Because of the complex and sensitive nature of nuclear power generation, Ontario Hydro feels that rigorous training is an important element in ensuring employee and public safety. In fact, safety meetings (ten per year) are another aspect of Randy's job. On-going safety training pertaining to chemical and radiation hazards is an integral part of working life for Randy and all his co-workers at the Pickering power plant.

Randy is happy with his role at Hydro, including the public relations side of working in such a high profile area. He enjoys answering questions about his job and the industry. He also appreciates the opportunity that Hydro has provided him to grow professionally.

- The discoveries of many scientists have contributed to our understanding of the structure of the atom.
- Radioactivity is the process in which an unstable nucleus of an atom splits apart producing other elements, particles and rays, and a lot of energy.
- Alpha (α) and beta (β) particles, and gamma (γ) rays are three possible forms of radiation.
- Gamma rays are more penetrating than beta particles, and beta particles are more penetrating than alpha particles.
- Everything is exposed to background radiation.
- Units used to measure radiation are the gray (Gy) and the sievert (Sv).
- Three principles to minimize radiation effects are shielding, distance, and time.
- Nuclear equations show what happens when a nucleus changes. The mass numbers and atomic numbers are balanced.
- In a fission reaction, a heavy nucleus splits into smaller nuclei.
- In a fusion reaction, light nuclei join to form a heavier nucleus.
- Nuclear power plants use a nuclear fuel in a reactor to produce the heat that turns water into steam. The steam is used to run electric generators.
- The essential parts in a nuclear reactor are nuclear fuel, moderator, coolant, and control rods.
- In the CANDU nuclear reactor, natural uranium is used as the fuel, and heavy water (D_2O) is used as the moderator and coolant.
- If a human or animal is exposed to a high dose of radiation, they will suffer from radiation sickness.
- The time it takes for half of the nuclei in a sample of a radioactive isotope to decay is called the half-life of the isotope.
- Radioisotopes can be used to date artifacts and rocks.
- Nuclear weapons and possible dangers associated with nuclear power plants are controversial issues.
- Radioisotopes have many industrial, scientific, and medical uses.

1. What happens to a radioactive nucleus? What is the process called?
2. What is a daughter nucleus?
3. List three types of radiation. Which is the least penetrating? Which is the most penetrating?
4. Which type of radiation is electromagnetic radiation?
5. What is background radiation? List four sources of background radiation.
6. List some illnesses that may be caused if a person is exposed to too much radiation.
7. Why do you think the government specifies 5 mSv as the maximum allowable dosage for the public, while it specifies 50 mSv for people working with nuclear materials?
8. Describe three precautions to take to minimize the effects of radiation if you have to work with radioisotopes.
9. Complete the following nuclear equations:

   (a) $^{59}_{27}Co$ + $^{1}_{0}n$ → ?

   (b) ? + $^{1}_{0}n$ → $^{3}_{1}H$ + $^{4}_{2}He$

10. What is a fission reaction?
11. A chain letter is like a chain reaction. Explain.
12. What is a fusion reaction?
13. What are the main parts of a nuclear reactor? Describe the role of each of these parts.
14. Why is Canada very particular about the countries to which it will sell its CANDU reactors?
15. When does radiation sickness occur? Describe the stages in radiation sickness.
16. What is meant by the term half-life?
17. Iodine-131 has a half life of approximately eight days. You start with 2000 radioactive nuclei at zero time. Plot a graph of number of radioactive iodine-131 nuclei versus time over 32 days.
18. List at least five beneficial uses of radioisotopes.

Acid. A substance which produces hydrogen ions when dissolved in water. In acid solutions, litmus is red, phenolphthalein is colourless. Acid solutions react with some metals to liberate hydrogen. An acid solution neutralizes a base solution to form a salt and water. Acid solutions have a pH value less than 7.

Acid rain. Precipitation caused by certain gases, some naturally formed, others formed in the burning of fossil fuels, which dissolve in atmospheric water to form an acid solution.

Active ingredient. The essential ingredient in a product which allows the product to do the task it was designed to do.

Activity series. An arrangement of the metals in order of reactivity. The order is based on their behaviour in single displacement reactions.

Additive. A material or mixture of materials added to a commericial product, usually a food, during production or processing to improve the product or help preserve the product.

Alchemy. The practice of very ancient chemistry. Alchemists were chiefly interested in converting metals, such as lead, into gold and seeking the universal cure. Modern chemistry developed from this work.

Alcohol. A class of organic chemicals containing the hydroxyl (OH) group.

Aldehyde. A class of organic chemicals containing a $-C\underset{\diagdown H}{\overset{\diagup O}{}}$ group.

Alkali. A material which dissolves in water to form a base solution. Such solutions have a pH value greater than 7.

Alkane. A class of organic compounds containing only carbon and hydrogen atoms. The carbon atoms are joined in a chain in which there are no double or triple covalent bonds between the carbon atoms.

Alkene. A class of organic compounds containing only carbon and hydrogen atoms. The carbon atoms are joined in a chain in which there is at least one double covalent bond between neighbouring carbon atoms.

Alkyne. A class of organic compounds containing only carbon and hydrogen atoms. The carbon atoms are joined in a chain in which there is at least one triple covalent bond between neighbouring carbon atoms.

Alpha particle. A positively charged particle given off by some radioactive elements when they undergo decay.

Amine. A class of organic chemicals containing a nitrogen atom. This group of compounds can be considered as being formed from ammonia, NH_3, in which one or more of the hydrogen atoms is replaced with a carbon-containing group.

Anode. The positive electrode in an electrolytic cell. The negative ions are attracted to this electrode and there undergo oxidation (loss of electrons).

Atom. The smallest particle of an element that still has the properties of that element.

Atomic mass. The mass of an atom when compared to the mass of the carbon-12 isotope. The value is given in atomic mass units, u.

Atomic number. The number of protons found in the nucleus of a particular element. In a neutral atom this number is also equal to the number of electrons found in the atom.

Background radiation. Radiation from natural sources in the earth and from space.

Balanced equation. A chemical equation showing the same number of atoms of each type on both sides of the equation.

Base. A substance which produces hydroxide ions when dissolved in water. In base solutions, litmus is blue, phenolphthalein is red. A base solution neutralizes an acid solution to form a salt and water. Base solutions have a pH value greater than 7.

Battery. A device containing chemicals that react to produce electrical energy.

Beta particle. A negatively charged particle given off by some radioactive elements when they undergo decay.

Binary compound. A compound made up of only two elements. The names of these compounds always end in *ide*.

Boiling point. The temperature at which a liquid comes to a full boil. This temperature changes if the air pressure changes.

Breeder reactor. A nuclear reactor that produces more radioactive material than it started with.

Buffer. A chemical solution that prevents large changes in pH value when small amounts of acid or base solution are added to it.

Carbon-14 dating. A technique using radioactive carbon-14 to date ancient once-living objects.

Catalyst. A chemical which speeds up a chemical reaction without itself being used up in the reaction.

Cathode. The negative electrode in an electrolytic cell. The positive ions are attracted to this electrode and there undergo reduction (gain of electrons).

Chain reaction. A process that goes on automatically once it has been started. For example, when uranium-235 is struck by a high energy neutron, it undergoes fission. Fission produces more high energy neutrons, which strike other uranium nuclei, thus allowing the fission process to continue.

Chemical change. A change in which new materials with completely different chemical compositions are produced.

Chemical family. A vertical group of elements in the periodic table having similar chemical properties.

Chemical formula. An expression using symbols of elements and numbers to describe how many of each type of atom is present in a substance.

Chemiluminescence. Light produced by a chemical reaction.

Chromatography. A technique used to separate small quantities of chemicals in a mixture.

Classification. A technique for grouping objects with similar properties.

Compound. A pure substance made from at least two different types of atoms.

Concentration. A term used to describe how much solute has been dissolved in a solvent.

Conductivity. The ability of a material or a solution to allow electricity to flow through it.

Continuous spectrum. The light spectrum in which all possible energies (colours of light) are present.

Controlled experiment. An experiment in which the variables are changed, one at a time, in order to determine which of them affects the outcome.

Control rod. Part of a nuclear reactor used to control the rate of nuclear decay.

Coolant. The substance used in a nuclear reactor to keep the heat produced under control. It is also used in the heat transferring process to produce steam for the turbine generators.

Corrosion. The slow destruction of a metal due to reaction with chemicals in the environment.

Covalent bond. A chemical bond between two elements, usually non-metals, in which a pair of electrons is shared between two atoms.

Covalent compound. A compound in which the elements are held together by covalent bonds.

Cracking. Using heat to break down large petroleum molecules into smaller molecules.

Crystal. A solid material in which the parts are arranged in a repeating pattern.

Daughter nuclei. The lighter nuclei produced during a nuclear fission process.

Decomposition. The breaking down of a compound into simpler substances.

Distillation. A purification process in which a liquid is boiled and then recondensed.

Double covalent bond. A covalent bond in which two pairs of electrons are being shared between the two bonding atoms.

Double displacement. A chemical reaction involving two compounds that exchange elements to produce two new compounds.

Dust explosion. The explosive burning of finely divided combustible material.

Electrochemical cell. A device containing chemicals that react to produce electrical energy.

Electrode. Electrical conducting material placed in a battery or electrochemical cell. The oxidation and reduction process takes place at the electrodes.

Electrolysis. The process of using electricity to break down a compound.

Electrolyte. A solute that dissolves in water to form an electrical conducting solution.

Electron. A negatively charged particle found in the atom.

Electron shell. One of the energy levels in which the electrons are located around the nucleus.

Electroplating. Using electrical current to deposit a thin layer of metal from an ionic solution onto a electrically charged surface.

Element. A pure substance containing only one type of atom.

Emulsifying agent. A chemical that enables two non-mixing liquids to mix together without separating. The mixture is called an emulsion.

End point. The point in a chemical titration in which a marked colour change is noted.

Endothermic process. A chemical reaction in which heat energy is taken in.

Energy level. One of the states, each with a fixed energy, in which an electron is allowed to move.

Ester. A class of organic compounds formed by the reaction between an alcohol and an organic acid.

Excited state. An atom in which one or more electrons are not in the lowest possible energy level.

Exothermic process. A chemical reaction in which heat energy is released.

Fat. A compound produced when a glycerol molecule reacts with three fatty acid molecules.

Fatty acid. An organic acid which comes from an animal or vegetable fat or oil.

Filtrate. The liquid portion that passes through the filter paper during filtration.

Filtration. The process of separating a mixture of large solid particles from a liquid by passing the mixture through porous filter paper.

Fission. The splitting of a large nucleus into small nuclei.

Flame test. A technique in which a compound of a metal is placed in a flame. The colour produced is used to identify the metal in the compound.

Foam. A mixture in which gas molecules are trapped within a liquid or, in some cases, a solid.

Formula mass. The sum of the atomic masses of all the atoms in a chemical formula.

Fractional distillation. A technique of separating a mixture of liquids which have different boiling points.

Freezing point. The temperature at which a liquid changes into its solid form.

Fuel cell. An electrochemical device which continuously converts a fuel and an oxidant into electrical energy.

Functional group. The group of atoms in an organic compound which is responsible for the properties of that compound.

Fusion. A nuclear reaction in which smaller nuclei combine to produce a larger nucleus.

Gamma rays. High energy radiation given off during nuclear fission reactions.

Gas. Matter which has no definite shape and no definite volume.

Gas chromatography. A chromatography technique in which the mixture is vaporized and introduced into a carrier gas. The carrier gas is then passed over a liquid or solid stationary phase. The parts of the mixture move over the stationary phase at different rates and are separated in the process.

Gel. A mixture in which the components have combined to form a thick, jelly-like product.

Gray. A unit of measurement used to measure the amount of radiation absorbed.

Ground state. The state of an atom in which the electrons are in the lowest possible energy levels.

Group. The vertical columns in the periodic table in which the elements with similar chemical properties are placed.

Half-life. The time taken for one half of an unstable radioactive material to decay.

Hard water. Water that contains dissolved minerals which make it difficult for the water to produce suds when mixed with soap.

Heavy water. Water that is made from two atoms of deuterium (^2_1H) and one atom of oxygen.

Hydrate. A compound in which water molecules are part of the crystalline structure.

Hydrocarbon. An organic compound which consists only of carbon and hydrogen atoms.

Indicator. A substance which through a change in its colour indicates the presence of a base or an acid.

Inference. A conclusion which is based on certain assumptions that may or may not be correct.

Ion. An atom that has lost or gained electrons.

Ionic bond. A chemical bond which forms as a result of two oppositely charged ions being attracted to each other.

Ionic compound. A compound in which the chemical bonding is mostly ionic.

Isomers. Molecules which have the same kind and number of atoms but arranged in different ways.

Isotope. Atoms of the same element but containing different numbers of neutrons in the nucleus.

Ketone. A class of organic chemicals containing a $\begin{smallmatrix}C\\C\end{smallmatrix}{>}C{=}O$ group.

Law of conservation of mass. During a chemical reaction, the total mass of all the reactants is equal to the total mass of all the products.

Lewis diagram. A diagram used to represent a molecule in which all the atoms and shared and unshared pairs of electrons are shown.

Line spectrum. The light spectrum in which only certain energies (colours of light) are present.

Liquid. Matter which has a fixed volume but no fixed shape.

Mass. The quantity of matter contained in an object.

Mass number. The number of protons plus neutrons found in the nucleus of an atom.

Matter. Anything that has mass and volume.

Mechanical mixture. A non-uniform mixture of two or more different substances.

Melting point/range. The temperature range over which a solid is changed into a liquid.

Metals. Elements that are good conductors of heat and electricity.

Mixture. A combination of two or more substances that are mixed together but keep their own properties.

Moderator. A substance used in a nuclear reactor to slow down the neutrons given off during nuclear decay.

Mole. A unit used to measure the amount of matter.

Molecular formula. See chemical formula.

Molecular mass. See formula mass.

Molecule. Two or more atoms chemically bonded together.

Monomer. A relatively small molecule or compound which is capable of being converted into a large molecule by combining with itself many times over.

Mordant. A compound that helps natural dyes to stay attached to fibres.

Mother liquor. The liquid portion that remains after a precipitate has settled.

Multivalent element. An element which has more than one valance value.

Neutral solution. A solution which is neither acidic nor basic and has a pH value of 7.0.

Neutralization. The process in which an acid and a base solution react with each other to produce a salt and water.

Neutron. A particle which has zero charge and is found in the nucleus of an atom.

Noble gas. One of the elements in the helium group of the periodic table. These elements are mostly non-reactive, although compounds of some of these elements are known.

Non-metals. Elements that are poor conductors of heat and electricity.

Non-polar solvent. A solvent which does not usually dissolve ionic materials.

Nuclear decay. The breakdown of an atomic nucleus usually accompanied by the release of large amounts of energy and some radiation.

Nuclear equation. An equation that describes a nuclear reaction.

Nuclear fallout. Radioactive materials in the atmosphere which eventually settle to the ground.

Nuclear reactor. A device which uses nuclear energy to produce electricity.

Nucleus. A tiny region in the centre of the atom which contains protons and neutrons. The nucleus is positively charged.

Observation. The use of the senses or instrumentation to obtain factual information.

Octet rule. A concept that elements react by losing or gaining electrons so that they end up having a valence shell electron structure similar to the nearest noble gas element. With the exception of helium, this means eight electrons.

Organic compound. A compound which contains carbon that is not in the form of an oxide, a carbonate or a cyanide.

Outer energy level electrons. The electrons in the valance shell that are involved in a chemical reaction.

Oxidation. A chemical reaction in which there is a loss of electrons.

Paper chromatography. A chromatography technique in which the fixed phase is an absorbent paper.

Patination. The process of using chemicals to colour a metallic surface.

Period. A horizontal row of elements within the periodic table.

Periodic table. An arrangement of the elements according to their atomic number. Elements with similar chemical properties are grouped together.

pH scale. A scale used to describe the acidity or alkalinity of a solution. pH values between 0 and 7 are acidic; values between 7 and 14 are basic; and a pH of 7 is neutral.

Physical change. A change in which the chemical composition of a material is not altered.

Plastic. Large molecular mass materials, usually synthetic, which can be molded and shaped with or without the use of heat.

Polar solvent. A solvent which readily dissolves many ionic substances.

Pollution. Materials introduced into our environment which are not normally there and which can be harmful to the things we value.

Polymer. A large molecule formed by joining together five or more identical monomer molecules.

Poly-unsaturated hydrocarbon. A hydrocarbon in which there are two or more double or triple covalent bonds between two carbon atoms.

Positron. A nuclear particle similar to the electron but which carries a positive charge.

Precipitate. The solid that forms when two solutions are mixed and react together.

Products. The materials that are formed during a chemical reaction.

Proton. A positively charged particle found in the nucleus of an atom.

Pure substance. A material in which every particle has identical composition and properties.

Qualitative analysis. The examination of a material to determine which molecules are present.

Qualitative observation. A descriptive observation.

Quantitative analysis. The examination of a material to determine the amount of a substance that is present.

Quantitative observation. An observation that requires a measurement.

Radiation. Energy associated with waves such as X-rays, ultraviolet, cosmic rays, gamma rays or with the release of alpha and beta particles when a nucleus undergoes decay.

Radiation sickness. Poor health caused by exposure to large doses of radiation.

Radical. A group of elements which behave chemically as if they were a single element.

Radioactivity. The natural or artificial breakdown of a nucleus accompanied by the release of radiation.

Radioisotope. An unstable isotope of an element which undergoes nuclear decay and releases radioactivity.

Reactants. The materials that react together during a chemical reaction.

Recrystallization. A process used to purify a solid material by dissolving the material and the impurities in a hot solvent and then allowing only the desired pure material to crystallize as the solvent is cooled down.

Reduction. A chemical reaction in which there is a gain of electrons.

Refluxing. A special technique in which rising vapour is made to condense and then allowed to flow back into the reaction vessel.

Residue. The material that is left behind on the filter paper during filtration.

Saturated hydrocarbon. A hydrocarbon where there are only single covalent bonds between the carbon atoms.

Saturated solution. A solution which contains the maximum amount of solute that can be dissolved at a given temperature.

Single covalent bond. A covalent bond in which only one pair of electrons is being shared between the two bonding atoms.

Single displacement reaction. A reaction in which the reactants are an element and a compound.

Sievert. A unit used to measure radiation.

Skeleton equation. An unbalanced chemical equation.

Solder. A low-melting alloy using to join metals.

Solid. Matter which has a fixed volume and a fixed shape.

Solubility. A measure of how much solute will dissolve in a given quantity of solvent at a given temperature.

Solute. The substance that dissolves in the solvent when forming a solution. In liquid-liquid and gas-gas solutions, this is usually the smaller component. In solid-liquid and gas-liquid solutions the solute is always the solid or the gas.

Solution. A uniform mixture of two or more substances. The dissolved particles are molecular sized.

Solvent. The substance that dissolves the solute when forming a solution.

Spectroscope. An instrument used to analyze the radiant light that is emitted from an object.

Spontaneous combustion. A process in which a substance ignites without an external flame or source of heat being applied.

Stick diagram. Similar to a Lewis diagram, stick diagrams use lines to represent each of the pairs of electrons being used for bonding. The electrons not used for bonding are not shown.

Structural formula. Similar to a stick diagram.

Surfactant. A substance that reduces the forces exerted by the molecules at the surface of a liquid when the substance is dissolved in the liquid.

Suspension. A mixture in which solid particles or very small liquid droplets are held uniformly throughout a liquid. If the particles are large enough they will eventually settle.

Synthesis reaction. A reaction in which the two reactants are both elements.

Ternary compound. A compound made from three different elements.

Theory. An idea used to explain the observations made in experiments and perhaps predict the outcome of future experiments.

Titration. A technique in which the volume of one solution needed to react with another solution is measured.

Transition metal. A metallic element located in the shorter groups of the periodic table.

Triple covalent bond. A covalent bond in which three pairs of electrons are being shared between the two bonding atoms.

Unsaturated hydrocarbon. A hydrocarbon which contains at least one double or triple covalent bond between two carbon atoms.

Unsaturated solution. A solution in which more solute can still dissolve at the same temperature.

Valence electron. An electron located in the outermost occupied energy level of the atom.

Valence shell. The outermost occupied energy level in an atom.

Valence value. The number of electrons an atom loses or gains when bonding with another atom.

Volatility. The tendency of a solid or liquid to pass into the vapour phase.

Word equation. A statement using words, not symbols, to describe a chemical reaction.

X-ray. A form of radiant energy produced when high speed electrons strike a metallic surface in a vacuum tube.

Zone melting. A technique used to purify a solid.

The Periodic Table of the Elements

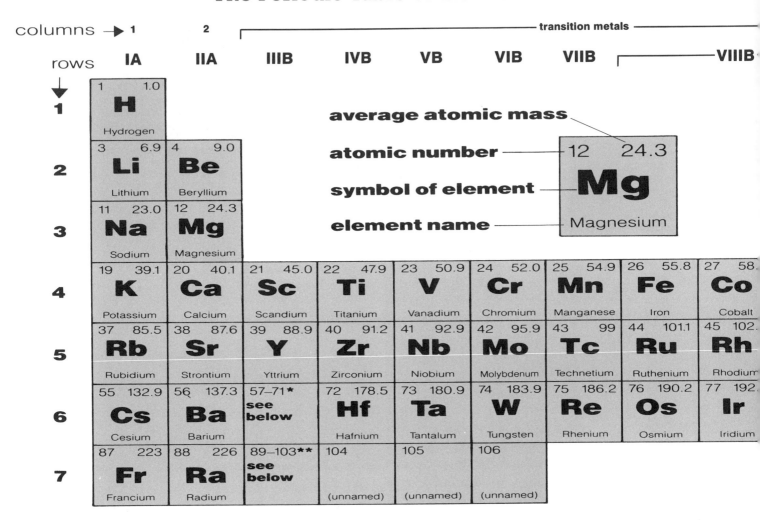

columns → 1   2   ────── transition metals ──────

rows   **IA**   **IIA**   **IIIB**   **IVB**   **VB**   **VIB**   **VIIB**   ┌──── **VIIIB**

average atomic mass

atomic number ——— 12   24.3

symbol of element ——— **Mg**

element name ——— Magnesium

1	1 1.0 **H** Hydrogen							
2	3 6.9 **Li** Lithium	4 9.0 **Be** Beryllium						
3	11 23.0 **Na** Sodium	12 24.3 **Mg** Magnesium						
4	19 39.1 **K** Potassium	20 40.1 **Ca** Calcium	21 45.0 **Sc** Scandium	22 47.9 **Ti** Titanium	23 50.9 **V** Vanadium	24 52.0 **Cr** Chromium	25 54.9 **Mn** Manganese	26 55.8 **Fe** Iron	27 58. **Co** Cobalt
5	37 85.5 **Rb** Rubidium	38 87.6 **Sr** Strontium	39 88.9 **Y** Yttrium	40 91.2 **Zr** Zirconium	41 92.9 **Nb** Niobium	42 95.9 **Mo** Molybdenum	43 99 **Tc** Technetium	44 101.1 **Ru** Ruthenium	45 102. **Rh** Rhodium
6	55 132.9 **Cs** Cesium	56 137.3 **Ba** Barium	57–71* see below	72 178.5 **Hf** Hafnium	73 180.9 **Ta** Tantalum	74 183.9 **W** Tungsten	75 186.2 **Re** Rhenium	76 190.2 **Os** Osmium	77 192. **Ir** Iridium
7	87 223 **Fr** Francium	88 226 **Ra** Radium	89–103** see below	104 (unnamed)	105 (unnamed)	106 (unnamed)			

*Lanthanide series

57 138.9 **La** Lanthanum	58 140.1 **Ce** Cerium	59 140.9 **Pr** Praseodymium	60 144.2 **Nd** Neodymium	61 147 **Pm** Promethium	62 150.4 **Sm** Samarium	63 15 **Eu** Europiur

**Actinide series

89 227 **Ac** Actinium	90 232.0 **Th** Thorium	91 231 **Pa** Protactinium	92 238.0 **U** Uranium	93 237 **Np** Neptunium	94 242 **Pu** Plutonium	95 2 **Am** Americiu

There are different ways for numbering the groups in the periodic table.

In this book, the eight longer columns are numbered as Groups 1 to 8, and the elements between Groups 2 and 3 are called transition metals.

			3	4	5	6	7	8
		IB	IIB	IIIA	IVA	VA	VIA	VIIA	VIIIA

rows →

1

	2 4.0
	He
	Helium

2

5 10.8	6 12.0	7 14.0	8 16.0	9 19.0	10 20.2
B	**C**	**N**	**O**	**F**	**Ne**
Boron	Carbon	Nitrogen	Oxygen	Fluorine	Neon

3

13 27.0	14 28.1	15 31.0	16 32.1	17 35.5	18 39.9
Al	**Si**	**P**	**S**	**Cl**	**Ar**
Aluminum	Silicon	Phosphorus	Sulfur	Chlorine	Argon

4

8 58.7	29 63.5	30 65.4	31 69.7	32 72.6	33 74.9	34 79.0	35 79.9	36 83.8
Ni	**Cu**	**Zn**	**Ga**	**Ge**	**As**	**Se**	**Br**	**Kr**
Nickel	Copper	Zinc	Gallium	Germanium	Arsenic	Selenium	Bromine	Krypton

5

6 106.4	47 107.9	48 112.4	49 114.8	50 118.7	51 121.8	52 127.6	53 126.9	54 131.3
Pd	**Ag**	**Cd**	**In**	**Sn**	**Sb**	**Te**	**I**	**Xe**
Palladium	Silver	Cadmium	Indium	Tin	Antimony	Tellurium	Iodine	Xenon

6

8 195.1	79 197.0	80 200.6	81 204.4	82 207.2	83 209.0	84 209	85 210	86 222
Pt	**Au**	**Hg**	**Tl**	**Pb**	**Bi**	**Po**	**At**	**Rn**
Platinum	Gold	Mercury	Thallium	Lead	Bismuth	Polonium	Astatine	Radon

4 157.3	65 158.9	66 162.5	67 164.9	68 167.3	69 168.9	70 173.0	71 175.0
Gd	**Tb**	**Dy**	**Ho**	**Er**	**Tm**	**Yb**	**Lu**
Gadolinium	Terbium	Dysprosium	Holmium	Erbium	Thulium	Ytterbium	Lutetium

6 247	97 249	98 251	99 254	100 253	101 256	102 259	103 257
Cm	**Bk**	**Cf**	**Es**	**Fm**	**Md**	**No**	**Lr**
Curium	Berkelium	Californium	Einsteinium	Fermium	Mendelevium	Nobelium	Lawrencium

Also shown above is the system using Roman numerals I to VIII,
with subgroups denoted by A and B.

Symbols and Valence Values of Some Elements and Radicals

Element	Symbol	Valence Value		Radical	Symbol	Valence Value
aluminum	Al	3		acetate	$C_2H_3O_2$	1
antimony	Sb	3, 5		ammonium	NH_4	1
arsenic	As	3, 5		arsenate	AsO_4	3
barium	Ba	2		arsenite	AsO_3	3
beryllium	Be	2		bicarbonate	HCO_3	1
bismuth	Bi	3		bisulfate	HSO_4	1
boron	B	3		bisulfide	HS	1
bromine	Br	1		bisulfite	HSO_3	1
cadmium	Cd	2		bromate	BrO_3	1
calcium	Ca	2		carbonate	CO_3	2
carbon	C	4		chlorate	ClO_3	1
cesium	Cs	1		chlorite	ClO_2	1
chlorine	Cl	1		chromate	CrO_4	2
chromium	Cr	2, 3		cyanate	CNO	1
cobalt	Co	2, 3		cyanide	CN	1
copper	Cu	1, 2		dichromate	Cr_2O_7	2
fluorine	F	1		dihydrogen phosphate	H_2PO_4	1
gold	Au	1, 3		hydrogen carbonate	HCO_3	1
hydrogen	H	1		hydrogen phosphate	HPO_4	2
iodine	I	1		hydrogen sulfate	HSO_4	1
iron	Fe	2, 3		hydrogen sulfide	HS	1
lead	Pb	2, 4		hydrogen sulfite	HSO_3	1
lithium	Li	1		hydroxide	OH	1
magnesium	Mg	2		hypochlorite	ClO	1
manganese	Mn	2, 3		iodate	IO_3	1
mercury	Hg	1, 2		monohydrogen phosphate	HPO_4	2
nickel	Ni	2, 3		nitrate	NO_3	1
nitrogen	N	3		nitrite	NO_2	1
oxygen	O	2		perchlorate	ClO_4	1
phosphorus	P	3		phosphate	PO_4	3
potassium	K	1		phosphite	PO_3	3
silicon	Si	4		sulfate	SO_4	2
silver	Ag	1		sulfite	SO_3	2
sodium	Na	1				
strontium	Sr	2				
sulfur	S	2				
tin	Sn	2, 4				
zinc	Zn	2				